THE UNDEVELOPED MINERAL RESOURCES OF THE SOUTH

By

DR. HENRY MACE PAYNE

Consulting Engineer
The American Mining Congress

AMERICAN MINING CONGRESS
WASHINGTON, D. C.
1928

Copyright, 1928
By
The American Mining Congress

Fleet-McGinley, Inc., Baltimore, U. S. A.

FOREWORD.

This survey was not undertaken nor this volume published for profit. It is, perhaps, the most extensive work ever undertaken voluntarily by any association, solely to stimulate industrial development, and in which its sponsors held no hope of direct or personal gain.

The work has been done with an altruistic purpose in the belief that mining is the basis of all modern civilization; that the marked difference in the advance of nations is measured by the extent to which their mineral resources have been developed; that this prosperity was brought about by the pioneers of the West who laid the foundation of our nation's financial supremacy by supplying $1,029,442,800 in gold and $645,518,100 in silver during the twenty-five years beginning in 1860, which enabled it to develop its other resources through the use of an abundance of real money (gold and silver).

This foundation of credit made possible the great development of iron, coal and other industrial minerals. Cheap power and cheap machinery with ample circulating medium made possible an industrial growth on these foundations which has been and is the marvel of the world.

The American Mining Congress, believing that the next great forward step would be through the utilization of non-metalliferrous minerals, turned to the South as the most promising and the most natural field for such development. The South had given but meager support to its state geological surveys. As a result, there had been no comprehensive survey of mining possibilities and there seemed to be a real need for such an effort.

With these facts in mind, the American Mining Congress secured the services of Dr. Henry Mace Payne to carry out the work which has made possible this volume. Dr. Payne first gathered together the information available from the United States Geological Survey, the several state geological surveys, the industrial agents of the many railroads, pieced together this information, and then by personal examination during a period of more than three years, has brought together in this volume what we believe to be a most complete survey of the mineral resources of thirteen Southern states, from Texas to Virginia.

The South has been thoroughly aware of its industrial advantages, but not of its mineral possibilities. The American Mining Congress hopes through this undertaking not only to awaken the South to the importance of its mineral possibilities, but also to bring these undeveloped opportunities to the attention of Northern and Western industrialists, and thus bring to Southern development more of steam-shovel operations.

The American Mining Congress believes that no greater service can be rendered the great farming industry of the South than to create local markets for farm products by the recovery of Southern mineral wealth and its home manufacture into marketable products. It believes that no greater service can be rendered to the railroads than the increase of freight tonnage of raw materials to points of fabrication, and through the return of those fabricated products, to fill the requirements of mining communities. It believes that no greater service can be rendered to the South than by increasing its taxable property, and thus making possible better schools, better roads and better public institutions, all of which are supported by taxation and by increasing business earnings and the more prosperous citizenship which makes possible higher development of religious and charitable organizations.

Absolutely accurate statements concerning undeveloped resources are, of course, impossible, but it is believed that the contents of this volume will furnish the basis of such further investigation as will demonstrate the value of the deposits herein described, and will lend assistance in the search for opportunities in the fabrication of these resources and in the marketing of the finished product.

J. F. CALLBREATH,

February 1, 1928. *Secretary.*

PREFACE

It has been the writer's experience for many years that whenever a call came for information about many of the mineral resources of the South, but little connected material was available. Hurried letters to the various geological surveys frequently brought the information that desired bulletins were out of print. Others, available, were many years behind the actual development taking place in the state.

The surveys, in turn, have been handicapped in most states by insufficient funds, and only those minerals most in demand, or those found contiguous to transportation, have been adequately studied. Books have appeared more recently on manufacturing processes, methods of marketing, and chemical properties. A few of the larger railroads have published maps and descriptive literature of their own resources. Commercial bodies have, in some instances, written glowingly of mineral deposits whose appeal instanced a local need. Large public utilities, in the construction of their plants and lines, have unearthed unsuspected and valuable acquisitions to a state's mineral wealth.

To review all these, to correlate them, then by personal field work to effect a reconnaissance of such areas as remained uncharted, and finally, to reduce this information to convenient reference form, has been the author's aim. In order that the work might be of still greater value, the uses to which these minerals are put, have been compiled from all available sources and included in the respective chapters.

The book is not offered as a strictly technical or geological work; but rather as a "commercially convenient" compilation of the mineral resources of the South, designed to afford the student, the consumer, the investor, and the producer a ready source of information regarding the nature and extent of these minerals; how they may be identified; where additional supplies have been proven up, or areas whose surface indications warrant further prospecting; what economic factors have speeded, retarded, or prevented their development; and new avenues of outlet for the product.

In the acquisition of this information, the writer has received the hearty and courteous support of the several Governors of the Southern states, the state geologists, the industrial agents of the various railroads, many staff members of the United States Geological Survey and the United States Bureau of Mines, the chief engineers of industrial corporations, professors of geology in the various universities and state colleges, and of industrial engineering firms and commercial bodies, to all of whom recognition is gratefully extended.

In the closing chapter on Bibliography will be found a list of the various printed sources which have been reviewed and drawn upon for pertinent data. To give page and chapter references would extend this volume beyond its possible limits. In the case of regular journals and Society proceedings, however, the annual indices will serve the reader equally well.

Particular attention is drawn to the fact that every effort has been made to avoid any savor of promotion either of particular industry or of individual property, and that statements of quantity or quality are based on what is believed to be credible information or personal examination. *In every instance,* the files of the American Mining Congress contain the specific source of the information, and frequently carry much intimate data wholly out of place in a publication, but available upon proper inquiry.

The author expresses his gratitude to Miss Bertha E. Chambers, who created and maintained the comprehensive files embodying the work while it was in process; to Miss Emily A. Spilman, who was in entire charge of the research work covering all the known uses of the various minerals; to the officials of the Washington City Public Library for research facilities and courtesies; and to Miss Virginia Taggart for her able assistance in the preparation of the index and bibliography, and her patient labors in checking the manuscript against the original field and file notes.

HENRY MACE PAYNE.

Washington, D. C.
February, 1928.

CONTENTS

Pages

Chapter I.—Problems of the Mineral Industry in the South 1-3
Chapter II.—Diatomaceous Earth, Tripoli, Fullers' Earth, Novaculite 4-18
Chapter III.—Bauxite—Baukite 19-29
Chapter IV.—Barytes, Ochre, Sienna, Umber and Pigment Clays 30-42
Chapter V.—Chalk, Whiting, Bentonite, Volcanic Ash 43-50
Chapter VI—Coal, Lignite, Peat 51-68
Chapter VII.—Petroleum, Oil Shale, Asphalt Rock 69-88
Chapter VIII.—Natural Gas, Carbon Black 89-92
Chapter IX.—Iron, Electric Smelting 93-115
Chapter X.—Chromite, Manganese, Antimony, Titanium, Rutile, Ilmenite, Monzonite, Zirconium, Columbium, Columbite, Samarskite, Cerium, Monazite, Thorium, Thoria, Godolinite, Carnotite, Uranium Vanadium, Tellurium, Selenium, Strontium 116-137
Chapter XI.—Molybdenum, Tungsten, Nickel, Magnesium 138-146
Chapter XII.—Corundum, Gems, Diamonds, Graphite 147-157
Chapter XIII.—Gold, Silver, Copper 158-178
Chapter XIV.—Pyrites, Gossan, Copperas, Sulphur, Salt 174-185
Chapter XV.—Zinc, Lead, Tin 186-197
Chapter XVI.—Kaolin, Clays, Cyanite, Sillimanite 198-231
Chapter XVII.—Mica, Chlorite, Sericite, Talc, Soapstone 232-244
Chapter XVIII.—Shales, Slate 245-251
Chapter XIX.—Fluorspar, Lithographic Stone.. 252-258
Chapter XX.—Potash, Feldspar, Cinnabar 259-272

Chapter XXI.—Building Stones, Marble, Granite 273-284
Chapter XXII.—Sand, Glass Sand, Molding Sand, Molding Clay, Gravel, Chert.......285-306
Chapter XXIII.—Phosphate Rock, Phosphoric Acid, Mineral Fertilizers................307-313
Chapter XXIV.—Limestone, Marls and the Cement and Calcium Arsenate Industries....314-336
Chapter XXV.—Asbestos, Gypsum, Mineral Waters 337-347
Chapter XXVI.—Bibliography 348-356
Index 357-368

Chapter I

PROBLEMS OF THE MINERAL INDUSTRY IN THE SOUTH

In a previous volume, "Natural Resources and National Problems," the author called attention to the great irregularity in mineral development in the South. That section, although viewing itself as agricultural, already supplies 22 per cent of the total mineral production of the United States. Over three-fifths of this is made up, however, of mineral fuels, since the great Southern fuel-producing states, actuated by increasing demand for coal and oil, have developed these industries far beyond the average of the country, while the production of the metallics and non-metallics is but a fraction of their logical potentiality.

Until very recently the non-metallics have received but slight consideration. Few inventions relating to these fields, and the names of but few engineers, have been added to the history of non-metallic mining.

The Southern Mineral Empire is incredibly rich in a diversity of both metallics and non-metallics. The former, however, have for the most part received the attention of metallurgists and the benefit of experienced operation elsewhere. The non-metallics have suffered from inefficiencies of mining, milling and marketing.

Lack of financial support and of appreciation of the value of their work has handicapped many of the State Geological Surveys. Much of the prospecting done has been at the instigation of the industrial departments of railroads traversing certain districts, and naturally has been confined to the territory contiguous to their lines.

When so developed, the product has naturally gravitated toward that market favored by the carrier. Prevailing ignorance of the non-metallics and their uses has encouraged nonchalant financial support and investment. The sporadic nature of the industry and, until recently, the limited attention paid in most of our universities and mining schools to the non-metallics have combined to direct the attention of mining engineers to other fields. Yet, long after the metallic minerals have been depleted, these least-treasured resources will remain and will become increasingly important and correspondingly valuable.

Under these conditions there has been but little co-ordination between the source of supply, the processes of preparation, and the ultimate consumer. There is still a lack of standardization in preparation and in required grades, and much remains to be learned by both producer and consumer concerning the operating conditions of the one and the manufacturing needs of the other.

Efforts to adapt improper equipment, absence of engineering experience and advice, and production on a scale too small to be economic have resulted in dissatisfaction and, in some cases, in financial ruin. Nevertheless, as the cost of labor has increased, mechanical methods of operation have become inevitable, and their financing has been dependent upon geological examinations and engineering supervision. This has led to new uses and new by-products. The new refractory baukite and the slightly known bentonite are assuming the same prominence as their more familiar bedfellows, bauxite and tripoli.

Advances in the arts of metallurgy, ceramics, and industrial chemistry have made possible the utilization of many mineral deposits of medium to low grade, hitherto unworkable. The same progress has educated the consumer to recognition of the economic value of uniform quality and the importance of established sources of supply.

To further this industrial march and to give these minerals the same impetus already acquired by coal and oil, salt and sulphur, it is essential that the entire South be studied as a unit; that markets and centers of production be correlated; that basic freight rates and methods of assessment and taxation receive collective consideration; and that the great fuel supply of the South, coupled with its unexcelled water powers, should be utilized in the fabrication of raw material into finished products carrying higher class freight rates, but reaching new centers of distribution; employing men in a thousand small towns rather than in a few large cities; and offering increased valuations of property as an offset to constantly mounting taxes.

CHAPTER II

DIATOMACEOUS EARTH, TRIPOLI, FULLERS EARTH, NOVACULITE

These materials, of siliceous origin, shading from ganister rock and glass sand down through the mild abrasives and polishing powders to impalpably fine diatomite, are found widely disseminated in many of the Southern states. Considerable confusion has existed regarding the line of demarcation between the finer and more valuable grades.

Diatomaceous earth derives its name from the diatom, whose skeletons settling to the bottom of a body of water in countless millions form the mineral deposit. These diatoms inhabit all the waters of the earth, both fresh and salt. They are always found on submerged objects, imparting a slimy feeling. Their purpose is to take the necessary elements from earth and water, and change them into compounds that animal life may use in their food. They also like land plants, take in carbon dioxide and give off oxygen, in this manner oxygenating the water that the fish may breathe.

Thus we have a continuous deposit of these siliceous skeletons in process of formation under water. If the water is still and clear the deposit will be of high grade. If the pool be muddy, or a part of a running stream, interstratification will occur with sand, clay or volcanic ash. Hence, it is usual to find the purer deposits along the coastal plain, rather than in the Piedmont area. One cubic inch of diatomataceous earth may contain fifty million diatoms, and 80 per cent of this volume will still be voids. The salt water deposits were originally considered superior to those in fresh water, but experience has indicated that there is little, if any, reason for this choice.

The earliest known deposits are in the Cretaceous chalk. The Tertiary deposits near Richmond, Va., cover several miles and extend to a depth of 40 feet, while those of Santa Barbara county, California, cover 12 square miles and are 1400 feet thick. In Florida the deposits are found in basins and former lake beds, and in Mississippi in a bluff along the south bank of the Tennessee River.

On account of its high absorptive quality it has been much used as an absorbent for nitroglycerine in the manufacture of dynamite, and it is known also as infusorial earth, and as kieselguhr. Current practice, however, uses the names diatomaceous earth and diatomite. It is usually white or gray in color, and the purest grades run 94 per cent or better in silica, and up to 6 per cent in combined water. It will absorb as high as 80 per cent of its own volume of water. In weight it varies from 8 to 30 pounds per cubic foot. Having a specific gravity of less than 1, it will float. The prospector will be aided in distinguishing it from chalk by its limited effervescence when treated by acid.

It is usually stacked or piled in windrows after mining in order that it may dry by evaporation. Great care must be observed in handling and in grinding to avoid destroying the delicate structure of the diatoms, which would not only decrease the absorbtivity, but would also increase the weight of the finished product.

It is marketed in the form of sawn blocks, in crude lumps, and as powder. The brick and blocks of crude material are so fragile that it is necessary to crate them.

The powder is shipped in burlap sacks of 100 pounds each. This expense for containers and the high freight rates on the product, due to its light weight and great bulk, are the outstanding problems of the industry. A maximum carload of diatomite is 20 tons. It is not suitable for ballast or for water transportation, both because of its specific gravity and its hygroscopic nature.

The logical solution, therefore, is the establishment of factories central to the sources of supply, and the development of a manufactured block which will be sufficiently strong to eliminate crating, at a fabricating cost less than that of the containers. Workmen in the industry suffer from a constant irritation by the impalpably fine dust, leading to pneumonia. Dust masks are, therefore, essential.

Virginia

The deposits in Virginia are best known around Richmond, in Henrico county. At Bermuda Hundred in Chesterfield county, northwest of Petersburg in Dinwiddie county, at Greenlaw's Wharf in King George county, south of Layton, and at Wilmont in Essex county, and at several points along the Rappahannock River, are deposits from 20 to 50 feet in thickness, in some cases resembling the famous chalk cliffs of England. The Virginia deposits grade into layers of clay, with occasional fissures filled with limonite and interspersed with tripoli.

South Carolina

Until recently but one commercial deposit of diatomaceous earth was known in South Carolina. This was at Salter's Depot, Williamsburg county, on the A. C. L. R. R. Another deposit has very recently been developed about 15 miles from Augusta, Ga., on the C. & W. C. R. R., at Cathwood, Jackson and Cowden, along the north side of the Savannah River.

Florida

The Florida deposits have assumed prominence in recent years. The Lake county beds are worked near Eustis and Clermont. There are a number of undeveloped sources in this county, and also in Polk county lying to the south, and it is probable that the entire Lake district will be found underlaid with valuable diatomaceous areas.

Mississippi

In Tishomingo county, Miss., along the Tennessee River, is a deposit 15 to 20 feet thick, underlying several square miles This has been variously described as fullers earth, tripoli, etc., but microscopic examination has shown a portion of it to be of diatomic origin, running 99 per cent silica, and of exceptional whiteness.

Arkansas

Diatomaceous earth is reported from several points in Arkansas, but is probably crystalline quartz.

Texas

Several deposits are reported in the southeast panhandle of Texas and in western Reeves county, but no development work has been done on them. In Wilson county, southeast of San Antonio, an extensive deposit is being opened up.

Uses

While diatomaceous earth possesses excellent soft abrasive qualities for silver polish and allied products, these properties are equally well served by the use of tripoli, reserving the diatomite for more valuable application, as an absorbent of essential oils for sachet powders, complexion creams, and toilet articles; as a filter material in the oil and sugar industries; as a wood filler; boiled with shellac as a base for phonograph records; as a carrying agent for liquid fertilizers; as a source of silica in making water glass, cement, tile glazing, ultramarine and other pigments, paper filling, sealing wax, fireworks, hard-rubber objects, matches, papier-mache, and for solidifying bromine; as a base for scouring soaps; and because of its porosity and light weight, as a fireproof filling for safes and filing cabinets, and for insulating packing around steam pipes, boilers, etc.; as an ingredient of Bohemian glass; as a sound deadener in floors, walls and ceilings of buildings, and in the form of hollow tile for inter-office partitions, where its combined fireproof qualities, lightness and porosity render it a superior material; as an inert filler for insecticides and plaster compositions; and in combination with magnesite and other refractories for refractory cement. It is also used as a super-filter in clarifying high-grade oils.

New uses are being rapidly found for this material. The *Manufacturers Record* of November 4, 1926, pages 102-104 contains many recent adaptations.

* * * * * *

Tripoli occurs in many of the Southern states. It has been said by some authorities to be an altered form of chert or siliceous limestone, but is now considered to be a form of novaculite, since the deposits of the one frequently shade into the other. Its specific gravity is from 2.15 to 2.63; its porosity from 45 per cent to 68 per cent;

its absorption from 38 per cent to 52 per cent of water; and its bulk from 30 to 45 cubic feet per ton.

The soluble elements having been removed by percolating waters, the silica skeleton or fibrous silica, devoid of diatoms, forms a soft, friable, porous deposit, either rose, cream or white in color, usually occurring in pockets or irregular beds associated with impure kaolin or chert. Like diatomite, it is easily distinguished from chalk and the calcareous formations by acid; but only a microscopic examination will differentiate the individual solid grains of tripoli from the hollow valve-like silica shells of the diatom. Its grains are hard enough to scratch steel, and when too coarse for inclusion in the polishing materials the deposit becomes novaculite or even glass sand.

Analogous to tripoli is pumiceous rhyolite, a form of volcanic ash which, when carried by the wind, fell on lakes and inland bodies of water and is now found on top of what was once boggy soil full of crawfish holes. There are areas 30,000 to 40,000 acres in extent in Western Texas, where nothing will grow and where this material forms the top soil. It is shipped North and East and used in various cleansers and scouring compounds.

Virginia

Much of the Virginia diatomite is marketed as tripoli. Scattering reports of workable deposits of tripoli have been made in North and South Carolina, but no substantial evidence has as yet been produced.

Georgia

The Murray county deposits in Georgia, like the Whitfield and Chattooga county beds, have been extensively worked and large reserves remain. Spring Place, Dalton, and Lyerly, Ga., are the centers of the industry in that state. Near Cohutta, in Whitfield county, the Southern Railway cuts through a tripoli bed for a distance of 100 feet, and exposes about 40 feet in depth. This is of the same grade as that mined farther north in Tennessee. There is also a larger operation at Silver Creek, Floyd county, Georgia, and the state geologist reports a high-grade deposit four miles southwest of Lafayette in Walker county.

Tennessee

The Tennessee deposits extend in a northeasterly direction through Hamilton, Bradley and McMinn counties, and at least one deposit in Blount county. Three miles north of Ooltewah is an exposure of at least 100 acres of pure white tripoli, wholly undeveloped. Near Cleveland many grades are mined, milled and shipped under trade names, the shipping point being Black Fox. Another extensive deposit lies slightly farther to the south of Black Fox.

Alabama

In Alabama, near Tredegar, Calhoun county, is a siliceous deposit grading into ganister rock. Near Piedmont, in the same county, is a deposit of light yellow tripoli.

Mississippi—Florida—Texas

The soft abrasives of Mississippi have been discussed under diatomaceous earth, as have those of Florida and Texas.

Arkansas

Tripoli occurs in Arkansas in Hot Spring, Garland, Ouachita, Montgomery, Washington, Pike, Benton and

Independence counties. Outside of Benton county, however, but little development has been attempted. There is an abundance of this material in the zinc region of the White River Valley, but no attempt has been made to exploit it.

Louisiana

In Vernon parish, Louisiana, about 12 miles west of Anacoco, and 4 miles east of Sabine River, is a deposit which has been drilled through at 100 feet depth, showing chalky clay, underlaid with tripoli.

Uses

The same general problems exist in the working and shipping of tripoli as with diatomite, except that the former, being more valuable, offers a slightly larger margin for operating costs. The abrasive industries which consume this material should be encouraged to fabricate their product near the source of supply, and the industries which utilize it as a filtering or absorbing medium should devote more experimental labor to the development of nearby supplies, many of which are of a superior quality.

Its uses are as an abrasive base for polishing powders and cleansers, scouring soaps and toilet articles; as a fireproof filler for safes and filing cabinets; as a heat insulating packing; as a parting sand in foundry work; as a paper, cloth and rubber filler; as a carrier for insecticides; as a filter; as a wood filler; and in refractory cements.

Approximately two-thirds of the total production is devoted to foundry parting because of the affinity for fats and oils which tripoli's porosity affords. It also resists deterioration for many months.

When used as a transporting base for stearic acid, tallow, paraffine or petroleum it maintains a stable form.

As a filter it is said to remove 98 per cent to 100 per cent of the micro-organisms found in water. The secret of its success as a cleanser is due to its high porosity, so that if a slightly alkaline water or soap are used, only three-fifths as much soap is necessary to form a lather, which is carried into the most minute crevices by the infinitesimal particles.

The process of grinding tripoli is attended with much detail; it must be accomplished at carefully controlled temperature and determined speed. The powder is shipped in four grades, from 40 to 500 mesh. Standard tripoli should dust perfectly with as high as 5 per cent moisture.

* * * * * *

Fullers' earth is not of definite composition, but consists essentially of clay mixed with sufficiently finely divided siliceous matter to destroy its plasticity, so that it falls to a fine powder when mixed with water. Its wide variations in chemical analysis lead to the conclusion that its properties are due to physical rather than chemical character.

It may be superficially tested by tasting; when dry it adheres strongly to the tongue. It gives a shiny streak, and is oily and smooth to the touch, with a specific gravity of 1.7 to 2.4.

The product goes principally to the oil companies, first for clearing mineral oils; second, for vegetable oils, and, third, for animal oils. It is shipped, in order of importance, to New York, Philadelphia, and the mid-continent oil fields. The imported English earth has for many years been used for the vegetable and animal oils because the earlier domestic supplies of fullers' earth left a residual odor, nothwithstanding the fact that for the edible oils the filtering medium is first treated by a secret steam process. In recent years, however, many sources of this earth have been developed in Georgia, Florida, Alabama and Mississippi, which have proven to be actually superior to the best imported product.

Uses

The Florida earth is particularly suited for oil use because it granulates well and the granules retain their size. The basis of tests is the cost of producing a pound of acceptable bleached oil. In filtering oil, all the carbon, tar and asphaltic materials are absorbed, and the color lightened. The filtering earth is then washed in naphtha, steamed and dried, burned to remove the carbon, and used again. The naphtha, in turn, is redistilled for further use. Fullers' earth may also be treated with acid and used for bleaching oils when it is desired to accomplish the process at greater speed. The product, however, is not of as high grade.

The earth when no longer suitable for oil filtering is used for hand soap, concrete waterproofing and asphalt preparations.

It is also used, after being dug, dried, ground and, in some cases, graded by water separation, in the manufacture of cocoanut butter, oleomargarine, cold-water paint, wall paper, and in detecting coloring matter in food products. In this latter capacity its use is being rapidly extended by food inspectors, as the absorption of oleaginous coloring matter is positive and rapid. It is sometimes used as an adulterant in talcum powders, as a poultice, and as an antidote for alkaloid poisons. Its use for fulling cloth (from which it derived its name), and for cleansing wool, has passed from major to minor importance. It has recently supplanted charcoal and freshly precipitated aluminum as a reagent for the removal of alkaloids from the aqueous solution of their salts.

Virginia

A deposit of fullers' earth is reported at White House, New Kent county, Virginia, and another below Chase City, in Mecklenburg county, on the opposite side of the river.

North Carolina

In North Carolina, on the Ellerbe branch of the Norfolk Southern Railway, in the northern part of Richmond county, a deposit is being operated. There are undeveloped deposits of good quality in Gaston and Madison counties.

South Carolina

Much of the fullers' earth in South Carolina is below water level, and the expense of removing the overburden, of pumping, and of keeping the product clean, has been prohibitive. Five and one-half miles southeast of Aiken, in Aiken county, and 3 miles southeast of Leesville, in Lexington county, are deposits of sufficient purity to supply the trade for cleansers. Other deposits exist 3 miles northwest of Orangeburg in Orangeburg county, and in Colletin and Beaufort counties, but these have never been opened on a commercial scale. A partly developed operation is located near Blaney, in Kershaw county, with a slight overburden. A deposit of high grade is reported along the A. C. L. R. R. in Clarendon county, above water level.

Georgia

The plants in operation, and the undeveloped resources

in fullers' earth in Georgia are many. Along the line of the Central of Georgia Railway are listed deposits and operations in Baldwin, Barbour, Covington, Houston, Jefferson, Randolph, Screeven, Washington and Wilkinson counties, a detailed description of which may be found in their *Mineral Directory*. Among the large producers are the operations in Twiggs and Decatur counties. Large deposits have also been proven up in Bibb and Columbia counties. South of Lumpkin, in Stewart county, is a 2000-acre deposit from 12 to 14 feet thick, with 12-foot overburden, lime-iron-and-grit-free, running between 60 per cent and 70 per cent silica, distinctly granular, and said to hold up for 24 filterings against 6 to 8 as obtained by ordinary fullers' earth. Also east of Waycross, in Ware county, on the south side of Satila River, is a good deposit. There have been a number of operations in Grady and Decatur counties, and along the A. C. L. R. R. from Whigham to Cairo, but no permanent development. Similar deposits are found along the G. F. & A. R. R., around Attapulgus, in Decatur county; and extending south in Grady county along the Pelham and Havana R. R. into Florida.

Alabama

Alabama also has a number of deposits of high grade. In the central-western portion of Choctaw county, near Toxey, on the A. T. & N. R. R. is a deposit of fine grade, tested at Alden College. At Thomasville, Alameda and Jackson, in Clarke county, and in the district around Fort Payne, in DeKalb county, the deposits have been intermittently worked. The power, labor, fuel and transportation situations are favorable. Extending southeastward from the Mississippi line, through Choctaw and Clarke counties into Monroe county, parallel to the lignite formations crossing the state, is a belt of high-grade fullers' earth from 5 to 6 miles wide. It has been repeatedly tested and pronounced of extra-fine quality, superior to the best English earth. It averages 86 per cent silica, and in many places forms mountains of the clear mineral. At Tunnel Springs, in Monroe county, the L. & N. R. R. tunnels through a fullers' earth mountain.

Florida

Florida, from the beginning of the industry, has been the leading producer. The industry, in turn, has been second only to phosphate rock in the state's mineral production. Eighty-five per cent of the Florida product comes from Gadsden county and much of the balance from Manatee county. There are good deposits also in Marion and Hernando counties, but slightly farther from present transportation.

Mississippi

For many years a buff-colored oil-clarifying clay has been mined in Mississippi in Clarke, Lauderdale and Newton counties, under the name of "claystone." It outcrops in high bluffs along the railroad in many places, making transportation easy. This material is really a valuable fullers' earth. About two miles southeast of Leesdale, in Franklin county, is an area one-quarter mile square, underlaid with a deposit 16 to 18 feet thick. In Smith county is a similar one. East of Louisville, Winston county, is an extensive deposit which has been tested with both vegetable and mineral oils and found to be of superior quality. The state geologist reports a number of deposits which are doubtless extensions of those in

Alabama, extending from southeast to northwest across the state, parallel to the lignite formation.

The area across Mississippi, south of the Vicksburg limestone belt and particularly centering around Leesdale, also carries extensive deposits of fullers' earth.

Arkansas

To Arkansas belongs the honor of the first discovery of fullers' earth in the United States, at a point east of Benton, in Saline county, in 1891. The state has fluctuated between second and third rank ever since in its production. Much of the output goes to the soap manufacturers, and comes entirely from Saline county. An undeveloped deposit, however, has been reported at Forrest City, Saint Francis county, on the C. R. I. & P. and Missouri Pacific railroads, and another at a point three miles north of Levesque, Cross county.

Texas

The Texas operations extend in a southwesterly direction from Walker and Grimes counties across Bexar county to Fayette county. The latter deposits have never been developed. They lie along the Colorado River, in territory covered by the M.-K.-T. and the S. A. & A. P., and the Southern Pacific railways.

* * * * * *

Novaculite is a fine-grained siliceous deposit, too hard and coarse to be included in the softer abrasives and used for oilstones and whetstones. It is frequently classed in commerce with **millstones and chasers,** which represent a still coarser grade. The principal source of the latter is in Montgomery County, Virginia. There is a small production in Jackson county, Alabama, and several promising deposits have been discussed in Bulletin 13 of the Alabama Geological Survey. Chasers are larger than regular millstones and are used for grinding quartz, feldspar, barytes, etc. **Rottenstone** is another intermediate abrasive, between tripoli and novaculite. It is the residue of siliceous limestone whose calcareous matter has been removed by the action of water.

Grindstone is a tough, even-grained sandstone, composed principally of angular quartz grains. It is found in West Virginia at Lone Cedar, Jackson county; Sattes, Kanawha county; Buckhannon, Upshur county; and in Wood county, north of Parkersburg.

Novaculite is found only in the Tyrol Mountains and in North Carolina, Tennessee, Mississippi and Arkansas.

The North Carolina deposits are in Anson county near Wadesboro; Orange county near Chapel Hill, and in Person county near Roxboro.

The Mississippi deposit is about four miles west of Blue Mountain, Union county. This material also carries a sufficient amount of iron and manganese to make it excellent umber paint pigment when roasted and ground.

The Southern Railway reports novaculite at Evansville, Tenn.

The Arkansas deposits occur in Hot Spring, Garland, Montgomery, Polk, Pike and Howard counties. Most of the product is shipped to New England, where it is cut and mounted and reshipped all over the country. This industry should be developed near the source of the raw material.

Novaculite does not disintegrate, but is easily crushed and makes excellent railroad ballast, for which purpose it is used by the C. R. I. & P. R. R. in Arkansas.

Chapter III.

BAUXITE — BAUKITE

Aluminum is not found in its native state. Its oxide, alumina, when in pure crystal form, is represented by corundum, sapphire and ruby, in the natural abrasive series. Hydrated alumina is **bauxite**, which grades into the bauxitic clays. These clays are white to buff in color and possess great plasticity, fusing at about 3300° F and having a silica-alumina ratio of 1.8 to 0.8. These were known in generations past as "Chimney Rock," because they were soft enough to quarry readily, but hardened on exposure.

Bauxite may be the result of the decomposition of feldspathic rocks, or derived by solution from sedimentaries, followed by deposition as grains, nodules or irregular pockets in limestones and dolomites. The Arkansas bauxites are of feldspathic origin, and those of the Appalachians are sedimentary.

The ore carries from 15 per cent to 33 per cent combined water, which necessitates grinding and drying before shipment. Some plants also calcine the ore, thus reducing the moisture to about one-half of 1 per cent.

High silica, iron and titanium are objectionable in bauxite, except where soda-ash fusion is used instead of the sulphuric acid process, when iron is allowable.

Dr. Eugene A. Smith of Alabama states that analyses of bauxite carry very little weight, because the character of the ore may vary from one extreme to the other within the limits of the same ore body.

The principal imports come from British Guiana, France and Dalmatia, and are of high grade, being used chiefly in the manufacture of aluminum and aluminum salts. In Eastern markets this imported ore undersells the domestic product, even with the import duty of $1.00 per ton. Over 70,000 tons per year are imported from Mediterranean ports to Gulf points and thence by inland waterways to points of reduction. So many bauxitic clays are available for refractory purposes that alum, alumina and artificial abrasives are the principal bauxite products. "Alum" is a general name for alkali metals and double sulphates of which the most important are ammonia, potash and soda alum. The artificial abrasives are made by fusing bauxite with carbon in an electric furnace, grinding the product and sizing the grains, which are then made up into abrasive papers and cloths, stones, wheels and various forms, under different trade names. The proportion of aluminous abrasives to silicon carbide abrasives is as 10:1.

Calcium aluminate of low silica content, when fused with bauxite, coke and limestone, and ground, makes a cement which hardens in 24 hours to a strength equal to that of Portland cement in 28 days. This cement also resists seawater and when used in wall plaster permits a rapid succession of coats. So satisfactory is this cement that 80 per cent of the demand in France is for it. Over 900,000 barrels of it were made there in 1923. If only 10 per cent of the American cement demand were for this kind, over two million tons of bauxite would be required annually for this purpose alone.

Until recently 52 per cent alumina content has been the minimum for commercial purposes. But the rapidly increasing use of aluminum wares and the various chemical products of the ore, have directed research to the economic utilization of lower grade bauxites and will ultimately bring many obscure properties into favor. In the variety of its uses aluminum is only exceeded by iron and copper. The future of aluminum and its price will be controlled by methods of mining the ore and processes of separation from its compounds.

Freight rates also enter into the problem. Bauxite, when shipped as "clay," takes a lower rate. On account of moisture and losses of the fines it is the opinion of many that the rates should carry on gross, instead of net tons.

Aluminum is principally a product of labor, whose manufactured value is about 2000 per cent of its raw material value. The bauxite must be mined, treated, transported and put through chemical process; the coal must be mined, transported and its energy turned into steam; the limestone must be quarried, transported and treated; salt must be mined and transformed by chemical process into soda-ash; cryolite must be mined in the Arctic and brought to the scene of reduction; by-product carbons of the coal tar and oil industries and fluorspar must similarly be produced and transported. It is estimated that five tons of bauxite require 27 tons of other materials to produce one ton of aluminum. Aluminum, therefore, more than any other metal, is a labor assemblage and a labor product.

Virginia

Eight miles northeast of Roanoke, Va., in Botetourt county is a bauxite deposit, also about one mile from Salem, Roanoke county, where a bauxite brick is being made from the slag. The merit of this brick lies in its being about one-half the weight of ordinary brick.

Bauxite ore of good grade is also found in Fluvanna county, about one mile from the Albemarle county line.

North Carolina—Kentucky

Bauxite also occurs in northern Stanly county, North Carolina, around Whitney. There is a little bauxite along the N. C. & St. L. R. R. in Hickman county, Kentucky, but of medium to poor grade.

Tennessee

The bauxite deposits of Missionary Ridge, around Chattanooga, have been opened in a few places, and additional prospecting is being carried on. Anywhere in Eastern Tennessee, where the volcanic ash bed is tilted up against the porous Knox dolomite (at an approximate elevation of 800 feet in the Chattanooga district), along the old peneplane, deposits of bauxite may occur and prospecting should be done. The peneplane rises to the north until it reaches an elevation of 1800 ft. at Johnson City and Elizabethton. From Johnson and Carter counties southwest to Chattanooga is all a promising field for bauxite prospecting. At Keenburg, Carter county, is a low-silica-and-iron bauxite, running 60 per cent alumina. This has been developed to a depth of 50 feet, and the ore gave no signs of running out. Based upon a theory of origin, wherever bentonite beds are faulted, they should be followed up along the fault line for bauxite.

Georgia

The bauxite areas of South Georgia are well defined. Those of North Georgia are similar to and merge into those of Eastern Tennessee. The South Georgia product is of high grade, and is used for the manufacture of alum more than for aluminum. The principal market for this ore is Pittsburgh, Pa. Wilkinson, Sumter and Floyd counties are active centers. About six miles from Rome, Floyd county, is a 10-foot vein, following the configuration of the mountain, and carrying only a four-foot overburden, thus offering steam shovel operation. Core drilling has shown this vein free from the usual pocket formation and to be low in iron.

The Central of Georgia Railway lists bauxite in 12 counties along its lines. An account of the Georgia deposits by R. T. Stull appeared in the *Journal of the American Ceramic Society* in July, 1924. Randolph, Meriwether, Macon and Bartow counties all produce a substantial tonnage.

Alabama

In Southeast Alabama, in Pike, Barbour, Houston, Henry and Dale counties, a high-iron bauxite occurs. In Franklin and Colbert counties are deposits high in silica and iron similar to that near Fort Payne, De Kalb county. Other deposits are found in Cherokee county. All these are suitable for brick purposes.

Deposits of chemical grade are reported around Jacksonville and Anniston, Calhoun county.

Mississippi

High grade bauxite is extensively found in Tippah county, Mississippi. From Tippah county, southward to Oktibbeha county and eastward into Alabama from the northeast corner of Kemper county, is a narrow zone, associated with gray clays outcropping along the western edge of the Flatwoods.

A few miles west of Falkner, Tippah county, the hills are capped with bauxite. The largest deposits are west of

Ecru and Pontotoc, in Pontotoc county, and are known as the Big Hill and Smoky Top areas. Webster, Oktibbeha and Noxubee counties also contain extensive deposits. Analyses show the Mississippi ore to be of superior quality. The development of hydro-electric power at Muscle Shoals should stimulate its development.

Bulletin No. 19 of the Mississippi Geological Survey, by Morse, and Bulletin No. 750-G of the United States Geological Survey, by Burchard, treat the Mississippi bauxite deposits exhaustively, and the reader is referred to them for maps and details.

Arkansas

Bauxite in Arkansas was discovered by the late Dr. John C. Branner in 1887. Up to 1899 shipments were small and no records were kept. There are two producing fields; the Bryant district, around the town of Bauxite in Saline county, and the Fourche mountain district adjacent to the southern limits of Little Rock, Pulaski county, the two lying about 15 miles apart.

Arkansas produces approximately 86 per cent of the entire output of the country. There are several competitive producers. A small producer with an advantageous location and a well-prepared product can frequently undersell a large producer.

Texas

Evidences of bauxite have been found in the Tertiary formation along the Gulf Coast of Texas, but have never been adequately prospected.

Uses

Because of its resistance to decomposition by corrosive slags in the reduction of metallic ores, bauxite is a valuable refractory. Among the abrasives made by fusing bauxite with carbon in an electric furnace are alundum, adamite, alowalt, aloxite, borocarbone, carbo-alumina, corowalt, corubin, exolon, metalite, oxalumina and rex.

Aluminum acetate is used as a mordant in dyeing and calico printing, waterproofing and fireproofing.

Aluminum chloride is used in refining mineral oils, for carbonizing wool, and in the manufacture of certain organic compounds.

Aluminum hydroxide, like the acetate, is used in the manufacture of lake colors and for waterproofing, and also for cement making and in medicine. The colloidal form is used in sugar refining.

Alum, the double sulphate of aluminum and an alakali in steel, such as iron or chromium, is made from aluminum sulphate.

Aluminum itself plays an important part in the automobile industry for pistons, connecting rods, forgings and bodies. It goes into all sorts of cooking utensils, collapsible tools, electric conductors, automatic screws, and as bronze powder, paint pigment and rubber filler.

The opacity of aluminum powder to light, and its waterproofing quality, give life and durability to aluminum paint. Because of its reflectivity it is used for painting interiors where light distribution is essential; and for painting the exterior of oil tanks to minimize volatilization.

For office equipment, such as guide cards, aluminum is light, stiff and durable.

One pound of aluminum is equivalent to two pounds of copper in the electrical industry, for the field coils of heavy motors, busbars and for overhead transmission lines. High-tension lines of 150,000 volts or over, require large diameter cables. A steel core is used to give structural strength. This core is covered with aluminum and double clamps are used, one for the core and one for the casing, to prevent slipping. There are in service in the United States 85,000 miles of steel reinforced aluminum cable and 40,000 miles of aluminum cable.

The aluminum industry is closely associated with the development of hydro-electric power because of the important part which electrolysis plays in its reduction. When brought into contact with oxygen for which it has an affinity, through the medium of a high-tension current, metallic aluminum is separated from its associated groups. This violent affection for oxygen is utilized in welding the rails of a street car track Aluminum powder and iron oxide are united with magnesium. The aluminum robs the iron of oxide, and in the terrific temperature attained, which approximates 6000° F. within 30 seconds, the iron liquifies and welds the rails. It is also used as a deoxidizer in steel manufacture.

Large tanks for sugar, soap and varnish, die castings, foil as a substitute for tin foil, powder in lithographic printing, and as an ingredient in the explosive ammonal, are other uses. Powdered aluminum is also used in the cyanide process. The sulphate is a water softener, and under the trade name of "concentrated alum" is used for paper sizing, in tanning, and for deodorizing and decolorizing mineral oils.

Because aluminum is light and does not rust it is in great favor. Duralumin is a structural material of aluminum base, made by secret process, and is so light that it is said that "a girder 16 feet long can be balanced on one's little finger, but so strong that if its ends are supported by blocks it will support 8 men." It is much used in the construction of dirigibles and aeroplanes.

Clippings from sheet aluminum and aluminum wire, filings from aluminum castings, aluminum borings and foil are all of value as secondary metal.

* * * * * *

Baukite is a highly refractory material, in appearance like silica sand and fine clay. Until 1921 it was found only in Austria. It was imported in small quantities and used for making glass pots. Attention having been called to the lining of some lime kilns near Knoxville, Tenn., which have been in continuous use for many years without attention, while other kilns lined with fire brick were repeatedly relined, it was found that this material came from near Apison, Hamilton county, Tenn., and upon further investigation it was pronounced baukite.

Tennessee

The deposit is a ledge in the ridge, extending for about one mile, and dipping about 42° along the north side of the Southern Railway.

It constitutes an "unburned refractory" and when mixed with water and silicate of soda for molding purposes it is unnecessary to burn it. The acetylene torch flame will not penetrate it one quarter of an inch.

It resembles Waverly sandstone, shows about 96 per cent silica, is not affected by any known reagent, and has a fusing point at about cone 32 or 3218° F. It may be defined as a non-spalling material which, upon the application of heat, forms an impenetrable glaze.

A plant is now in operation and the product is shipped

to the Pittsburgh district for use in steel mills and glass factories. When mixed with bauxite it adds strength to saggers and increases their life by many heats. For glass and zinc pots and bridge walls in furnaces it is incomparable. An acid furnace is generally lined with pure silica sand, which is silicon dioxide, and has an acid chemical reaction. Basic furnaces are generally lined with magnesite or dolomite, or a mixture of these. Baukite has been tested for slag resistance, and is not affected by either basic or acid slag.

In the work on the electro-thermic metallurgy of zinc difficulty has been encountered in the breaking down of the refractory condenser linings, due to carbon deposition around particles of iron oxide contained in the material. The treatment of complex ores and the behavior of the metals commonly associated with zinc, such as cadmium, lead and silver, during distillation and condensation, constitutes an important field of research and the newly-found baukite offers substantial assistance to the work.

Mississippi

Subsequent to the opening up of the Apison deposit, a similar and much larger one was located east of Louisville, Winston county, Mississippi, on the G. M. & N. R. R. Extensive tests have been made with this material, and much literature has appeared about it within the past year.

It is applied, also, with the cement-gun for tunnel linings, patching firebox linings, etc., and renders greatest efficiency when ground to about 60 mesh, and mixed with 25 to 40 per cent of any good refractory, or old fire brick properly pulverized.

Experimental work now being carried on with this

material indicates that when heated in accordance with established methods, it inverts to tridymite and then to christobalite. Microscopic examination discloses that the silica crystals lie imbedded in a matrix of highly refractory clay, which presumably acts as a cushion in the expansion of the silica and accounts for its non-spalling qualities.

Chapter IV

BARYTES, OCHRE, SIENNA, UMBER AND PIGMENT CLAYS

Barytes occurs in veins or masses in limestone, as nodules in clay, or as a gangue mineral with fluorspar, and ores of lead, zinc, iron and copper. It is classified as "hard" or "soft" ore. When especially hard, it takes a high polish and is substituted for ornamental marble. The market is active and expanding. Competition, however, is keen, and long distance distribution of the product is precluded by freight rates.

Uses

Barytes is widely used in the manufacture of paper, rubber and paints, and as the base of a material for hermetically sealing meats and other food products for export. An inferior grade of paint pigment is made by grinding barytes so fine it will float on water. A better grade is made by chemical treatment, and a superior grade by mixing chemically with zinc. The best grade of pigment in the form of barium sulphate is sold commercially as "blanc fixe." It may be used as a pure white pigment, or as a filler, and is a base for lake colors, lithographic ink and "battleship gray" (which is 45 per cent blanc fixe). It is marketed as a paste containing 30 per cent water, and also as a dry powder.

Lithopone is a white pigment, 70 per cent blanc fixe and 30 per cent zinc sulphide. To manufacture 100 tons of lithopone, 125 tons of barytes and 275 tons of zinc, sulphuric acid and coal are required.

Manufacturing plants should, therefore, be located near

the sources of raw materials. As a substitute for white lead, it requires less grinding, is more easily mixed, does not check or peel off, or yellow with age, and spreads easily and evenly.

With ground cork it is the base of linoleum; it is used to make window shades light-proof, and as a non-corrosive filler in printer's and lithographic inks; in the manufacture of Bristol board and playing cards, calcimines, photo mats, and artificial ivory.

Barium sulphide precipitated with soda ash is used in the manufacture of optical glass and for "flat" wall paints. The carbonate is also used to neutralize sulphur in pressed brick and rubber.

Barium binoxide is used in the distillation of peroxide of hydrogen. Barium chloride is used as a mordant in dyeing and in the tanning of leather, as a water softener, in rat poisons, in ceramics, in the purification of table salts, and for battery plates. Barium nitrate is used in munitions and in lead fire material and military signal lights. Blanc fixe has also recently been used as a detector in taking interior X-ray pictures of the human body.

In cases where there is too much stain from the iron oxide for paint pigment, the material is used for chemical purposes. Much of the material mined is sold in the crude state with only a preliminary washing. On account of unstandardized product, many consumers have found it advisable to operate their own mines and regulate the quality of the product.

Virginia

There are a number of barytes deposits in Virginia which have been operated, and others awaiting development. Those in Russell, Campbell, Pittsylvania, Bedford and Smythe counties are in active operation. Louisa, Prince William, Tazewell, Washington and Wythe county deposits are extensive and in many cases of high grade and available to transportation. Deposits in Lee and Russell counties have never been proven up, but are known to exist.

At Stone Mountain, Bedford county, on the Virginian Railway; and at numerous places in Campbell county are barytes deposits intermittently operated as wagon mines.

West Virginia

The West Virginia barytes deposits are along the north slope of East River Mountain, in Mercer county. They have not been developed.

North Carolina

One of the difficulties in marketing North Carolina barytes has been the presence of calcium fluorite (CaF_2) which early shippers ignored, with the result that the product was viewed with apprehension.

At Runion, Madison county, a high-grade barytes deposit occurs along the Southern Railway. There are several wagon mines operating in the western part of the county, along the Tennessee State Line. The deposits disappear in Madison county, east of Barnard. About 400,000 tons have been shipped from around Hot Springs and Stackhouse, and it is estimated that at least three-quarters of a million tons remain available above water level. The region around Stackhouse is particularly susceptible to economic operation because the deposits are well segregated, the barytes boulders separating easily from the clay, mud or sand matrix and transportation facilities are good.

Barytes is found at a number of points in the vicinity of King's and Crowder's Mountains, in southern Gaston county, about five miles south of Bessemer City, on the headwaters of Wateree River. It occurs in well defined veins from 2½ to 12 feet in thickness, with walls of mica schist, dipping steeply to the west. The weathered outcrop is usually iron stained, but wherever operated to a considerable depth this has disappeared, and the deposit has improved in purity and thickness.

To the northeast, at Concord, Cabarrus county, and still farther northeast, at Hillsboro, Orange county, sporadic mining of barytes has been attempted but no substantial operations have resulted.

South Carolina

The Gaston county deposits extend southwesterly into South Carolina, and at Gaffney and Blacksburg, Cherokee county, compare favorably with the best Georgia product. Barytes is also mined at Rock Hill, York county, and Lockhart, Union county.

Georgia

Georgia vies with Missouri in barytes production. The mineral is frequently found as a gangue of lead, zinc or copper, and also as irregular ore bodies in limestones, sand stones and residual clays. The state's production comes from Cartersville, Bartow county, and Eton, Murray county, in the northwestern part of the state, and occurs in association with ochre and other minerals. An opening is also reported near the Central of Georgia R. R., four miles north of Lafayette, Walker county.

Alabama

Alabama barytes is found in Jefferson, Shelby, Bibb,

Calhoun, Clay, Lee, St. Clair, Etowah and Talledega counties, all north and east of the "Fall Line." At most of these occurrences it is exceptionally pure and white, and is found as loose boulders in residual clays. The Southern Railway also reports barytes north of Heflin, Cleburne county, and Fort Payne, De Kalb county. Residual weathered deposits from sub-carboniferous limestones have recently been opened up near New Market, Madison county. The Alabama product is pure and well suited to lithopone manufacture, but local grinding facilities are needed.

Kentucky

Although Kentucky supplies a minor portion of the annual production, there are many deposits in the state. In Woodford county, near Shyrock Ferry, it occurs as lead-zinc gangue. In Fayette county, around Lexington; Jessamine county, at Ambrose; Garrard county, along Dix River, west of Lancaster; Boyle county, along both the Southern and L. & N. Railroads, around Danville and Junction City; Mercer county, near Harrodsburg; Anderson County, at Lawrenceburg; Bourbon county, at Millersburg and Paris; and in scattered deposits of Franklin, Lincoln and Madison counties, we have an extensive central area in this state which has never been thoroughly prospected.

Russell county, on the south, and Caldwell county in the western part, at Fredonia, have been producers. The Gratz mine in Owen county, the limestones of Harrison county, the gangue minerals of Scott county and the area around Lockport, in Henry county, comprise the northern group. Thus we see four producing sections of which the central counties are the largest. Many of these districts are idle at present.

Tennessee

Both hard and soft ores of barytes are mined in Tennessee. They are found in the limestone areas, both calcite and dolomite. Many deposits are known to exist, but have never been prospected. The oldest operations are around Del Rio, in Cocke county, in the valley of the French Broad. These veins are a continuation of the Madison county, North Carolina, deposits. There are a number of plants in operation around Sweetwater, Monroe county, where the occurrence is in loose lumps of residual clay as a result of the weathering of the Knox dolomite. Many wagon mines are working around Philadelphia and Lenore City, Loudon county; Etowah, McMinn county; and Eagan, Claiborne county.

Of all these the Cocke county district first referred to, is the most extensively prospected. The barytes occurs here as a disseminated deposit averaging 6 ft. in thickness. It has been mined in several places to a depth of 100 feet and improves at the lower level. Across the river from Del Rio, in the same county, is a 4-foot vein outcropping for more than half a mile. At Rankin, Cocke county, slightly farther northwest, is a similar deposit. The basic reason for the Cocke county development is its excellent transportation facilities. Davidson, Greene, Smith, Bradley, Jefferson and Washington counties have also entered the market under favorable prices.

Arkansas

Arkansas is not a producer of barytes, although lenticular deposits are reported in the counties extending southwestward from Pulaski to Sevier. The entire area is traversed by several different lines of railroad, so that should the quality and extent of the Arkansas deposits be proven commercial, no difficulty would be experienced in marketing the product.

Texas

In Texas, sulphur and barytes are frequently associated with gypsum underlying the cap rock of the various salt domes (vide Chap. XIV). A small amount has been shipped from Llano county and an occurrence of commercial size noted at Burkeville, Newton county.

Without a protective tariff, the industry would quickly die, because the foreign cost of production with cheap labor is about 50 per cent of the domestic cost. The increased use of blanc fixe and lithopone will furnish a steadily growing market for barytes carrying 90 per cent or better of barium sulphate.

* * * * * *

Ochre, sienna, umber, and mineral pigments, are a variety of mineral earths of varying colors, usually derived from combinations of iron, silica, alumina, or manganese. Incrustations of oxides of other metals, such as bismuth and nickel, are occasionally called ochres, but they are of minor importance.

Ochre ranges in color from light yellow to brown. It may be considered for practical purposes, as an earthy and powdery form of hematite and limonite, usually impure, and requiring grinding, washing, and sometimes roasting, to improve the color.

It may occur as branching veins, or as residual masses in pockets or lenses. It is essential that all pigments should be free from grit. Much of this is removed by washing. The material is then ground between soapstone disks until not a trace of crystalline structure remains.

Some colors can be finished in one grinding, while others must pass through the mill five times before meeting the requirement "butter smooth." The work cannot be speeded, as this would burn the pigments and ruin the colors. Three days are required to grind 250 pounds of certain high grade pigments.

Sienna is a mixture of iron oxide and manganese dioxide with clay. The raw material is dull brown and burnt sienna a bright red.

Umber varies from sienna only in the substitution of manganese oxide for manganese dioxide. When washed and dried at 212° F. it becomes "raw umber," and when calcined and turned to a deeper color is sold as "burnt umber."

"Sap Brown" is a mixture of silica, organic matter and nitrogenous material used in paints and dyes.

Of the various pigment minerals, many have been treated in other chapters; as e. g., carbon black in Chapter VIII, zinc white in Chapter XV, white lead in Chapter XV, and chrome yellow in Chapter X.

Mineral pigments to be of value must be insoluble in the medium through which they are applied. "Substantive pigments" have an original color. "Adjective pigments" (e. g., crimson lake) are precipitated on a colorless base (e. g., alumina).

They are finely ground in a drying oil for oil paints, or in gum water for water colors. It is essential that they shall have stability and body and should not interact when mixed.

Virginia

Any basic igneous rocks in the Piedmont region, when weathered, will yield yellow ochre. The principal sources are the Piedmont counties and the northwestern slope of the Blue Ridge Mountains. Western Chesterfield county, Virginia, is rich in ochres. At Stanley, Page county, Hiwassee, Pulaski county, and McCoy, Montgomery county, are deposits which are available for paints and mortar colors. Warren, Grayson and Page counties supply umber of excellent grade. Bedford, Loudon and Rockingham counties have several developments and many deposits which have never been opened.

Various colored pigments are exhibited by the Southern Railway from Virginia. Yellow, black, gray and orange from Edinburgh, Shenandoah county; white from Orange, Orange county; and red ochre from Orange, Orange county.

West Virginia

Many deposits of yellow ochre are found in West Virginia, in Summers, Cabell and Wayne counties along the Chesapeake and Ohio, R. R.; Hardy, Lewis and Jefferson counties on the Baltimore and Ohio Railroad; and at Kline, Pendleton county.

North Carolina

The ochre industry in Madison county, North Carolina, has never been developed, but the deposits are very large. Ochres are also found in Cherokee and Clay counties, near the brown iron ores.

Georgia

Bartow county, Georgia, which embraces the Cartersville district, produces approximately one-half the yellow ochre output of the United States. The area is a narrow belt about 8 miles long and 2 miles wide, along the Etowah River. Fourteen miles north of Cuthbert, Randolph county, is a promising ochre deposit awaiting development. Between La Crosse and Ellaville, Schley county, is a 4-foot outcrop of ochre which has never been prospected. About 14 miles west of Savannah, Chatham county, is a large area which is underlain with "sap brown" in thickness from one to three feet. There has recently been discovered a short distance east of Saint George, Charlton county, an extensive deposit of "sap brown" and Van Dyke brown.

Kentucky

That area of Western Kentucky lying between the Tennessee, the Mississippi and the Ohio Rivers, and known as "Jackson's Purchase" carries large beds of yellow ochre. At Highland Landing, on the Tennessee River in Marshall county, the outcrop may be seen exposed in the river bank.

Tennessee

The ochre deposits of Eastern Tennessee are a continuation of the Blue Ridge deposits. At Butler, Johnson county, is a bed of very light colored ochre, about 2 miles from the railroad. At Athens, McMinn county, is a slightly darker colored deposit. The barytes beds of Cocke county are associated with ochre at Del Rio and Bluffton, grading in color from brown to yellow.

Alabama

Ochre is extensively distributed over Alabama. It is reported across the river from Columbus, Georgia, in Russell county, Alabama. Red ochre is mined at Attalla, Etowah county. Yellow ochre is shipped from Coosada, Elmore county, on the Louisville and Nashville Railroad, and from various points on the Mobile and Ohio Railroad, in Autauga county, lying to the west. Along the Mississippi-Alabama line, in Colbert county, about three miles south of the Southern Railway is a yellow ochre deposit of exceptionally fine grain, uniform coloring and purity.

Twenty-two miles north of Mobile, on the Gulf, Mobile & Northern R. R., in Mobile county, and at Guntersville, Marshall county, on the Nashville, Chattanooga and St. Louis Ry., are deposits available to transportation.

Macon county has a mineral clay which runs 45 per cent silica, 45 per cent alumina and 9 per cent iron oxide. This has been used by Prof. G. W. Carver of Tuskegee Institute in the production of Venetian reds, paint pigments and dyes. On account of its high alumina content it should also receive attention in the development of a suitable method of extraction. Fayette, Marion and Tuscaloosa counties also carry both red and yellow ochre.

At Oxford, Cherokee county, is a sienna deposit. Umber is found around Piedmont, Calhoun county, and pink paint pigment at Anniston, in the same county.

Mississippi

The ochre situation in Mississippi is good. Rail and water transportation are good, labor is plentiful, and the purely local developments have secured permanent markets in Kansas City and New Orleans, where the product is used in ceramics and paints. A wide variety of colors is available. In Tishomingo county, both red and yellow ochre are shipped. The yellow ochre is of superior quality and considerable extent, easily loaded from the hillside. On a branch of Leaf River, near the Gulf and Ship Island Railway in Smith county, is a deposit of pure yellow ochre two feet in thickness.

In Southern Benton and Tippah counties and in northern Union county, a ferruginous novaculite is found, which when burned and ground is a source of "mineral red" much used for painting telephone and telegraph pole cross-arms, railroad box cars, etc.

Large quantities of this material are available between Hickory Flat and Blue Mountain. It contains sufficient manganese to yield a rich umber when ground and roasted and is of very uniform texture.

Arkansas

In many localities in Arkansas, an ochre-clay or red chalk known as "reddle" is found. In Pulaski county brown ochre occurs in contact with brown iron ore, in Fourche Mountain. Yellow ochre is found near Monticello, Drew county, and Piggott, Clay county, but none of these have ever been developed beyond local consumption for home-made paints. A reddish ochre is also found on Hurricane creek in Saline county.

Texas

Yellow ochre beds were recently opened at Anderson, Newton county, Texas.

Uses

A fair grade of paint may be made by drying high grade ochrous clays and then grinding them with linseed oil. In addition to their use for paint pigments and dyes, these mineral pigments find a large market as a filler for linoleum and oilcloth. They are also used to color tiling and for various earthenware products, and as mortar color in connection with fancy building brick. Adequate facilities for washing and grinding, and good transportation are the principal requisites of the industry. Foreign competition is principally in the cheaper grades, as the higher grades of Southern ochre are recognized as equal or superior to any other.

Chapter V

CHALK, WHITING, BENTONITE, VOLCANIC ASH

Uses

Chalk is soft, pure white, or gray carbonate of lime, composed of microscopic marine shells. The imported chalk from England is called "Cliffstone." In addition to chemical purposes, where soft pure calcium carbonate is desired, it is used for cement, and for whiting. Chalk is also used for burnt and unburnt lime products, plaster, fire-brick, soap, bone ash, artificial gas, paper, pottery, egg preservatives, tanning materials, and the dehydration of alcohol.

Alabama

The Alabama deposits have been extensively studied, and a full account of them is to be found in Bulletin 522 of the United States Geological Survey. At Demopolis, Alabama, from 500 to 600 tons per day are produced for cement purposes.

Mississippi

The Selma chalk beds of Mississippi extend from Corinth in the northeast corner of the state, southward through Okolona and West Point, and pass out eastward into Alabama along the line between Noxubee and Kemper counties. They occupy a strip varying from 30 to 50 miles in width. The eastern edge of the deposit is approximately 100 feet thick, but to the south and west it increases.

Arkansas

The chalk cliffs of Arkansas are referred to in Chapter

XXV under limestones. These deposits being soft and pure, requiring little or no grinding, and being easily calcined are of great value. The cliffs are 150 feet in height, and are the only known deposits of their kind in the United States.

Texas

The Austin chalk of Texas extends northeastwardly from San Antonio through Austin, Waco and Dallas to Sherman. The northern part of the bed is about 600 feet thick, and the deposit dips south and east about 1 per cent. Near Dallas it is operated extensively. Chalks have been reported from Georgia, Tennessee and North Carolina, but it is not probable that these are true chalk.

Imported and domestic **whiting** are strong competitors of each other. The requirements of whiting for most uses depend on its physical properties, its color, grain and colloidal content. For ceramic purposes it must be low in iron oxide and at least 98 per cent calcium carbonate. It must show a minimum of 30 per cent colloidal particles and totally pass 150 mesh.

Uses

Whiting made from pure white marble contains 98 to 99 per cent calcium carbonate, the remainder being lime-magnesia-silicate. This is used for rubber filler and optical glass, and must pass 100 per cent through a 300 mesh screen. The marbles used for this grade, which is crystalline and not colloidal, come principally from Georgia, Tennessee, and North Carolina.

Since 1918 the domestic production of both crystalline and colloidal types has been much improved in quality, and is superior in stretching power in putty to the

English imported article. The Belgian product has never been a strong competitor.

The uses are for putty, gilding, linoleum, paint, chemicals used in the glass industry, and "paris white" for special moldings.

* * * * * *

Bentonite is a transported volcanic ash, altered after deposition. It swells to several times its actual size when soaked in water and becomes a soft creamy mass. It is colloidal, and after swelling will remain in suspension indefinitely in mixtures as dilute as one part of bentonite to 50 parts of water. It has much greater suspending power than ordinary enamelling clays. One part of bentonite is equivalent to five parts of clay. It is frequently called "colloidite." It may be easily distinguished from tripoli, fullers' earth and kaolin because these are not permanently colloidal. It may be waxy in appearance, or dull and powdery, cutting into pulverized grains or soapy shavings.

Uses

Bentonite is of such fine grain that one billion particles would be required to dot a surface one inch square, and it will pass through ordinary filters. It is distinctly adsorptive; that is, selectively absorbent, and therefore of particular value in de-inking processes.

It has a counterpart called montmorillonite, so similar as to require colloidal tests for determination. As a substitute for fullers' earth in bleaching oils, the montmorillonite is treated with sulphuric acid to remove the alkaline earths, and being non-colloidal, is found to be remarkably efficient, equivalent to 16 times that of corresponding amounts of fullers' earth.

As a water softener, true bentonite exhibits interchangeable properties, permitting easy replacement of alkaline oxides, and restoration by sodium chloride solution, so that it may be used repeatedly and easily rejuvenated.

It has for years been used in the form of antiphlogistine as a medical preparation and for packing horses' hoofs in desert travel. It has been found that as much as 50 per cent of soap substance can be replaced with bentonite and still give a good ordinary soap. This is due to its high porosity, so that if a slightly alkaline water or soap are used, only one-half as much soap is necessary to form a lather, which is carried into the most minute crevices by the infinitesimal particles.

Labels pasted on metal with bentonite glue will neither curl nor drop off. It is also a base for massage cream and toilet articles, one part of bentonite being equivalent to from three to five parts of other earths.

It is used in the dehydration of crude petroleum and other oils; as a heavy lubricant when mixed with oil; for the manufacture of lake colors; as a filler or dressing for leather; mixed with asphalt as an ingredient of felt and waterproof paper board; as a super-absorbent of glycerine in the manufacture of explosives; as a harmless adulterant of drugs and candies; as paper filler; as rubber filler; as a filler for phonograph records, textiles, cordage, and pressed and molded electrical insulation.

Its high plasticity makes it available with decreased quantities of bonding clays, molding sand in ceramics, and the manufacture of abrasive wheels, and graphite crucibles. Although increasing the drying shrinkage, it is nevertheless a valuable retarder for gypsum and lime plasters. Its use enables the enameler to reduce the amount of raw materials in the brit, or semi-fused material, before vitrification, and in wet-finish coats, especially white, the bentonite enamel has the best appearance.

Of greater economic importance than all of these, however, is the recent development in de-inking newspapers, so that they may be again used for news print, thus lessening the stupendous consumption of wood pulp for that purpose. Old newspapers have heretofore passed into the limbo of various grades of cardboard. When a mixture of varnish, oil, glue and carbon black, in the form of printers ink, is treated with soda ash or caustic soda, and filtered with a solution of bentonite, the carbon black is adsorbed and carried away from the mixture, leaving it decolored.

One ton of bentonite will thoroughly de-ink ten tons of newspaper, and the total cost of the clay, the gathering of the newspapers, and the process itself, is less than that of new pulp. The de-inked macerated paper pulp, with a small percentage of new wood pulp to strengthen the fibre, is again ready for the news print process.

Kentucky—Tennessee—Alabama

Bentonite was discovered in Bedford county, Tennessee, in 1920. It has been found to extend from Bessemer, Jefferson county, Alabama on the south, to Highbridge, Jessamine county, Kentucky, on the north, a distance of over 300 miles. The Jessamine county deposit, on the Southern Railway, is 10 feet thick. About 100 yards west of the C. N. O. & T. P. R. R. at Dayton, Rhea county, on the west side of the big spring which supplies the town with water, is a bentonite deposit about three feet thick, which dips about 25° under the mountain. On the Kentucky-Tennessee state line, in Pickett county, Tennessee, it is four feet thick. Fifty miles south, at Pikeville, Bledsoe county, Tennessee, it is three feet thick, while south of Birmingham, in Jefferson county, Alabama, it is 18 inches thick. These beds, which apparently cut out in Jefferson county, reappear as isolated deposits of exceptional purity about two miles from Montgomery, and of slightly lower grade near Mobile.

It is also found in Hamilton county, Tennessee, between Chattanooga and Ooltewah, and in Hawkins county, in northeast Tennessee, a deposit apparently parallel to the greater one, noted above. As noted in Chapter III, wherever bentonite beds are faulted, they should be followed up along the fault line for bauxite.

Mississippi

Deposits have also been noted along the G. M. & N. R. R. in southwest Tippah county, Mississippi, western Union county, and across Pontotoc county, in that state. Outcrops of bentonite are also exposed at Houlka, Chickasaw county, west of Woodland, in the same county, and near Maben, in both Webster and Oktibbeha counties. The State Geological Survey of Mississippi reports a deposit of bentonite in the Eutaw formation of Monroe county, southeast of Aberdeen, the deposit being from two to six feet thick. A similar deposit has been located just east of Booneville in the same formation.

Texas

At Riverside, in northern Walker county, Texas, along Trinity River, is a deposit which is being developed. A so-called fullers' earth has recently been found in the Taylor marls of Bexar county, in a horizon containing hydrated volcanic dust, which it is expected will prove, under sufficient prospecting, to be bentonite. This horizon is exposed in various parts of the Tertiary and the Cretaceous beds of the state, extending in a northeast and southwest direction about 175 feet above the Austin chalk.

Arkansas

The same situation exists in Arkansas, where in the southwestern section between Arkadelphia and Texarkana, it is necessary to determine the colloidal nature of the deposits.

It is probable that the development of the bentonite industry will prove one of the most rapid of all the minerals. Its bulk and hygroscopic qualities, however, make it necessary to establish other industries using it as raw material, near the source of supply. The chief mechanical difficulty encountered is the necessity for a special type of grinding machine, as the powder clogs the machine unless removed as fast as it is made.

* * * * * *

Uses

Volcanic ash, either loose or solid, is used in cement and as an abrasive in various polishing and cleansing compounds, in tooth powders and for insulating purposes. Sometimes known as "tuff," it is frequently found well sorted as a result of deposition in water.

When altered after such deposition it is commonly classed as bentonite, particularly when proven colloidal.

Louisiana

A deposit of considerable extent and very finely grained, covering several square miles, is found about eight miles southeast of Columbia, Louisiana. It will vitrify and glaze at comparatively low temperature and is available for soft abrasive and buff compounds. The bed is reported by the Missouri Pacific Railroad to be from 5 to 25 feet thick.

Chapter VI

COAL, LIGNITE, PEAT

The coal resources of the country have been so exhaustively treated by various authorities that less attention need be paid them, in a work of this kind, than to other minerals which have not been so exploited. The minable areas are well known, and for the most part the qualities of the various coals have been determined.

Reference is made in Chapter I to the overdevelopment of fuels in the South in comparison with other minerals. This, however, means simply that ample fuel development is already available for almost unlimited extension of the mining industry in the Southern states. The coal industry as a whole has become overdeveloped. Wage scale agreements and restricted immigration have, during the past year, tended somewhat to reduce this surplus so that uneconomic mines have in many instances been closed.

Improved methods of power generation, new mechanical devices for efficient fuel consumption, and greater attention to the selection of coals suited to local purposes, have all served to better the industry. One of the principal factors in determining the economic operation of any given district is freight rates. Inasmuch as coal is a bulk article of commerce, its future must always be determined by the markets available in competition with other sources of supply.

Divided into anthracite and bituminous, the latter is again subdivided into high volatile or gas coal, and medium and low volatile or steam coals. A characteristic of most gas coals and some steam coals is their coking quality.

Virginia

The reserves of Virginia are in three separate groups, the Richmond Basin, the Merrimac and the southwest fields. The deposits of the Richmond Basin are extensive, especially in Henrico and Chesterfield counties. Developments have all been on the east side of the area. The Basin is four to five thousand feet deep in the center; it is uneconomical to develop, except around the edges, at the present time. The Merrimac or "Valley" coal fields comprise Montgomery, Pulaski, Wythe, Bland and Roanoke counties, with limited extensions along the Botetourt-Craig county line, and a separate area in Augusta and Rockingham counties. The first three are the most important. This coal is a good grade of semi-anthracite, and is the only substitute east of Arkansas for Pennsylvania anthracite. The present tonnage is good, and there remains a considerable area to be developed. The product is similar to Lykens Valley coal and sells at approximately the Pennsylvania price when properly prepared. Because of its quality, it should be considered a valuable asset for domestic fuel supply wherever freight rates will permit it to compete.

The southwest Virginia field comprises Tazewell, Dickinson, Buchanan, Russell, Wise, Lee and Scott counties, and is the principal producer from point of tonnage. Scott county contains very little compared to the others. The entire area is held by a few controlling interests. The coal reserves are defined in Bulletins 9, 12, 18, 19, 21, 22, 24, and notably 25, of the State Geological Survey. Railroad service is available to all of these fields, and water service to a portion of the Richmond Basin.

West Virginia

West Virginia coals are voluminously covered by state and county reports. The state contains all grades of bituminous coal from the highest volatile low sulphur gas to low volatile smokeless coal. The smokeless coal area is principally in Wyoming, Mercer, McDowell, Raleigh and western Summers counties. The counties with undeveloped coal deposits of magnitude are Greenbrier, which has been opened up along the edge, and Nicholas, which is practically undeveloped. A general process of consolidation has taken place, so that vast areas are controlled by holding interests in the counties of older development. Much money was spent on a pseudo-anthracite deposit in Morgan county, which is really a series of horizontal alternating layers of slate and coal, which were crumbled together when the Blue Ridge was formed. A vein sample would show high ash, and it is commercially impracticable to wash the product.

The available merchantable coal in West Virginia has been estimated at 60,080,000,000 tons. To this may be added 100,000,000,000 tons of thin seams not now salable, but ultimately valuable. The state could thus provide for an annual consumption of 600,000,000 tons, in the United States, for a period of 250 years. Of the reserves mentioned, about 13,233,000,000 tons are smokeless, or low volatile coal.

North Carolina

The Deep River coal field of North Carolina has assumed importance not only because this coal is of good grade, but because its location is such as to command a considerable market, with favorable freight rates. Sixty-seven million tons have been blocked out in Moore, Lee and Chatham counties. It has been found to be a good steam coal, a fair gas coal, and a good coking coal. The basin is approximately 4 miles from rim to rim, with a maximum central depth of 2200 feet. This is a promising field for the production of metallurgical coke, which can also be crushed for domestic briquettes, while the by-product gas is used for power, and the by-product bitumen as a binder for the briquettes. In 1922 the state assumed sufficient importance in the industry to be numbered among the real coal producing states. It is of historical interest to note that this coal was used for the manufacture of illuminating gas, at the first commercial plant for this purpose, being sent by boat in 1853 to the Green Point, Long Island, gas works.

At the intersection of Lee, Moore and Chatham counties, along the Norfolk Southern Railway, near Carbonton, and extending westward along the Chatham-Moore county line, is a 3-foot vein of semi-anthracite, similar to the Virginia "Valley" coal, which has never been developed.

Georgia

The coal fields of Georgia are limited to Dade, Walker and Chattooga counties, in the northwest corner of the state, and are an extension of the Alabama fields. It is all coking coal, a good substitute for Pocahontas coal, and is nearly all shipped out of the state as coke. Over 900,000,000 tons remain available, so that there is no shortage of coal for Georgia industry.

Alabama

The Alabama fields, because of the great iron and steel industry, show a constant development. When the furnaces and mills are idle, or when labor troubles affect the coal industry, the usual economic fluctuations occur.

In connection with iron ore development in the same section, a tract of over a half million acres has been blocked into one organization in northwestern Alabama to ship coal down the Warrior River for export, and to develop chemical and other industries. The company claims its property to be underlain with three billion tons of Black Creek coal, a high volatile, low sulphur, low ash coal with high fusing point of ash. This is an excellent by-product coal and promises much for western and northern Alabama. Many Alabama coals are suitable for briquetting, and also for grinding and use as pulverized fuel. Mechanical atomization provides high efficiency under overload. More heat from an equal amount of fuel means lower costs, larger production, and prosperity for industry.

Mississippi

During the summer of 1924, while drilling a well at Guntown, Lee county, Mississippi, a vein of coal was encountered at about 250 feet. As the Selma chalk is at the surface at Guntown, with 250 to 300 feet of Eutaw sand between it and the Tuscaloosa lignite, it is probable that this is lignite, and not bituminous coal as at first reported.

Kentucky

The coals of southeastern Kentucky, which are an extension of the southern West Virginia high volatile coals on the one hand, and of southwestern Virginia on the other, are celebrated for their high heat value and coking quality. This coke has attained rank with the best Connellsville coke, and is largely used for metallurgical purposes. The largest undeveloped coal deposits occur at the headwaters of the Middle and South forks of Kentucky River, and in Martin and Pike counties, on Tug Fork of Big Sandy river. They reach outlet over several railroads and form the nucleus of a transportation area, which includes the great industrial consumers of the North, East and South.

Considerable attention has also been paid to the development of by-products and briquettes from these coals. Their by-product yield is very high. The problem of low temperature carbonization of coal, which gives a smokeless semi-coke for domestic use, and a large supply of liquid fuel, is receiving concerted scientific study abroad, and claiming greater attention in America. The Western district of Kentucky is also a high volatile coal area, whose product is used for gas and steam purposes. On account of existing freight rate structures it does not reach as large a market as the coals from the eastern end of the state.

Tennessee

The Cumberland Mountain coal field of Tennessee is 50 miles wide and extends north and south across the state. There are large areas of high grade coking coal, and others of lower grade. The Sewanee seam is the best coking coal in the state and the Jellico the best domestic coal. The northeastern coal field is similar to the Kentucky and Virginia coals. A considerable area of available high volatile, low ash and low sulphur coal occurs in Rhea county, and a cannel coal deposit is found in Campbell county.

Arkansas

The Arkansas coal field is in the west central part of

the state, in the valley of the Arkansas river. It was first opened for domestic purposes in 1841, but no material output was had until the railroads reached the field in 1883. Sebastian county, which is the most active field in the state, was opened in 1887. The coal ranges from sub-bituminous and bituminous into semi-anthracite, and in the extreme eastern part of the field, on the north side of the river, to anthracite. This furnishes the active domestic trade, and the balance suffers from keen competition with oil and gas from Oklahoma, Louisiana and Texas. Many individual undeveloped properties are offered for sale. The coal resources of the state have only been scratched.

Texas

Texas has three distinct coal fields, the bituminous of the north central, the cannel or sub-bituminous of the extreme south, and the great lignite belt which extends from below San Antonio to the Arkansas line. Most of the state's production is shipped as run-of-mine. The Eagle Pass coal, in Maverick county, is washed to reduce sulphur and ash. Over one-half the coal mined in the state comes from Erath county, the district being served by ten railroads. The cannel coal of Webb county runs over 50 per cent volatile combustible matter and takes high rank because of its low moisture content. It shades off in Zavala and Dimmitt counties, into sub-bituminous, which still farther northeast becomes lignite. There are several veins of coal from 2 to 3 feet in thickness in the north central area which have never been developed.

In west Texas, in the Chisos Mountain district, and south of Van Horn, in the Vieja valley, are some sub-bituminous veins running 2 to 4 feet thick, but all are cut by faults and folds. The Chisos quicksilver mine used cord wood for reduction until four years ago. They now use this coal, which is mined by Mexicans on free land.

Uses

In addition to its direct use as a fuel, coal when coked, supplies gas, ammonia, benzol and tar. Each of these is again susceptible of re-combination into a wide variety of further by-products. The tars especially yield valuable contributions to chemistry, dyestuffs and medicine. Among the most important of the coal tar derivatives are phenol, naphthalene, benzine, solvent naphtha, cresylic acid, pyridine, salicylates, aniline oil and salt, anthracene, creosote, dimethylaniline and xylene. Nitrated coal is a new material for paints and varnishes.

* * * * * *

The Gulf Coast **lignite** field includes parts of Alabama, Mississippi, Louisiana and Texas, covering about 83,700 square miles. Lignite has been reported in Houston county, Georgia, but it is not considered to be in commercial quantity, east of the Chattahoochee River, as the beds thin out in eastern Alabama.

Alabama

The Alabama lignites extend in a belt about 25 miles in width, from Choctaw and Washington counties on the west, through Clarke and Marengo counties, eastward across Wilcox, Butler, Crenshaw and Pike counties to the Chattahoochee River. They are best known in Marengo county, where at Nanafalia the bed exposed by the Tombigbee River is 6 to 7 feet thick. The strata are very flat, dipping about 30 to 40 feet to the mile. Other seams outcrop to the south, in Clarke county, on both the Tombigbee and the Alabama Rivers. The Nanafalia horizon is characterized by a conglomerate of little oyster shells, which may be traced from the Mississippi line to the Chattahoochee valley.

Mississippi

The Mississippi deposits begin at the Tennessee line and sweep southward in a belt from 20 to 40 miles wide to Webster and Choctaw counties, then bearing eastward through Kemper and Lauderdale counties where they join the Alabama beds described above. They vary in thickness from 1 to 6 feet, and dip about 30 feet to the mile. Where opened they have shown a good shale roof, and appear exceptionally clean, running up to 12,000 B. T. U. They are too friable, after exposure to the air, to stand transportation for domestic use and should therefore be briquetted or used for the manufacture of producer-gas. Although lying outside the well defined lignite belt, three seams of lignite outcrop in Smith county, north and east of the G. & S. I. R. R. A detailed report of the state's lignites has been published by the Mississippi Geological Survey, 1907, as Bulletin No. 3. The development of scientific and efficient methods of utilizing these great deposits is of importance to the people of Mississippi, for their forests are being rapidly exhausted, and other industries utilizing the clays and mineral deposits must have cheap fuel available if they are to be fostered.

At Louisville, Winston county, a limited deposit of sub-bituminous coal has been found, 44 inches thick, with sandstone roof. The G. M. & N. R. R. had a test entry driven in the hill a distance of 100 feet and a carload was shipped to Mobile, where it gave excellent service in the railroad shops and proved to be midway in quality between bituminous coal and typical lignite. This coal burns to a fine white waxy ash and stands handling very well. It is mined in large lumps, suitable for domestic fuel.

The lignite deposits of Louisiana and Mississippi have been found to contain approximately 80 pounds of ammonium sulphate per ton, as compared to a maximum of 35 pounds per ton from Texas lignites, lying farther west in the Gulf Coast area. This is equivalent to 65 pounds of recoverable nitrogen, which is of value in the manufacture of fertilizer.

Louisiana

Louisiana has issued a similar lignite report, Bulletin No. 8, which describes in detail the lignite formations which occur in the 15 northwest parishes of that state. DeSoto parish is the center of the industry, the beds increasing in thickness as they extend westward. The same problems regarding its marketing occur as in Mississippi, except that there is a keener competition with oil and natural gas in Louisiana.

The extensions of the lignites into Arkansas and Tennessee need receive no consideration at this time, as both these states have an abundance of true bituminous coal, and in Arkansas, the Smackover gas and oil field is adjacent.

Texas

As noted in the discussion of coal, in the earlier portion of this chapter, the lignite fields of Texas extend from the Arkansas-Louisiana line southwestwardly for a distance of 800 miles until they approach the cannel coal fields along the Rio Grande. Activities center about Milam, Lee, Bastrop and Fayette counties, although numerous operations dot the lines of railroads traversing the entire territory. The veins vary from 1 to 25 feet in thickness, and dip to the southeast. In Shelby and Wood counties a number of mines are in operation and there are many available properties undeveloped. The Milan county field around Rockdale produces a high grade lignite equal to the best Saskatchewan product. The minable reserves of Texas have been estimated at thirty billion tons.

The high moisture content and rapid disintegration of lignite after production necessitate large grate areas and mechanical stokers. When forced blast is employed it must be operated at low pressure or the fuel is blown from the fuel bed. When coking coal is available a mixture is found very satisfactory.

It is estimated that at a point distant from the mine one ton of high-grade coal is equivalent to two tons of lignite when both must be mined, handled, loaded, shipped, unloaded, stored and charged into the fire box. This ratio determines the distance from the mine in which lignite can compete in its natural state for industrial purposes. This would not apply, however, to domestic fuel, which is not purchased on the basis of heating value alone.

The problem of low temperature carbonization of this great fuel supply and the profitable extraction of its by-products should attract the attention of Texas industry. Tests made on the Milam county lignites show:

Gas .... 7571 cu. ft. per dry ton
Oil-mixed base .... Paraffin and coal tar. Oil sp. gr. 0.93 with a large amount of phenol
Ammonium sulphate .... 18 to 35 lbs. per ton
Motor spirits .... 6.89% per bbl. of oil
Kerosene ....21.38%   "   "   "   "
Gas oil .... 9.55%   "   "   "   "
Lubricants .... 4.74%   "   "   "   "
Paraffin .... 1.75%   "   "   "   "
Still coke left in oil ...... 6.86%   "   "   "   "
Creosote oil ....20.54%   "   "   "   "
Asphalt pitch ....20.89%   "   "   "   "

The briquettes resulting after these by-products have been extracted are an ideal smokeless domestic fuel which can be sold at one-third the price of delivered Arkansas anthracite and which contains only 10 per cent less heat units. The producer gas has a heating value of 360 to 400 B. T. U. per cubic foot.

The U. S. Bureau of Mines has designed a carbonizer in which the principle of internal combustion is used as heat. Some of the tar is used as a binder for the briquettes. It has been estimated that 40 pounds of tar per ton of air-dried lignite may be recovered under certain conditions and temperatures and that of this amount 25 per cent or more of lignite oil may be obtained. This in turn is an efficient fuel for internal combustion engines.

In European countries gas plants have been operated on powdered coal, powdered lignite, sawdust and various other powdered solids. Mr. Hamilton K. Avery of the Association of Commerce in New Orleans, La., has made a study of the various fuels with the following results:

Based on oil of 18,500 B. T. U., coal with 6 per cent moisture:

	Bit. coal	Lignite	Crude oil
Boiler efficiency	63.	75.	78.
Fuel in lbs. as fired, per boiler H. P.	5.13	3.97	2.34
Oil at $1. per bbl. equivalent to coal at $5. per ton	$1.85	$1.13	$1.00

The American Railway Association recommends as a basis for comparison 160 gallons of oil to 1 ton of coal. The cost of conversion from coal to oil burning is about $1500 per locomotive. When the price of oil per barrel on the tender decreases to less than one-third the price of coal per ton on the tender a change over is logical. Similar comparisons may be made with lignite, the average steam coal being assumed at 12,500 B. T. U.

A new process has recently been developed at the University of Texas whereby raw lignite is dehydrated by heating with oil in a closed retainer. Excess high volatile oil is removed after processing by superheated steam and the lignite charge cooled by a cold-water shower. The heavy oil remaining serves to film the pores of the lignite so that it will not reabsorb moisture or air-slack. It is claimed that by this process dehydrated lignite of improved fuel value can be delivered at Austin for less than the present raw product, when considered on a B. T. U. basis.

Uses

In addition to the making of briquettes many synthetic products may be produced from lignite, such as aniline dyes, photo-chemicals and coal-tar preparations. From the carbolic and creosote fractions are derived carbolic acid, creosote, lysol, creoline, salycilic acid, asperin, oil of wintergreen, picric acid, phenacetin, and many dyes, chemicals and perfumes. Carbolineum, used as a wood preservative in road making, and in the manufacture of lamp black; gas-enriching oils, paraffin, disinfectants, asphalt pitches for roofing, insulating and waterproofing, all offer remunerative inducement for industry.

Powdered lignite is used to preserve eggs in summer and as a mixture with cane juice for filtration, its colloidal properties serving as a de-colorizer, the filtrate being bright and almost colorless, and the residue from the filters being afterwards used as fuel under the evaporating pans. Powdered lignite is also used as an ingredient of hollow tiles. The lignite, on burning out, imparts a certain porosity which is desirable.

Carbonized lignite is equal to animal charcoal as a decolorizer. When purified with hydrochloric acid it is superior to either animal charcoal or rice hull carbon, and as a commercial proposition is a promising competitor of the various vegetable carbons used in sugar manufacture. When fully carbonized it is highly gas-adsorptive (selectively absorbent) and when treated with hydrochloric acid and dilute ammonia it adsorbs and retains 145 volumes of chlorine gas. Hence, as a catalyzer it is of great value in the production of carbon tetrachloride, used in chemical warfare.

Lignite is used in Germany for the creation of montan wax which is extracted by the use of benzol and other solvents. Its early uses were for blacking, phonograph cylinders, impregnating woven belts, cable covering, roofing composition, adhesive greases, stove polish, insulting material and paper sizing. During the war it was used as a lubricating grease.

The crude wax is dark brown in color with a slight aromatic odor but when refined and bleached to a white or pale yellow it is used for candles consumed in tropical temperatures, carbon papers and crayons.

The bleached wax is also added to paraffin to offset its low melting point while the by-products of the bleaching process are used for impregnating explosives in polishing metals and in the manufacture of varnishes.

A combination of montan wax and soda, when mixed with seven parts of water, is used as a protective coating against water and chemical action for containers, packing bags and special printing papers.

Six American companies are engaged in experimentation in wood preservation with montan wax and also in the creation of oil soluble dyes.

* * * * * *

Peat ranges in color from light brown to black, and in texture from loosely-fibrous woody material to a structureless cheesey mass nearly as plastic as clay or putty. In all cases it contains 80 per cent to 90 per cent water, and the first problem in connection with its commercial use is drying. It owes its preservation to the presence of humic acid. As a direct fertilizer and a culture medium for nitrifying organisms, peat offers a domestic source of nitrogen at a price economical to the farmer.

Uses

Originally viewed solely as a fuel, which, however, requires briquetting to make it commercially available, peat developed into a fertilizer filler, and has been used as an insulator in packing, and as fibre in the manufacture of paper. It also finds a market as an absorbent for the uncrystallized residues of beet and cane sugar for the manufacture of stock feed. During the war it was used in

Europe as a substitute for absorbent dressings and as cloth fibre.

If crude peat is allowed to air dry and the remaining moisture is then driven off with waste heat from the flues it can be pulverized and used as powdered fuel with good success, the ignition being instantaneous and the resulting gas giving uniform heat. Peat powder is also available for cement and other kilns; and producer-gas from peat is similar to that from lignite.

North Carolina peat, which is high in carbon and volatile matter, has been used for the production of wood tar, wood alcohol, and ammonia compounds.

As an absorbent and deodorizer of stable liquids peat is superior to lime or ashes. It is used in refrigerating plants as an absorbent with mineral wool; and as packing and stuffing for furniture and mattresses in place of excelsior and as a mineral absorbent for waterproofing. The disintegrated grades, with certain clays, are used for medicinal mud baths.

In Germany peat fibre is used for weaving carpets, draperies, sacking and working clothing. Peat is also combined with wax under pressure, and the product impervious to water is used for railroad ties and paving material.

Virginia—North Carolina

The extent and quality of the peat deposits in the swamps of Eastern Virginia have never been carefully studied. The Great Dismal Swamp, beginning in Virginia, finds its major portion in North Carolina. The peat bogs of the swamp itself rarely exceed six feet in depth. But peat from the marginal swamps around the sounds and estuaries near Elizabeth City, Pasquotank county, at a depth of sixteen feet gives off a strong hydrogen sulphide odor and has been readily briquetted. A large acreage is available in Pasquotank, Craven, Camden, Currituck, Perquimans and Sampson counties.

Florida

While peat formations are found along the coastal plain of the entire Eastern United States, the next great deposit south of Virginia-North Carolina is that of Florida. There are vast deposits of peat in the Everglades and other separate areas, as at Palatka and Canal Point, where on the south edge of Lake Okeechobee an experimental plant is working out fuel values, producer-gas possibilities and improved fertilizer fillers. The peat around Fellsmere, St. Lucie county, is exceptionally high in nitrogen and should make an excellent fertilizer base.

An entirely recent development, and one offering sufficient inducement to warrant attention, is the utilization of peat for the propagation of micro-organic fertilizers. Farms are abandoned and farming communities scattered because of progressive impoverishment of the soil, which makes profitable operation an economic impossibility. Nor does a mere plant stimulant meet the requirement.

A nitrogenous supply of plant food is essential. Peat, which is of itself nitrogenous humus, is capable of a rapid increase in soluble nitrogen by bacterial action. When a mixture consisting of 90 per cent peat and 10 per cent lime and phosphorous is added to the soil, its decomposition furnishes the food necessary for the bacteria which render the nitrogen available to the plants at a much lower cost than the usual methods of fertilization. Such a mixture restores the porous quality to clay land and prevents too rapid drainage of sandy soils.

In commercial fertilizer, such as is commonly used throughout the South, known as "8-3-3" mixture, each 200-pound sack contains 16 pounds of phosphates, 3 pounds of nitrates, and 3 pounds of potash, or a total of 28 pounds of plant food and 172 pounds of inert filler. Filler is necessary in order that the potent ingredients may have a proper distribution over the surface of the soil and not be applied in such concentrated form that they would burn out plant life, but as fertilizer the average filler is useless. If, instead, as a filler, we use well decomposed peat combined with lime, we secure a nitrogenous humate of lime which is immediately available for plant life.

To develop a peat bed to high bacteriological efficiency it is necessary to drain it and also to impound water above it so that its irrigation may be controlled. Its acidity is regulated by the application of lime and wood ashes. Many bacterial fungi of the soil are vitamine producers; others are nitrogen gathering; while others act as anti-toxins. A peat-humus fertilizing compound should show 1 per cent alkaline reaction. In Virginia in 1918 nine first prizes were awarded farmers for crops raised on micro-organic fertilizer to the extent of only 500 pounds per acre.

When we consider that in 1910 the thirteen Southern states used four million tons of commercial fertilizer, and in 1920 five and one-quarter million tons, an increase of nearly one-third, the opportunity to increase the value of the fertilizer itself, to utilize the great peat resources of Virginia, the Carolinas and Florida, and to increase the productivity of weak or impoverished soils by the addition of this nitrogenous component so close at hand, becomes apparent.

Chapter VII

PETROLEUM, OIL SHALE, ASPHALT ROCK

The general subject of oil and oil resources, like coal and clay, might well justify an entire volume in itself. So much valuable literature is available, and the subject has been so adequately covered, however, in current periodicals and works of reference, the writer will confine this chapter to the direct interest of the Southern states in their own oil reserves.

In 1922 the American Association of Petroleum Geologists and the United States Geological Survey estimated the reserves of the South as follows:

West Virginia	200 million barrels
Kentucky, Missippi, Northern Alabama	175 " "
Northern Louisiana, Arkansas	525 " "
Texas (except Gulf Coast)	670 " "
Texas Gulf Coast, Southern Louisiana	2100 " "
East Gulf Coastal Plain and Atlantic Coast States	10 " "
	3680 " "

or approximately 40 per cent of the total reserves in the United States.

Until 1906 the petroleum industry existed primarily to supply the world with kerosene. With the development of the internal combustion engine and its application to motor cars, vessels and airplanes, the gasoline and lubricating oil business caused an increase in investment from $750,000,000 to over $12,000,000,000.

In 1923 the South produced 59 per cent of the country's

output and 40 per cent of the world's output. The oil industry is, therefore, of particular interest in these states. The Bureau of Mines reports a loss of 6 per cent between the well and the refinery and another 4 per cent at the refinery. These wastes are a part of the economic problem in connection with oil production and supply, which is receiving marked attention and intensive application. The United States consumes 70 per cent of the world's oil. The per capita consumption in 1924 was 225.8 gallons, as compared to 8.2 gallons for the balance of the world. Approximately 50,000,000 barrels of oil are now consumed for industrial heating each year.

Advocates of fuel conservation look forward to the day when coal will be turned into by-product gas for domestic heating and fuel oil will be confined to industries and transportation. Already the wood distillates have become a factor, one plant in Northern Michigan turning out 135 pounds of acetate of lime, 61 gallons of methyl alcohol, 610 pounds of charcoal, 15 gallons of tar, heavy oils, light oils and creosote and 600 cubic feet of fuel gas, per ton of wood distilled. The higher extraction of gasoline from crude oil and natural gas, and the evolution of internal combustion fuels from distillates all tend toward an extention of reserves.

West Virginia

Special reports of the West Virginia Geological Survey cover that state adequately, with the exception of eastern Nicholas county, where the structure is not wholly worked out.

North Carolina

Speculation regarding the presence of oil in commercial quantities along the Coastal Plain in North Carolina has been rife for many years. A few months ago a company was organized and financed to drill at a point about five miles west of Havelock, Craven county, on the edge of Lake Ellis, to a depth, if necessary, of 3500 feet, at which level the question of oil should no longer sustain any degree of dispute. Drilling has reached a white water-bearing sand at 121 feet and was proceeding at last reports.

This hole will prove of great scientific value concerning the structure of the Northeast Coastal Plain, as it will for the first time make available the relative thickness of the various horizons and the depth and character of the "basement rock" lying below the tertiary formations.

Georgia

The Georgia Geological Survey has recently issued a report on petroleum possibilities in that state. The formations in Georgia, so far as known and tested, are not very encouraging for any large fields. The Southeast Coastal Plain, if oil bearing, is at too great a depth for drilling, and their value would lie in being a source from which migration of oil to higher horizons could take place.

The most promising field is along a structural arch in the Thomasville, Thomas county, area. Next is along the crest extending from Camilla, Mitchell county, through Valdosta, Lowndes county, and eastward between Statenville, Echols county, and Thelma, Clinch county. A third structure is found along a line drawn midway between Douglas and Broxton, Coffee county, and Osierfield and Ocilla, Irwin county, in an east and west direction. The fourth and last is along an arch from Claxton, Evans county, northward to Metter, Candler county, and passing about twelve miles east of Swainsboro, Emanuel county, still farther north.

Oil has been reported, but not proven up, at Carnesville, Franklin county.

Florida

At Oldsmar, Pinellas county, Florida, an exploration syndicate has done considerable drilling, and a 1000-barrel well was reported at a depth of 3200 feet, passing through sands at 700 and 2100 feet. Because of the coral formation, Florida has been considered barren territory for oil. This opens up a new district for drilling and, if true, proves the existence of oil on all sides of the Gulf of Mexico. Further prospecting is reported in "The Petroleum Possibilities of Florida," 1922, by E. H. Sellers and Herman Gunter, state geologist, in which the Sumter, Citrus, Escambia, Wakulla, Brevard, Gadsden, Calhoun, Walton, Washington, Leon and Lee county wells are logged and detailed stratigraphy discussed.

In Okeechobee county, a drilling operation in April, 1926, reported bailing oil at 2770 feet. Other operations in this county and at Brooksville, Hernando county, Monticello, Jefferson county, and at Bradentown, Manatee county, have been reported, but it is impossible to segregate legitimate development from promotion and real estate selling.

Kentucky

The undeveloped petroleum fields of Kentucky occur in Lawrence, Elliott, Carter, Morgan, Owsley and Jackson counties in the eastern part of the state, and a problematical stretch extending southwestward into Clinton, Cumberland, Monroe, Metcalfe and Adair counties. Warren, Estill, Lee and other counties, where development is already under way, have been discussed in the oil trade papers and survey reports.

Tennessee

Oil is now being produced in Scott and Clay counties, Tennessee, in small units, and has been produced in past years in Pickett, Overton, Fentress and Dixon counties. These pools were small and no others were found. Excessive county taxes have held up prospecting in many counties.

Tennessee oil production may logically be expected to increase from year to year, with a small annual production, plus the unknown possibilities of Western Tennessee, which is underlaid with the same sands as Smackover and El Dorado, Arkansas, and also Northern Mississippi.

Alabama

Alabama has been carefully surveyed for oil. There are limited areas, analogous to those in Georgia, where wild catting would probably bring in some small pools and establish minor domes. The valuable petroliferous rocks and shales of Alabama appear to be around Cherokee and Margerum, Colbert county, where both sandstone and limestone are saturated and where asphalt rock occurs, as will be noted below.

Mississippi

The Mississippi situation is decidedly interesting. Funds have not been available for the State Geological Survey to extend its work on structures, although a considerable amount of field work is recorded in the Biennial Report for 1921-23.

While the anticline, dome or fault is the structure to be sought in determining the location of oil or gas accumulations, such structure is by no means always evident on the surface, due to deformation by erosion. Most of the hills and ridges in Mississippi are erosional, and not structural; yet there are anticlines in the state. The city of Jackson is located in a valley, yet it is built on a broad anticline. Drilling and careful comparison of the logs is the only scientific method of correlating the structural series. This is reduced to an exact science by the system of peg models in use in California and elsewhere, in which a large scale map of any district is mounted on the top of a soft pine table. Holes are drilled at the exact location of the well and a dowel some 18 or more inches in length inserted securely. The log of the well is then drawn to scale, usually 100 feet to the inch, and mounted, with reference to a given datum, on the dowel pin. As soon as a few wells have been drilled in the given area the points on the various pegs, where any given formation was encountered, are connected by colored strings. In this manner the dip and strike of the series may be visualized and by the insertion of a peg at any given point the contact depth of any structure may be projected.

The total cost of installation and maintenance of such a system is more than recovered in drilling any one well after its inauguration. To accomplish the proper results, however, all logs must be carefully recorded and pass through a central department of mines, or the Geological Survey, whose function it is to plat these logs and keep the peg model up to date, where it may be available to all interested.

The anticlinal work in Mississippi is not completed. At Columbus, Lowndes county, a 2000-foot well has not yet reach the Paleozoic. Just west of the prairies in Chickasaw county and north in Union county it was struck at 1400 feet. This would appear to be faulting, which is not visible on the surface. Drilling is being done in Washington county, near Pascagoula, Jackson county, and at least 50 wells in various parts of the state were completed and several under way in 1924. These are described in "Petroleum Prospecting in Mississippi," by Prof. P. F. Morse, in Vol. VII, No. 6, of the *Bulletin of the American Association of Petroleum Geologists*.

A gas well recently brought in at Amory, Monroe county, offers an accurate log upon which further development may be predicated.

The conclusion is inescapable that the majority of these wells are not drilled on the proper structure, and that the balance are either too shallow or were abandoned because of financial or mechanical difficulties before completion. The physical characteristics and fauna of Mississippi are identical with those of Louisiana and Arkansas. The field is, therefore, a legitimate one for further exploitation. The reader is referred to pages 34-60 of the biennial report mentioned above for a discussion of possible oil horizons.

Louisiana

The fields of Louisiana vary from fourth to seventh in national production, depending upon new production from year to year. This growth has only been a factor since 1901. Prospecting is carried on under the supervision of the State Department of Conservation along scientific and economic lines. Principal development has been in Northern Louisiana adjacent to the Smackover field in Arkansas. In 1927 three new fields were brought in in Sabine, Calcasieu and Cameron parishes and two new deep productive oil horizons in the old Pine Island field in Caddo parish.

Arkansas

The first production of oil in commercial quantities in Arkansas came from the Hunter well, near Stephens, Ouachita county, late in 1920. The second well was about eight miles southwest of El Dorado, Union county, and came in about a month later. Neither well created much excitement, and the Arkansas oil boom really dates from a third well which came in about one mile southwest of El Dorado in January, 1921, with a daily production of 10,000 barrels. The state first appeared in the reports of the United States Geological Survey as an oil-producing state in March, 1921, and on July 1st of that year stood seventh in production. In April, 1924, it had assumed fourth place.

There are seven and, possibly, eight producing fields in Arkansas at the present time, the El Dorado, East El Dorado, Lisbon, Smackover, Stephens, Irma and Bradley, with an eighth potential field near Urbana in Union county. The El Dorado field has produced 37,966,360 barrels from 1380 wells up to January 1, 1926. The East El Dorado field reached a maximum production of 10,000 barrels daily in 1923. The Lisbon field in 1926 averaged 11,750 barrels per day. The Smackover field reached peak production of 443,950 barrels per day in May, 1925. The Stephens field, from 252 wells now averages 1500 per day. The Irma field, with 56 wells, produces about 1900 barrels per day. Five small producing wells have been drilled in the Bradley field and two wells near Urbana. Total 1927 production was 37,533,650 barrels, a slight decrease of peak production previously.

As development continues in the Smackover field, in recently discovered deep sands, a flood of heavy oil is resulting. It is below 20 gravity and almost devoid of gasoline content.

The outcropping Quaternary rocks form a thin covering of alluvial materials on the Tertiary beds along the flood plains. These beds are carbonaceous clay, marl and sandstone, dipping and thickening to the southeast, reaching a maximum thickness of 2000 feet.

The oil is a distinctly Coastal Plain oil; and one-half the state of Arkansas is Coastal Plain. The rocks have not been altered to a degree that would injure oil accumulations, and the entire area, which was once the shore of the Gulf of Mexico, has accumulated organic matter of the sea and adjacent land. The same conditions obtain in Western Tennessee and Mississippi, and it is logical, therefore, to anticipate interesting developments in these littoral beds.

It is to be hoped that funds will be provided for the establishment and maintenance of peg models in this state, as a direct means of conservation and intelligent prospecting.

Texas

In Texas, beginning at the Rio Grande, there is a chain of shallow oil fields extending northward from Zapata and Webb counties into Wilson and Bexar counties. The present operations in this district are in the upper Cretaceous structure. To the east are found the salt dome formations, in Duval county, and extending north into McMullen, Live Oak and Atacosa counties. Shallow fields are in operation from Wilson county northward through Bastrop, Fayette and Milam counties to Navarro county and westward through Medina and Uvalde counties to Val Verde county. Milam county is a center for oil, lignite and clay, and should, therefore, be a logical center for manufacturing and distribution over its several railroad lines. The same situation is found in Texas as in Arkansas, regarding the need for peg models.

The older pools are described in the "Mineral Resources of the United States" for 1922, pp. 367-368. The oil structures of the entire state are discussed in Bulletin 44, 3rd edition, 1919, of the University of Texas, on pp. 138-149, inclusive, together with maps and charts.

* * * * * *

Oil shale is a shaly deposit from which petroleum may be obtained by distillation, but not by trituration or by solvents. In oil sand the oil is contained in the sand, as oil. The two forms should not be confused.

Oil shales will normally be mined like coal. Most of the richer shales are soft, tough and springy, and will require slow-burning, low-strength explosives. It is probable that coal-cutting machines and mechanical loaders will be used. Operations should be on a large scale and conducted with engineering skill, and chemical efficiency. On a tonnage basis analogous to coal mining, the cost should be somewhat less than that of mining coal.

Uses

Water-white gasoline can be made from crude shale oil with a refining loss of 5 per cent, at an operating cost favorably comparable to that of refining well oil. Satisfactory progress has been made in the production of high-grade lubricants, paraffin wax, kerosene, fuel oils and **minor** products. Carbon black of high quality can **be** made at small cost. Other by-products are cement materials, furniture polish, and automobile polish.

It is conceded that oil prices must eventually rise. Refiners would welcome stabilization, if a constant supply were assured, since wide fluctuations in both price and supply do not promote profits. Oil shale appears to be the ultimate stabilizing medium. There is an almost inexhaustible supply; retorting processes have proved successful; shale oil is superior to well oil, not only for the crude, but for fractional distillation and refining. The flash point, viscosity, body and wearing qualities of shale oil are also said to be superior. Shale gasoline has a higher specific gravity than petroleum gasoline, but volatilizes as readily and gives more power.

Upon distillation, American oil shales yield from 15 gallons up to 100 gallons of oil per ton. An oil shale plant with its own local refinery would be a permanent development. The by-products of oil shale at present-day prices reach a gross jobbing value of $15 per barrel; while the cost of plant installation will run from $100,000 to $300,000.

Even though substantial additions are made to known oil reserves, both at home and abroad, the problem of meeting increased demand is of vital importance. As domestic demand increases, prices will likewise increase, and after a time depletion is inevitable. In the past ten years automobiles have increased 260 per cent, while gasoline production has only increased 145 per cent. Oil pools are merely reservoirs certain to become exhausted in a few years, while a steady and almost inexhaustible supply of shale oil is available in advantageous locations for distribution.

When the cost of supplying oil from wells approximates that from oil shale, the latter will become an established and paying industry. An interesting sidelight on consumption of gasoline is the estimate that if all the coal mined in the United States in one year were coked in by-product ovens, the quantity of motor fuel so produced would amount to 20 per cent of the annual domestic consumption of gasoline.

A price of $2.50 to $3.00 per barrel in the mid-continent field will mean pronounced activity in oil-shale mining. Regulations promulgated in 1916 by the United States Geological Survey for oil shale operation on public lands provide that open-cut mining must yield 750 barrels of oil per acre in beds not less than 6 inches thick and yielding not less than 15 gallons per ton. Where the beds are too deep for open cutting and must be mined they must be not less than one foot thick and capable of yielding not less than 1500 barrels of oil per acre, or 15 gallons per ton. It is considered that one gallon of oil per ton of rock is equivalent to 50 barrels of 42 gallons each, of crude shale oil per acre-foot.

Pioneer oil shale research in the United States has been carried on by Dr. Victor C. Alderson, formerly president of Colorado School of Mines, to whose book, "The Oil Shale Industry," the reader is referred for an enlightening treatise on the subject. Dr. Alderson felicitously states that "If oil is 'king,' oil shale is the 'heir apparent.'"

West Virginia

The oil shales of West Virginia are thin, but very rich in yield. They are found principally in Fayette and Kanawha counties, and are described in the Kanawha county report of the West Virginia Geological Survey.

North Carolina

No attention has been paid to oil shale development in North Carolina; but at Gulf, in southern Chatham county, is a considerable area of oil shale, apparently shading into and overlain by oil sand. After a heavy rain, the country road is greasy with "oil float," which is reported by test to be mineral oil.

Kentucky

The Kentucky oil shales lie in a horseshoe of fifty miles radius around Lexington, Fayette county. These bluffs and escarpments of Devonian shale cross from Indiana, curving southward, eastward and northward into Ohio, a total distance of 250 miles. Another bed is found along the Cumberland River in Southern Kentucky, and a third of lesser importance in the cannel and Sunbury shales of the Eastern and Western Kentucky coal fields. Commercial outcrops are found in 33 counties.

Much attention has been given to these deposits by Dr. W. R. Jillson, state geologist, and Prof. C. S. Crouse, of the University of Kentucky. The average thickness of the horseshoe-shaped deposit is 50 feet, although much of it is 200 feet, and can be worked for three miles back from the outcrop. The average weight is 130 pounds per cubic foot, from which it is estimated that in this one deposit in the state of Kentucky alone there are available 90,604,800,000 tons of shale. The average oil content is 16 gallons per ton, with a recovery of 25-30 gallons per ton in selected areas. The specific gravity of the shale is 2.173, and the sulphur content varies from 1.5 per cent to 4.15

per cent. The sulphur occurs as pyrites and is unevenly distributed. The nitrogen equivalent is 97.8 pounds of ammonium sulphate per ton, of which Prof. Crouse estimates 50 per cent recoverable, thus yielding a further offset to the cost of producing oil from shale. The recoverable K_2O runs from 38-58 pounds per ton.

It is claimed for this deposit, which is the largest east of the Mississippi River, that it more nearly resembles the Scotch shales than any other, yielding more ammonium sulphate. The Kentucky shales, alone, contain, by Prof. Crouse's estimate, more than four times as much recoverable oil as the combined well-oil reserves of the United States, recoverable without undue expense or effort. Nor is the deposit limited to the area of the eroded Cincinnati uplift. It has been encountered in oil drilling in Breathitt county, at 340 feet depth, 30 miles east of the shale outcrop.

The oil production of Kentucky is so limited that within the next few years it is probable shale distillation will be commercially in operation.

Tennessee

The oil shale area of Tennessee covers 30 out of 93 counties. The Chattanooga black shale yields 8-40 gallons of oil per ton, averaging 10-15 gallons. The refined products and by-products should all be made on the ground, using the waste gas and heat for distillation.

A shipment of cannel shale was made to Switzerland from a 6000-acre tract near Newcomb, Campbell county, and reported as yielding 100 gallons of oil per ton. If this test is authentic, such a shale would approach the Australian shale in yield, and would be well worth development.

The Cheatham county shale along the Tennessee Central R. R. yields 10 gallons per ton and is used as a base for paint.

Alabama

The shale formations of Kentucky and Tennessee extend into Northern Alabama. They occur in Etowah and De Kalb counties in the northeast and around Cherokee and Margerum, Colbert county, in the northwest. They thin out, however, to the south. Experimental plants are being built and developments closely watched. The shales are said to bear marked resemblance to the Colorado deposits.

Mississippi

It is possible that a limited amount may be found in northeastern Mississippi under the limestones, as an extension of the Alabama beds, but no prospecting has been done.

Arkansas

The Chattanooga, Bloyd and Fayetteville shales of northwest Arkansas carry oil, but have never been developed. Branner's report, Arkansas Geological Survey, 1888, and Folio 202 of the United States Geological Survey discuss these formations.

Texas

The Eagle Ford shales of East Central Texas in Bell, McClennon, Williamson and Burnet counties have shown a good oil yield in such tests as have been made, but with the present oil resources of the state, no inducement at present exists toward their development.

Special mention may be made of the Burnet county deposits, which are gray in color and contain many marine fossils. The Engineering and Mining Journal-Press of November 10, 1923, says:

"**Ichthyol,** according to Sir Edward Thorpe, in his dictionary of applied chemistry, is a pharmaceutical product of oily consistency, distilled from fossilized fish remains found in the Tyrol, on the coast of the Adriatic, and in other places in Europe. The chief source of the crude product is in the Seefeld district between southern Bavaria and the Tyrol, where it has long been used as an antiseptic. The crude rock oil is obtained by simple distillation from the shale. It is extensively used by the medical profession."

Uses

In Burnet county, crude ichthyol is being mined, the shale yielding about 125 pounds of ichthyol per ton. By-products such as shellac, paint, stove polish and disinfectants are produced. The crude material ranges in the United States from $5 to $10 per pound, while the refined product has sold as high as $7 per ounce. In Bexar county, west of San Antonio, an ichthyol deposit is reported at 167-foot depth.

* * * * * *

The **asphalt** industry depends for its principal markets on the roofing and paving industry. In this chapter only asphalt sand and rock, used principally for road material, will be considered. Asphalt sand and rock are the oldest waterproofing material known to man, and antedate all other known road materials. They were used to pave a street in Babylon by King Nabapolassar 2500 B. C., or practically four and one-half centuries ago.

Asphalt impregnated limestone and sandstone were discovered in Trinidad and Venezuela, mixed with vegetable and mineral matter in pools and lakes. Within the last ten years apparently inexhaustible quantities have been found embodied in the heavy petroleums of Mexico and California. These are now refined, the lighter oils removed, and a 99.5 per cent bitumen remains. Sixty-eight per cent of the road building asphalt used in the United States at the present time is obtained from Mexican petroleum.

Bulletin 691-J of the U. S. Geological Survey on "Asphalt and Oil" is pertinent to this Chapter.

Kentucky

Rock asphalt constitutes one of Kentucky's largest undeveloped resources. The deposits are essentially bituminous sandstones, known as the "Big Clifty" of the Mississippian age, and the "Pottsville Conglomerate," of the Pennsylvanian. In western Kentucky the deposits occur in Edmonson, Grayson, Hart, Hardin, Warren, Logan, Todd, Butler, Ohio, Breckenridge, Christian, Muhlenberg and Hopkins counties. The eastern Kentucky deposits are not as numerous. It is found near Soldier, Carter county, along the Chesapeake and Ohio R. R. and on the border of Rowan and Elliott counties. There are deposits of problematical value in Johnson, Letcher, Bell and other counties along the western border of the eastern coalfield.

In western Kentucky, commercial operations have been under way for upwards of 20 years, on a small scale. In 1916 a tract of 50,000 acres was blocked and leased on the Nolin River, a tributary of Green River, around Kyrock, Edmondson county.

Another operation was installed in 1922 at Bear Creek in the same county. Two other plants are working, at Summit, Hardin county, and Big Clifty, Grayson county. These various plants ship by both rail and water. At least six others are being promoted.

Up to the present time, the chief obstacles have been transportation, quarrying and milling methods. These have been to some extent solved, but transportation problems retard the largest development, those on Nolin River and Bear Creek. Small stream transportation is a serious and expensive obstacle to large production.

The rock asphalt which occurs in Carter county is a much more volatile sandstone than that which occurs in Edmondson, Hardin and Grayson counties. Asphalt impregnated limestones of undetermined commercial value are found in Bell and Nelson counties.

In general, the Kentucky asphalt rock varies from 10 to 50 feet in thickness, in old oil sands brought to volatilization by erosion. There has been invested in the mines of Kentucky in the production of natural rock asphalt approximately $7,500,000, and shipments from these mines during 1925 amount to enough material to lay in streets and roads approximately 5,000,000 square yards of surfacing, and there was a decided increase in this production during 1926.

"Kentucky stands at the head of any other locality in the world in the production of natural rock asphalt."

Alabama

The petroleum formation around Margerum, Colbert county, Alabama, has been previously referred to. This formation extends north into Lauderdale county and south into Franklin county, along the Southern Ry. In most cases the asphaltic material is available for steam shovel operation.

Mississippi

At Iuka, Tishomingo county, Mississippi, the asphaltic limestone area is of several thousand acres extent. If 4 per cent bitumen is added when it is heated and rolled, it makes an exceptional road material and is shipped as far as Dallas, Texas, in competition with other materials.

Louisiana

In Terre Bonne parish, Louisiana, asphalt from the bed of the Gulf of Mexico is washed up along the shore. As the midway formation is 2700 feet down at this point, its outcropping must evidently be far out in the Gulf.

Uses

So active is the demand for road binder in Louisiana, the pine stump distillation process has been actively developed. The charcoal finds a good market; the heavy oils go into turpentine, and the oil of pine is used in flotation. The waste pitch and tar are then available for road oil, road binder, and as a binder for lignite briquettes.

Proligneous acid and acetate of lime are also waste products from this process. The former is used for destroying mosquito larvae, and from the latter are obtained acetone, acetic acid and allied derivatives.

Arkansas

In 1918 the U. S. Geological Survey issued Bulletin 691-J on asphalt deposits in southwest Arkansas. Three deposits were noted in Pike county and four in Sevier county. They occur in the Trinity sands, and are obviously an extension of the Texas deposits, noted below.

The Iron Mountain and the Kansas City Southern Rys. serve the district. Opened in 1903, the asphalt sand from Pike county has long been shipped to Little Rock and elsewhere, and used for street paving. It has but little cover, and is mined by stripping and open cutting. The sand hardens on exposure to the sun and makes a natural paving mixture. Occasional portions are too rich to be used in the natural state. No experiments have been made, however, toward refining it for pure asphaltum.

Texas

Asphalt is generally distributed in Texas as in Arkansas, in the Trinity sands, in which it occurs in many of the northern counties. It is also found in the Port Hudson clays at Sour Lake, Hardin county. In south Texas it is found in the shell breccia of the Anacacho limestone in Uvalde, Kinney, Maverick and Zavalla counties. The breccia voids are filled by the asphalt which is apparently a residue from liquid bitumens of earlier time. The material is used extensively for building hard-surfaced roads and for street paving. The southern area is contiguous to the Southern Pacific and the San Antonio, Uvalde and Gulf R. Rs.

Chapter VIII

NATURAL GAS, CARBON BLACK

Natural gas is the ideal fuel, stored in the subterranean tanks of nature, under pressure, a fuel in which the United States has a monopoly. Its history begins with the burning springs recorded by the early explorers. Its earliest use for illumination was in the village of Fredonia, N. Y., where after 1821 a shallow well supplied thirty street lights for many years. In 1838 a well drilled for water in Ohio, became a source of domestic fuel instead, and in 1841 natural gas was adopted as a fuel for evaporating brine in the salt industry in West Virginia. From that time to the present, its development and utilization have been rapid and constant. Great industries have been made possible because of it. The glass factories and potteries of the Ohio valley depend upon it. As the supply declines manufactured gas replaces it for domestic purposes, but this movement must necessarily be restricted to areas where the materials for the manufactured product may be economically procured.

For many years, but little attention was paid to the intelligent conservation of natural gas, with the result that at a conference of Governors held in Washington, D. C. in 1908, the State Geologist of West Virginia sounded a warning against the early depletion of the leading gas fields, due to wasteful practices. Many of the states now regulate its use and control its production. The extraction of natural gas gasoline before selling the gas has been a distinct economy.

In 1923, the astounding quantity of over one trillion cubic feet of natural gas, valued at approximately $240,-

000,000, was consumed in the United States. New fields are continually being brought in, and old fields extended as well as abandoned, and the history of the industry closely parallels that of petroleum.

Of the southern states, West Virginia and Louisiana lead in production, with Texas, Arkansas, Kentucky and Tennessee in the order named. The natural gas fields of eastern Kentucky are somewhat removed from the present pipe lines, and supply small town consumers in Perry, Leslie, Clay and Owsley counties. The largest gas wells are in Floyd, Johnson, Magnoffin, Lawrence and Martin counties.

It is used mainly for domestic and industrial fuel, and the manufacture of carbon black. Gasoline extracted from natural gas in the United States now amounts to over half a billion gallons per year, of which over one-third comes from Texas, West Virginia, Louisiana, Kentucky and Arkansas.

In Texas we find helium, a valuable constituent of natural gas, in a limited field. This is extracted for its non-inflammable qualities and is used for inflation of the dirigibles of the Army and Navy.

It is probable that new gas fields will be brought in from time to time, as present oil fields are extended. Attention is now directed to several promising fields in Texas, and especially to northern Mississippi, where the structures being similar to those of producing fields in Arkansas, it is not unlikely that both oil and gas will be found. During 1927, a 4,500,000 cubic foot gas well was brought in at Amory, Mississippi; and, it is confidently expected that the gas belt will be extended south from Aberdeen and Columbus. Should a well-defined gas area be developed adjacent and parallel to the Cincinnati Arch, the mineralized area of northeast Mississippi would receive great impetus due to the introduction and availability of this high grade fuel.

Price is a determining factor in the use of natural gas for fuel. Its leading industrial use aside from fuel is in the manufacture of carbon black. For many years this industry centered in West Virginia, but with the advent of the Monroe field in Louisiana, the lead has been assumed there, to the distinct advantage of the waning West Virginia fields, whose reserves will serve domestic and industrial purposes, although a considerable quantity of black is still made in that state.

Carbon black has supplanted lamp black for printers ink. The latter, a product of the incomplete combustion of oil, results in a grayish black ink, while carbon black is recognized as a perfect base. The Bureau of Mines has developed an arc process whereby carbon black may be produced from light oil distillates. This has the advantage of being applicable wherever cheap power and the requisite oil are available, and enables off-peak power to be used.

One of the handicaps of the black industry is the long distances over which the product must be shipped, at freight rates which are high because of the bulkiness of the product. The average production is about one pound of black for every thousand cubic feet of gas. One pound of black, with eight pounds of oil and varnish, will make enough printers ink to print 2250 copies of a 16-page paper. The annual consumption of printers ink amounts to one hundred million pounds per year, exclusive of lithographic, embossing and other special inks. Recent developments in the industry in southern Union parish, Louisiana, are producing ten pounds of carbon black per thousand cubic feet of gas. This black, under microscopic examination, shows an entirely different structure from the regular commercial black, being round instead of jagged particles, and of special value to the rubber trade. Six million cubic feet of 80 per cent hydrogen are also recovered daily in the form of CH_4 by this process, as compared to 55 per cent recovered by coke oven processes. The hydrogen is utilized in the manufacture of ammonia and other chemical industries.

Uses

The use of carbon black in automobile tires has enabled the manufacturers to extend mileage guarantees from 3,000 to 10,000 or more miles. Its action on rubber is not only to toughen the tread and increase the non-skidding quality, but to increase the life of the tire by making it opaque.

Carbon black, in addition to its use in printers' ink and automobile tires, is used in paints, varnishes, enamels, stove and shoe polish, phonograph records, black leather, book binders' boards, buttons, carbon paper, typewriter ribbons, carriage cloth, celluloid buttons, electric insulators, cement colors, crayons, drawing and marking inks, artificial stone, black tile, tarpaulins, wall tints and colors, oil cloths and linoleums. A potential consumption of carbon black will be in liquid oxygen explosives. A cartridge of carbon black is soaked in liquid oxygen, charged in the drill hole, and exploded by a detonator in the usual manner.

Chapter IX

IRON, ELECTRIC SMELTING

Iron occurs in nature in many forms. It appears as oxides in the form of hematite, magnetite and limonite, and as carbonate in the form of siderite. Wrought iron is used for forged parts of machinery, boiler plate, water and gas pipe, and structural material. Cast iron is an intermediate product between steel and wrought iron. Inasmuch as 750,000 cubic feet of free air are required to reduce one ton of iron ore in the blast furnace, and four-fifths of this are inert nitrogen, the dream of the metallurgist is for cheap oxygen to replace the use of common air to sustain combustion in furnace practice.

The consumption of Southern made pig iron in Southern industry is increasing much more rapidly than the output. Southern iron formerly had a national distribution, and its prices fixed the market for the rest of America. In those days the South had preferential freight rates that helped greatly in the wide distribution of its iron. At one time the rate was $1.00 per ton from Birmingham to Mobile, to encourage export shipments. The development of diversified iron consuming industries in the South will necessitate more furnaces to take care of local trade and the opening up of new ore deposits.

Progress in methods of beneficiation for the utilization of medium and low grade ores, both of iron and of manganese, and the development of electric smelting, will have a far reaching effect on iron and steel fabrication and distribution.

Experiments have been carried on in England for the reduction of iron ore at low temperature by rotary kilns.

By this method it is claimed that a 99 per cent nodular iron may be produced with 1,000 pounds of raw coal per ton of iron. The product is then cast into ingots and worked. Ores as low as 20 per cent metallic, as well as high-grade Swedish ore and Welsh hematite, are alike amenable to the process.

Swedish attempts to produce forge iron without the melting furnace are variously reported, but have so far been confined to experimental plants.

The United States Bureau of Mines has made a careful study of the metallurgical requirements in connection with the production of sponge iron and has developed a furnace which can be used for that purpose. The reason for the Bureau's interest in this subject is in connection with the possible utilization of low-grade fuels and medium-grade ores, which, at the present time, it is not commercially feasible to use in the blast-furnace. The Bureau has also made a careful study of the feasibility of converting sponge iron in the electric furnace into iron and steel products.

Sponge iron, which is more porous than iron and steel scrap, can also be used to advantage as a reducing agent in hydrometallurgical work in the precipitation of metals from their solutions, and especially in connection with the hydrometallurgy of lead and copper.

Although many "direct steel" processes have been attempted, it is evident that the manufacture of either steel or pig iron from sponge iron in regions where coke is expensive and electric power cheap, would offer an economic means of small or large scale utilization of many iron ore deposits now dormant. The Bureau of Mines states that any type of iron ore is satisfactory for this process, and that slags of high iron content may also be utilized. The process is described in Serial 2578 of the Bureau of Mines.

Thus it will be observed that the substantial progress made in the past two years, along the lines of direct reduction of iron ores, lends hope of the utilization of cheaply mined low-grade ores which, now, are not considered economical for use in the blast furnace.

It, indeed, appears safe to say that, by direct reduction on both high and low-grade ores, the production of a steel and wrought iron intermediate can be forecast at a cost which will encourage large developments.

Virginia

The iron ore resources of Virginia have been elaborately described in a report of that name, by Dr. Thos. L. Watson, published in 1907, and by frequent technical articles. The magnetites were first worked in the northwest corner of Pittsylvania county. The undeveloped magnetite deposits are in the crystalline region, scattered throughout the Piedmont district and part of the Blue Ridge.

The hematites were worked for many years in the James River basin east of Lynchburg, and also in the Blue Ridge. The Clinton fossil ore of Wise and Lee counties is now being worked. Those of Alleghany county are idle.

The principal resources are the brown limonite, or so-called "mountain and valley" ores, the distinction being that the mountain ores occur on the northwest slope of the Blue Ridge, while the valley ores occur in the limestone section on the northeast border of the valley. They differ also as to the size of the deposit and chemical composition. In some, the manganese content ranges into ferruginous manganese. In addition to the limestone limonites, which are all residual deposits, the so-called "Oriskany" district—Alleghany, Botetourt and Bath counties—have several productive mines. The ores are in the Hilderberg limestone and should be called "Hilderberg" ore.

Gossan ore, in the Piedmont or gold pyrite belt, was the pre-revolutionary source of iron. These are fairly well exhausted, with the exception of Carroll, Floyd and Grayson counties, where the pyrrhotite capping constitutes a splendid deposit as yet scarcely touched. This corresponds to the Ducktown, Tennessee, deposits, which also show intermediate outcroppings at Ore Knob, N. C. "Blue Billy" is the trade name of the iron by-product of gossan ore.

There are many undeveloped iron deposits in Virginia which offer good possibilities for future production, and coke is not far distant. These are of the same general character, mineralogically, as those mined at present and in the past. The industry, therefore, is capable of expansion.

The Southern Railway calls attention to the iron deposits near Blacksburg, Montgomery county, and Amherst, Amherst county. The Virginian Railway traverses the northern border of the Pittsylvania county deposits along Staunton River, and those between Narrows and Rich Creek, in Giles county.

West Virginia

From a geological standpoint, Hampshire, Hardy and Grant counties, West Virginia, are splendid adjuncts to the Lowmoor, Alleghany county, Virginia, deposits and furnaces. These three West Virginia counties will some day be counted valuable. Wagonload ore from this district will run 48 per cent metallic iron. Hand picked ore will reach 52 per cent. But the "Oriskany" (Hilderberg) and some of the Clinton ores run as high as 12 to 15 per cent silica, which requires more fuel to melt them, and hence are more expensive to reduce than Lake Superior ores. They are, however, tributary to the Atlantic Coast limestones for fluxing and contiguous to West Virginia coal. Vol. IV of the West Virginia Geological Survey treats of these in detail.

North Carolina

The brown iron ores of Cherokee and Clay counties, North Carolina, have been worked, in a good market. There is sufficient tonnage to warrant development under a consolidated operation, with competent metallurgical research. Sufficient brown ore and magnetite exist to support a smelter for an indefinite period.

The magnetite of Ashe county has not been developed for lack of railroad transportation. A branch of the Norfolk and Western R. R. from Abingdon, Va. now taps the ore belt at Lansing, on the head of the north fork of New River. From the Virginia state line, near the junction of the forks of New River, and extending to the southwest is an area of about one hundred square miles carrying magnetite averaging 12 feet in thickness. Both forks of the river hold large potential waterpower reserves.

A joint survey of the "Magnetic Iron Ores of East Tennessee and Western North Carolina," has recently been completed and issued by the joint Geological Surveys of these states and the United States, as Bulletin No.

32, of the North Carolina Geological and Economic Survey. In this, the hematites, the titaniferous, and the non-titaniferous ores, are located and discussed. The first of these is remote from the railroad, in both states. The second will become of value when the supply of high-grade non-titaniferous ore is exhausted. The titaniferous ores are recognized in the basic rocks like gabbro.

The third, or non-titaniferous magnetites are low in phosphorous, and sulphur, and utilized for making very low-phosphorous iron. The ore that has not been concentrated by magnetic processes rarely exceeds 41 per cent metallic content. It yields readily, however, to concentration after grinding, and as high as 71 per cent metallic iron is recovered.

A portion of these are available to the furnaces at **Johnson City, Tennessee.** Those in the Piedmont area are not of present day economic importance. A belt passing through Cranberry, Avery county, North Carolina, northwest into Carter county, Tennessee, has supplied the furnaces for many years. The Cranberry ore is in gneissoid granite, while the Lansing, Ashe county, ore occurs in marble. It is estimated that between the Cranberry and Peg Leg mines there are two and one-quarter million tons for every 100 feet in depth.

The development of the iron ores of both Virginia and North Carolina is dependent on improved transportation and adjustment of freight rates.

The American Mining Congress has long advocated such freight rates on raw materials as would stimulate their production. If this theory shall be adopted by the railroads, the resultant rate would certainly develop a large business in the communities in which these iron ore deposits are located, to the general benefit of these communities, and with peculiar advantage to the railroads whose profits on the in-going freight to support such industries would more than offset any rate reduction necessary to bring about the first shipment of these basic raw materials and the natural flow of traffic thereafter. These problems should be worked out by local contact between the railroads and the communities to their mutual benefit.

The Cranberry ores have received special favor because of their peculiar fitness for the making of cutlery, long before the days of ferro-alloys. There is also an abundance of potential hydro-electric power in the district, which will doubtless hasten the development of the remote and lower grade deposits. On both sides of the Cranberry ore belt, at Fort Blackmore, Scott county, Virginia, and at Avery and Sevier, McDowell county, and Forbes and Huntdale, Mitchell county, North Carolina, along the Clinchfield railroad, are large hematite deposits, in close proximity to coal and limestone. The Southern Railway also exhibits ores from Mitchell county, from Salisbury, Rowan county, and King's Mountain, Cleveland county, North Carolina.

South Carolina

At Smyrna, York county, and Blacksburg, Cherokee county, the Southern Railway also reports a fairly good magnetite.

Kentucky

Kentucky iron ore is of low grade. Deposits are found on the Red River in Estill, Powell and Menifee counties. In Bath county is a soft Oolitic ore commonly but erroneously called "Clinton." This is mixed with high grade Lake ore at the Ashland furnaces. There are many iron ores found in the shales of the coal measures in the state which will ultimately be worked. In the Cumberland River district in Livingstone, Lyon and Caldwell counties, iron was smelted for years, for boiler plate. In the Red River district the iron is used for car wheels.

Efforts were made to coke Hopkins county coal and treat it for reduction of sulphur, but the process was too expensive for commercial practice, since all their coke finds a ready market at nearby lead smelters, which want sulphur in their coke. The transportation expense of securing Virginia coke has so far been prohibitive. When Cumberland River ores can be supplied with a low sulphur coke, at competitive rates, these deposits will again be worked. In the area constituting the divide between Blaine Creek and Little Sandy Rivers, where Elliott, Lawrence, Carter and Boyd counties join, is a considerable area of siderite extensively mined many years ago, of which about 20,000 acres still remain available to economic operation and requiring only adequate transportation facilities.

Tennessee

The largest undeveloped deposit in Tennessee is on the narrow gage railroad from Johnson City, Tenn., to Cranberry, North Carolina. This is an extension of the Cranberry ore. There are several undeveloped properties in Johnson and Carter counties. These require magnetic surveys and careful drilling.

It would be well worth while for a large company to go into this area, and by careful prospecting, to develop low phosphorous pig iron for armor plate. The only other similar deposit is in northern New Jersey.

The most active operations are at Rockwood, Roane

county, where a red ore is being mined about three miles from the furnaces. At Lafollette, Campbell county, the furnace operates intermittently. There are big possibilities in drilling, under the Cumberland mountains, north of Rockwood, along the Queen and Crescent line as far north as Stearns, Kentucky. Deep oil wells in this section have cut three feet of red ore at less than 2000 foot depth. The analysis showed unleached ore averaging 30 per cent metallic content.

Coking coal lies above, and limestone within 50 miles. This is the old shore of the Brassfield formation ("Clinton Sea") where the iron accumulations occur. The same conditions exist in Walden's Ridge under Signal Mountain, and east of the Sequatchie ("Hog Trough") valley. Thirty miles north of the state line this disappears, but from here south to Chattanooga is a synclinal area where deposits thicken and offer a splendid field for prospecting. Good ore has also been passed up northeast of Rockwood, where there are some down-faulted areas which should be prospected.

The brown ores of east Tennessee require concentration or beneficiation. From the 100 year standpoint we are short on iron ore, but inexhaustibly supplied with coal and lime.

In middle Tennessee, on the western highland rim, are also found ores requiring beneficiation. Standard grades of iron cannot be made in Tennessee except at Rockwood and Chattanooga, unless the good ores from the South can be brought in on a cheap freight rate and used in connection with coking coal along the N. C. & St. L. R. R., and with the by-product ovens at Chattanooga—or by tying in with a furnace making standard pig and manufacturing industry using it—or by the development of beneficiation processes and mechanical puddling or electric smelting, which are discussed elsewhere. The economic solution in any event, would be a combination of Tennessee ores and manufacturing consumption.

Chattanooga is the foundry center of the United States. The cast iron pipe industry of the country lies between Chattanooga and Birmingham along the A. G. S. and the T. A. & G. R. Rs.

Cumberland Furnace, formerly making high silicon pig iron, is now out of blast, due to high cost of production and shortage of ore.

Ferro-phos is made at the Gray furnace at Rockdale, Maury county. There are charcoal iron furnaces at Collinwood, Wayne county, built by the Government during the war. Wood alcohol and acetic acid are also made there. This district being only about 50 miles from Muscle Shoals, is likely to reach a high stage of development. The Bon Air furnace at Wrigley, Hickman county, also makes charcoal iron. The principal trouble with this process is that one-third more Southern charcoal is required to carry the load, than Minnesota and northern woods, hence, a slightly higher cost.

A specially fine iron, for foundry trade and stove plate, is produced at Napier, Lewis county. This furnace in the past has used largely a high phosphorous ore. Examinations of the past year have disclosed additional ore bodies of low phosphorous ore on which they will now operate.

At the intersection of Knox, Sevier and Jefferson counties is a 14-mile syncline of hematite ore, extending northeast and southwest, and flanked on either side by lenticles of brown ore. This area has been prospected and drilled for three years, and is estimated to carry 30,000,000 tons, much of which can be operated by steam shovel. The brown ore is estimated at 10,000,000 tons, running .022 in phosphorous, and 54 per cent metallic by beneficiation. The hematite is 52 to 55 per cent metallic run-of-mine, and is accessible to both river and rail. It shows an average thickness of 22½ feet at over 100 openings with a minimum of 6 feet and a maximum of 55 feet. This is in the Tellico series and occurs as an alteration of ferruginous limestone, free from shales or partings.

From 3½ to 4 miles across a barren anticline to the northwest, occurs the so-called "Clinton," or No. 5 ore, which is entirely leached out from top to bottom, and runs 55 to 57 per cent metallic. It is an anhydrous ore. The belt is 30 miles long and entirely detached from the ore which underlies the coal measures at Chattanooga. The veins run from 3 to 4 feet thick and could easily be worked as a strip proposition.

From Newport, Cocke county, southwestward to Walland, Blount county, for a distance of 40 miles, is a third horizon of non-fossiliferous hematite, showing a marked amount of heat action. This belt is flanked at a distance of 50 feet by a body of marcasite or "white pyrites." It is obscured in many places by an overburden of manganese carbonate, which merges into iron ore. The three horizons together, would total from 225 to 250 million tons of ore.

Tennessee, therefore, has low phosphorous ore at Cranberry and Napier; high phosphorous ore in middle Tennessee; high silicon at Allen's Creek; charcoal iron at Wrigley and Collinwood; and ferro-phosphorous at

Rockdale. The combination of these interests into one group and the making of specialty iron, would be a logical conclusion, which it is understood is already receiving consideration.

The Southern Ry. has on exhibition, iron ore from Embreeville, Washington county, Clinton, Anderson county, Calhoun, McKimm county, and a maganiferous iron ore from Sweetwater, Monroe county. This latter is so fine in texture that it passes through the stack. It should be amenable to the matte and electric smelting process.

Georgia

Brown iron ore is distributed principally in Georgia, in Polk, Bartow, and Floyd counties. It occurs in pockets in the residual clays. These pockets vary from a few carloads, to deposits which have been continuously worked for over 20 years and are still in operation. The ore also varies greatly in depth, in some instances extending below water level. Near Emerson, Bartow county, it is also found as an irregular vein, with mica-schist walls, as the result of precipitation from circulating chalybeate water.

Beginning in 1840, charcoal furnaces operated on the brown ores, until the Civil War. They resumed about 1870, but in recent years, due to low prices for ore, high labor cost and freight rates, the value of the state's output fell from around $400,000 per year to less than $80,000.

The fossil, or "Clinton" ores of Georgia are found in Dade, Walker, Catoosa and Chattooga counties, near the Tennessee line. Much of this ore is ground and used for ochre, or sold for paint pigment.

Unprospected deposits of magnetite occur near Union Point, Greene county, Dahlonega, Lumpkin county, and Draketown, Haralson county.

Alabama

Iron ore being one of the primary resources of Alabama, there remain fewer areas of undeveloped deposits in that state. The industry is well developed. There have been many discussions on the part of textile machinery manufacturers as to the advisability of fabricating their product near the sources of raw material and ultimate consumption. Such a move would be logical and economical, and would materially assist in balancing labor and distribution. Coal and limestone are found in close proximity to the red iron ore beds. Centering around Birmingham, the industry has expanded to Anniston and Gadsden. Fabricating plants are increasing and old plants are being enlarged.

Groupings of raw materials are being formed at numerous points, as around Guntersville, Marshall county, from which point it is proposed to ship ore and limestone, coal and coke, to St. Louis via the Tennessee River.

In Talladega county is a gray, slatelike ore, running 47 to 50 per cent metallic and high in silica. It is a hard ore, in two veins, the deposit showing over 100,000,000 tons, of so high metallic content as to overcome the high silica. This and adjoining properties are said to be the highest metallic-content ores in the state. They have been erratically worked by outside methods, which resulted in dirty ore and the plants were shut down. They lie close to Anniston, and if operated by modern methods would support a large plant.

Another group has blocked over a half million acres

of coal and iron properties in northwestern Alabama, with terminal facilities on Little and Big Dauphin islands, in Mobile Bay, with expectation of using the Warrior River for transportation. The coal is available for export purposes, and it is proposed to construct by-product plants for the extraction of anthracene and other chemicals. The property is being prospected by drill to ascertain the extent of the underlying red ore. Limestone and cement materials also occur contiguous to the river, and along the five railroads which traverse the property, thus making both the Warrior and the Tennessee rivers available.

The U. S. Bureau of Mines is engaged, at its experiment station in Tuscaloosa, in solving the problem of handling the high silicate ores, such as those of Talladega county referred to above, and in improved methods of beneficiation and concentration.

An interesting sidelight on the iron industry in Alabama, is the use of Cuban ore at the port of Mobile. Alabama coal and limestone, taken down the Warrior River meet Cuban ore there, at a lower figure than the smelters at Birmingham, on native ore. Cuban and Chilean ores are said to require one-third less coke than Alabama ores, and the slag is worth $2 per ton along the Gulf Coast for building purposes. Iron pig from Mobile can be laid down in Liverpool in combination with cotton cargoes as ballast. Coke-oven gas would also have a ready sale in Mobile and in combination with Mississippi Sound glass sands would open another industry.

Cuban ores are said to compare favorably with Mesabi ore. One ton of Alabama iron ore requires approximately 3000 pounds of coke; Pittsburgh furnaces require about 1900 pounds, while Cuban ore uses 2000 pounds. Were it not for the fact that only 25 per cent of the Alabama product today is shipped out of the South, and that within the next two or three years industry will consume practically the entire output, the problem of utilizing Cuban ores would present little attraction. As it is, it would permit the inland ores to go into nearby fabrication, and the coal and limestones to follow down-stream traffic to the coast, where the combination would furnish employment for hundreds of men and open up new Alabama industries.

Mississippi

The "Iron Ores of Mississippi" are the subject of special report, Bulletin No. 10, of the Mississippi Geological Survey.

For many years charcoal iron was made in southeast Marshall and northwest Union counties. The ore was brown oxide, and considerable carbonate ore, strip-mining, and of good grade, an extension doubtless of the Alabama deposits. It runs as low as .01 phosphorous, and is reached by an extension from the G. M. & N. R. R. Along the state line between Monroe county, Mississippi, and Lamar county, Alabama, near Vernon, Alabama, was a Confederate iron furnace which made cannon and cannon balls during the Civil War, and shipped them to Mobile by the Mobile and Ohio R. R.

At Duck Hill, Montgomery county, an iron boom occurred in the early eighties. Another boom followed, at Enterprise, Clarke county, in 1887. A deposit of high-grade carbonate ore has since been found in a belt 8 to 10 miles wide and 20 miles long in Marshall and Benton counties, centering around Potts Camp, and extending northeast and southwest. The Tallahatchie River forms the southern boundary of the district.

The ore occurs in kidneys varying from a few pounds to a ton or more in weight. Overlying the lenticular mass is a capping of brown ore, presumably oxidized by exposure. The same deposit is encountered outside this belt, in drilling wells, the average thickness being from 1 foot to 14 inches. The State Geologist states that the averages of these analyses indicate better than 40 per cent metallic iron and about 7.81 per cent silica. The ore beds extend into Tippah county, and are accessible to the railroad. Twenty-five carloads which were shipped to Birmingham for mixture with the red ore met with ready acceptance. An abundance of timber is available for calcining the carbonate ore. It is also possible to put the low phosphorous ore of northern Mississippi for transshipment to Gulf and Atlantic ports into competition with imported Swedish ore in the eastern steel plants.

Memphis would also be a logical point for a furnace, utilizing coke and flux from up-river points, and distributing the output by inland waterways. The beneficiation and concentration and electric smelting research referred to later in this chapter, will likewise react to the encouragement of iron ore development in Mississippi.

In addition to the areas mentioned, Yalobusha, Lafayette, Grenada, and Webster counties have deposits which are well worth systematic prospecting.

A movement is on foot in Clarke and Lauderdale counties, to develop the charcoal iron industry, in connection with a by-product chemical company, and to sell the slag for road material. For such a proposition, properly engineered and financed, there is a promising field for its products and an abundance of raw material on which to operate.

Arkansas

A survey of Arkansas, made in 1890, said that there were no commercial deposits of iron in the state. There are many scattered deposits of limonite, hematite and magnetite. The counties of Montgomery, Garland, Saline, Grant, Dallas, Nevada and Ouachita are considered in a later (1892) report to be susceptible of development. Ores also occur in Crawford, Franklin, Johnson, Pope, Van Buren, Conway, Sebastian, Logan, Yell, Scott, Washington, Madison, Thorp, Lawrence, Fulton, and Randolph counties to such extent that the concentration and beneficiation processes of recent years lend hope for their ultimate operation, in connection with hydro-electric development now taking place in the state. Of the entire group, Lawrence and Sharp counties, on the Frisco and Missouri Pacific R. Rs. hold greatest promise, in connection with the possible developments at Memphis, discussed in connection with Mississippi ores.

Texas

Texas has commercial deposits of iron ore in 17 of its northeastern counties. These are discussed in Bulletin 44 of the University of Texas. They are limonite and carbonate ores, in laminated, nodular and conglomerate forms, frequently as in Mississippi, capping the broad flat hills, and offering opportunity for open cut and stripping operations. North of the Sabine River the ores are nodular. South of the Sabine they are laminated. No commercial deposits have been developed west of the Trinity River.

About three million dollars worth of pig iron has been

produced in Anderson, Cass, Cherokee, Gregg, Henderson, Marion, Morris, Smith, Upshur, and Wood counties. Two cargoes of Cherokee county ore were shipped for experimental purposes to northern furnaces. The metallic content varies from a maximum of 59 per cent or almost pure limonite to an average of 30 to 35 per cent.

Llano, Mason and Burnet counties carry magnetite which occurs in gneiss, but has never been developed commercially. Its metallic content ranges from 25 to 65 per cent, some of the deposit being high-grade lump magnetic ore, of the highest grade and in other cases occurring as pyrrhotite, high in sulphur. There is such a large quantity in evidence, however, as to warrant scientific prospecting. The smelters at Pueblo could receive direct line shipments from Burnet county, and the same advances in metallurgy and electric smelting which have been discussed above, would create a Pittsburgh or a Birmingham in northeast Texas, to be served by the Missouri Pacific, Katy, Frisco, Rock Island, Cotton Belt, Southern Pacific, Santa Fe, Colorado and Southern, and associated groups, in connection with the ports of Houston, Galveston and Corpus Christi.

Uses

In addition to the normal, every day and universally recognized uses of iron and steel, for which there is no need to recount, we find steel fishing rods which only appeared a few years ago, and yet today, 90 per cent of the country's production is of steel. Fish hooks were formerly all imported from Europe. Today they are made in America. A leading sporting goods authority estimates that 500 tons of steel fishing tackle is made in the United States annually. For large uses in small ways, we have phonograph needles, knives and forks, surgical instruments, fence posts, eyeglass cases, sewing, knitting and crochet needles, key rings, golf clubs, eyeglass frames and nose pieces, curling irons, button hooks, and shoe horns, buckles and ornaments, corsets, pins, pens, cotton ties, steel wool, toys, license plates, spinning rings and travelers, shoe steel, tie plates, tacks, and skates.

Steel and iron have replaced rubber for dredging sleeves, and go into gun parts, tools of all kinds, structural forms of every design, automobiles, engines, boilers, battleships, nails, screws, rivets, bolts, frogs, and switches, rail, architectural and machine design, and in fact, the whole fabric of national existence. The great iron and steel nations must always lead the van of commerce and industry.

* * * * * *

Reference has already been made to processes for the production of sponge or matte iron, and to the liklihood of electric smelting development for the direct reduction of iron to steel. This situation is admirably summed up in a recent article in "Mining and Metallurgy," as follows:

> "The production of pig iron in the blast furnace requires a large investment in furnace, coke ovens, and accessory equipment. Large output is necessary for economical operation. **Electric furnace smelting** requires only one-third as much coke or charcoal per ton of pig iron as does the blast furnace, and operates on a small scale, 25 or 30 tons per day being the usual output. The power consumption is 2000

to 2400 k.w.h. per ton. Two-thirds of the power required for electric smelting is used in reducing the iron oxide to metal, and only one-third in melting and carburizing the iron to produce the finished product. Hence, if the reduction of the oxide to metal can be carried out with heat, rather than from electric energy, the power consumption can be cut down two-thirds and a large saving made in the most expensive item.

"If iron ore is subjected to reducing gases at a temperature suitable for reduction but not high enough to melt the ore or the metal produced, the iron oxide is converted into metallic iron. The product, being the original iron oxide, minus its oxygen, is sponge-like, and is called 'sponge iron.' The work of the Bureau of Mines has demonstrated that five sizes of coal, lignite or sub-bituminous coal are as satisfactory for making sponge iron as higher grade fuel, and the process can be economically operated where the price of coke is high, and there is cheap electric power for the finishing process. Much less labor is required; also a smaller plant."

The tremendous significance of the rapid depletion of high-grade iron ore has not yet impressed itself upon the American people. China, Japan, Brazil and India, with immense quantities of iron ore, cheap labor, and water power, are already reducing their ores by the electric furnace. At least 70 direct processes have been invented. The Swedish process has 27 large installations in various parts of the world. With the falling off of high-grade ore and the development of hydro-electric power, vast supplies of medium and low-grade ore, which cannot be economically handled in the ordinary blast furnace, will be opened up. The electric product is markedly superior to that of the standard blast furnace.

It has also been suggested that hot metal from either type of furnace can be poured directly into a large metal mixer where additions of ore, cheap borings, or turnings could be made, and transferred to a Bessemer converter, where the metal would be given a partial blow only, and the deoxidizing and finishing off quickly completed in the electric furnace.

The electric smelting method is particularly applicable in non-ferrous metallurgy, where it is desired to conserve sulphur. As the electric furnace atmosphere is either neutral or reducing, the principal oxidation loss in other types of furnace is eliminated. Also, owing to the unlimited but perfectly controlled temperature, few copper ores require a flux in the electric furnace, and there is low metal loss in the slag.

In electric steel making, phosphorous is controlled by the use of steel scrap, silicon and manganese. Pouring does not interfere with molding, and confusion from dull heats is gone. Iron may be tapped in any amount from a few pounds to the whole charge, the remainder being held at any required temperature. Due to the thoroughly deoxidized metal and the absence of occluded gases, electric furnace gray iron has a uniformly fine grain.

So rapidly has the electric furnace earned a place in the steel industry, that the output of electric steel in the

United States jumped from 30,180 tons in 1913 to 511,364 tons in 1918, and there are at the present time over 450 electric steel furnaces in this country.

Double versus single voltage receives much discussion. Double voltage increases the thermal efficiency of furnace, thus increasing the tonnage. Double voltage of 115-125 high and 75-85 low is current practice. Single voltage is usually operated at 95.

Mechanically there is no limitation to the size of the electric furnace. The removal of three-electrode limitation opens a new field of design and utility. Power consumption depends upon whether the charge is melted in a cold furnace or after a previous heat. In one test run on 25 consecutive heats, in a 20-ton furnace, the average consumption was 746 k.w.h. per ton of iron and 872 k.w.h. per ton of steel. The lower the voltage used the greater the life of the refractory lining.

A modification of the usual type of electric furnace, which is in use at Anniston, Alabama, has electrodes of artificial graphite surrounded by a combustion flame of oil, gas, or powdered coal, sprayed under pressure. The voltage is 2300. It is estimated that 100 pounds of oil per hour is the equivalent of 600 k.w. fuel energy. Compressed air sprays the fuel and a secondary air supply passes through pipes into the combustion chamber. A temperature of 3600° F. is attained, and three grades of open hearth steel are melted per hour. By utilizing waste gas this method could be utilized anywhere. A space of 16 inches is maintained between the tips of the electrodes, and an 8-inch arc to each is made by the continuous oil or gas flame. The three electrodes converge, so that the arcs meet. This adaptation is available for foundry melting of iron or steel, for direct smelting on a small scale at low investment cost, for brass melting, for phosphate smelting in the production of phosphoric acid, or for any high temperature chemical and metallurgical processes. It simplifies slag reduction and offers a means of maintaining high temperatures under reducing conditions.

Because of the even distribution of heat and its absolute control, the electric furnace is rapidly supplanting the fuel fired furnace for smelting of iron, the manufacture of steel, heat treatment in the automobile industry, the manufacture of calcium carbide, and in the annealing of glass.

Chapter X

CHROMITE, MANGANESE, ANTIMONY, TITANIUM, RUTILE, ILMENITE, MONZONITE, ZIRCONIUM, COLUMBIUM, COLUMBITE, SAMARSKITE, CERIUM, MONAZITE, THORIUM, THORIA, GADOLINITE, CARNOTITE, URANIUM, VANADIUM, TELLURIUM, SELENIUM, STRONTIUM

Chromite, or chrome ore, is a compound of iron containing 68 per cent chromic acid. It is an essential mineral of which over 90 per cent comes from foreign sources. Being a metal of specialized uses, and those deposits which do exist in this country being so irregular and under the handicap of remote transportation or high transportation charges, any thought of tariff protection has always seemed futile.

Uses

An electro-chemical process of chromium plating, producing wearing surfaces harder than any other known metal, with a finish 20 times the life of nickel plate, which will neither rust nor tarnish, has recently been developed. Next to the diamond, this is the hardest substance in existence.

Experience at the United States Bureau of Engraving and Printing has shown that by the application of a thin layer of chromium only 1-5000 inch thick to electrotype plates used for printing paper currency, the life of the plates is increased to over twice that of case hardened steel plates, and several times that of the nickel-faced electrolytic plates prior to the application of the chromium upon them.

This increased service is due to the extreme hardness of chromium, the hardest metal known. Chromium plating has long been known to be possible, but until recently it has not been commercially practicable.

Subsequent tests have shown that chromium plating is likewise valuable on other types of printing plates, especially those used for long editions. It will also probably be useful on dies and gauges where extreme hardness is required, and may obviate case hardening them.

Because of its bright color, it is also used for dyes and paints in the form of chrome yellow, orange, red and green. In tanning as bi-chromate of soda and potash, chromic acid and chrome alum, it gives softness and durability to leather, and its high fusing point makes it valuable for furnace linings and fire brick. The chief value of chrome brick lies in its neutral character and high refractoriness. The disadvantages are its sensitiveness to rapid thermal changes, and inability to support heavy loads at high temperatures. It is shiny black in color, much heavier than fire clay or silica, and slightly heavier than magnesia.

Chrome refractories are used in the steel and copper industries, crucible furnaces, blast furnace settlers, converter linings, and refinery furnace linings. They have been used with limited success in the smelting of lead, antimony, tin and nickel.

Chrome steels are used for high speed tools, armor plate, armor piercing projectiles, crushing machinery, safes and automobile parts. Chromium raises the elastic limit of steel, increases the hardness, and intensifies the effect of other alloys. Among the chemical uses are dry batteries, medicines and various applications of metallurgy.

Virginia

At Dranesville, Fairfax county, Virginia, west of Great Falls, some chromite has been found in the serpentines.

North Carolina

The Jackson and Yancey county deposits in North Carolina are of good quality and quantity. Excellent ore is exhibited from Webster, Willetts, Balsam and Sylva, in Jackson county, which appears to be the center of the North Carolina deposits. A number of prospects near Burnsville, Yancey county, and Democrat and Stocksville in Buncombe county, and in Mitchell county, have yielded high grade ore, free from foreign matter. During the war several carloads of ore were shipped from Mine Hill, in Yancey county.

The development of chromite in North Carolina depends on market, freight rates, and tariff. It has been announced through several sources that no difficulty would be experienced in disposing of a chromite property, properly prospected and proven up, if it was also near to a water power of 800 H.P. for reduction purposes.

Georgia

The U. S. Geological Survey reports chromite disseminated in crystals through chrysolite (green garnet) near Hiwassee, Towns county, Georgia, and other exposures in Heard and Fayette counties.

Alabama

Chromite is also found, but has never been developed, in Tallapoosa county, Alabama, near Dudleyville.

* * * * * *

Manganese occurs in many forms, but chiefly as an oxide. When found as pyrolusite or manganese dioxide it is especially useful for the production of chlorine, bromine, and in the manufacture of permanganates, because it is richer in oxygen.

High grade chemical ore runs 35 per cent or better, metallic manganese. Ferruginous manganese runs from 10 per cent to 35 per cent, while ores below 10 per cent are classified as manganiferous iron ore. Methods of beneficiation, which are rapidly reaching higher development, have made possible the utilization of many medium grade deposits, until recently considered uneconomically workable.

Uses

The high grade ore, when free from iron, is used to decolorize glass, as a depolarizer in dry batteries, and as drier in varnishes and paints. It is also a valuable chemical for use in disinfectants and the manufacture of oxygen, and for making manganese bronze and similar alloys. High grade ore which contains iron is utilized chiefly in the manufacture of ferromanganese and spiegeleisen, also for coloring glass, pottery, and brick, and as paint pigments.

The low grade ore, frequently beneficiated, goes into all of these, and is used for flux in lead, copper and silver smelting. When containing less than 5 per cent metallic manganese, it is not considered. The limit for impurities is approximately 8 per cent silica, and 0.2 per cent phosphorous. Clean, well prepared ore, free from iron, lime or other substances, are requisites of manganese used in the manufacture of chemicals, dry batteries and plate glass. As an alloy, 13 per cent of manganese will suppress the magnetic properties of 87 per cent iron. Every ton of steel made in the United States requires the use, on an average, of 40 pounds of manganese.

Of the southern states, Arkansas takes the lead, and is also second in the United States. Georgia is a substantial producer. The imported product comes from Brazil, West Africa, India, Russia, Cuba, Argentine, Chile, Panama and Turkey.

There is a wide divergence of opinion on the result to American industry of the tariff on manganese. Certainly it has stimulated the production of manganiferous iron ore, and those changes in furnace practice equally beneficial to the ore producer and to the steel manufacturer, which were predicted in its passage. In Arkansas there has been considerable development of manganese of good grade. A rather large deposit has been opened on the Pacific Coast (Washington). The development of the many other manganiferous ore deposits in the United States will depend upon the quality of the ore, development of the beneficiation processes, transportation facilities, and freight rates.

Virginia

Manganese and manganiferous ore deposits occur in three districts in Virginia. The first, and principal district is along the northwestern foot of the Blue Ridge, across the entire state. Certain of these areas run high in metallic manganese. The second is in western Virginia, comprising the Oriskany and Hilderberg horizons in

Tazewell, Bland, Giles, Shenandoah and Frederick counties. The third is east of the Blue Ridge in the Piedmont region, comprising Campbell and Appomatox counties. There are also some isolated deposits. Bulletins 17 and 23 of the Virginia Geological Survey cover the first and second districts in detail. Bulletin 640-C of the U. S. Geological Survey describes the third district. Bulletin 660-J of the U. S. Geological Survey discusses areas available for manganese prospecting.

The deposits occur principally in sandstone and chert, filling the crevices. Those occurring in clays are nodular replacements of shale or argillaceous sandstone.

West Virginia

Manganese was mined in West Virginia along the Virginia border during the war. In Greenbrier county it occurs at numerous places, usually in stringers ½ inch to 4 inches in thickness, forming veins up to 36 inches wide. The general recoverage is around 50 per cent metallic manganese, but the expense of cleaning and preparing the product requires an active market. The Hardy county deposits have not been worked. They are an extension of the Virginia ores on the west side of the Blue Ridge.

There is a vein of manganese near Sweet Springs, Monroe county, W. Va., which extends for about one mile and is ten miles from the C. & O. R. R. A shaft has been sunk 6x6 feet and a carload of manganese assaying 50 per cent metallic is on the dump

Tennessee

There are some 40 per cent manganese deposits in Tennessee, occurring in nodules irregularly scattered through clay. The labor cost of segregation is high, and only an emergency demand would appear to warrant their operation. Bulletin 737 of the U. S. Geological Survey describes the east Tennessee deposits and operations.

Northeastward from Unicoi, Unicoi county, are several deposits analyzing 50 per cent metallic manganese, and running low in silica. Bradley county shipped over $100,000 of high grade ore during the war. Much of this was hydrauliced along the hillsides, where the nodules are found in residual clay. Between Newport and Del Rio in Cocke county; in Monroe and Carter counties; and in Hickman, Lawrence and Wayne counties, are deposits of manganese, psilomelane, pyrolusite and wad, which were operated to greater or less extent during the war.

North Carolina

The manganiferous ores of North Carolina are common to the iron deposit areas. Caldwell, Chatham, Cleveland, Catawba, Gaston and Lincoln counties all have prospects in varying stages of development. The Southern Ry. shows an exhibit of manganese from North Wilkesboro, Wilkes county. In Surry county the garnet deposits are manganiferous.

South Carolina

The South Carolina deposits of manganese in Abbeville county are of economic importance. They occur in mica schists in the form of psilomelane and pyrolusite. Greenwood county has several deposits around Greenwood and Breezewood, and the Smith Mountain area in Cherokee county, and on Hard Labor Creek, Edgefield county are other commercial fields. Wad, or bog ore, is extensively found along the Seaboard Air Line and

Southern R. Rs. on the west side of Wateree River, near the junction of York and Chester counties.

Georgia

The manganese ores of Georgia are found in two groups, the one comprising the ten northwest counties of the state, and the other, the area lying between the "Cartersville Fault," and the "Fall Line." Considerable mining has been done in the Cartersville and Cave Spring sections, but such prospecting as has been done elsewhere does not indicate any substantial reserves. Bartow, Floyd and Polk counties are the principal producers, ore from this district having at one time been exported to England. The Southern Ry. also reports manganese at Temple, Carroll county, and the Cen. of Ga. Ry. in western Walker county. Whenever any promising specimens come in to the Georgia Geological Survey, the State Geologist endeavors to provide for examination of the prospect.

Alabama

Around Murphree's Valley, Blount county, southwest of Raccoon Mountain, and near Altoona and Walnut Grove, Etowah county, Alabama, several deposits of oxide ore occur. Near Selma, Dallas county, and extending northeastward into Autauga county, is a sandy siliceous surface crust carrying manganese ore which is used in the furnaces near Birmingham for special purposes.

Coosa, Lee, Randolph and Tallapoosa counties carry manganese in combination with iron, mica schist, or gold. Bibb, Cherokee and Cleburne counties carry nodular ore in residual clays, while Calhoun and Tuscaloosa counties show psilomelane formation. Bibb county also mines manganiferous limonite near Woodstock.

The local situation is seriously affected by the importation of Brazilian ore which comes to Mobile and up the Warrior River.

Arkansas

The first manganese was mined in Arkansas about 1851 when Matthew Martin shipped small quantities of ore from Batesville. This is said to have been the second manganese deposit mined in the United States. There are two well defined fields in the state. The first, known as the Batesville district, is in the northern part of Independence county, extending into Izard and Sharp counties. The second field extends from the Pulaski county line to the western boundary of the state.

A survey made during the World War, embracing 180 mines and prospects gave as an estimate of reserves in Arkansas, 250,000 tons of ore, 40 per cent or better, and 170,000 tons containing less than 40 per cent manganese. It is probable that this estimate is entirely too low. The field covers 120 square miles, and the ore runs in pockets. New ore bodies are continually being uncovered. An estimate of several billion tons would be as accurate as one of several hundred thousand. Nothing but years of prospecting will serve to adequately measure the actual extent of the manganese reserves of the state. The Batesville district enjoys better railroad facilities than the balance of the field. The fine ore occurs mixed with clay. It is screened and sluiced, and the concentrates jigged. Labor is paid on a tonnage basis, of metallic manganese produced from $1.50 per ton on low grade to $10.00 per tone on chemical grade fine.

The latest lead of manganese found in the field was uncovered by the graders who are building the dump for an industrial railroad near Cushman. Several thousand pounds of high grade ore were recovered, where the cut crossed the lead.

The outstanding development of 1927 in the Arkansas manganese field was the installation of a plant near Batesville, and beneficiation of medium to low grade ores with a view to electric furnace production of ferromanganese.

Texas

Manganese has been produced in Texas at the Spiller mine, in Mason county, runing over 40 per cent metallic content. During the war, this ore was hauled 40 miles to the railroad. Many prospects have been opened and a few operated, in Llano county. In the east escarpment of the Llano Estacado manganese oxide is found in association with petrified wood.

* * * * * *

Antimony is an element of metallic appearance and crystalline structure, which occurs in a free state and also combined with various minerals. Its chief source is stibnite ore, which is antimony sulphide, although it is also recovered as a by-product of lead and silver. Chemically it has been classed both as a metal and a non-metal.

It is detected in prospecting by a yellowish coating of antimony oxide which forms on the exposed surface of the sulphide.

Uses

It has the property of expanding when solidifying, and of imparting this characteristic to its alloys. It is prepared by roasting and reducing with charcoal or by reducing directly with iron in crucibles. It is extensively used for type metal, which consists of antimony, lead and tin.

It also goes into chemicals, paints, and pigments. An alloy of antimony, tin and copper is called "Britannia metal." Antimony acts as a severe poison, similar to arsenic. One of its compounds, tartar emetic, is used as a medicine. Red antimony sulphide is used in vulcanizing rubber, and in safety matches. Antimony tetroxide renders enamels opaque. Battery plates, solder, pewter and Babbitt metal are also compounds of antimony.

Arkansas

It has been mined since 1873 in Sevier and Howard counties, Arkansas. The veins vary from 6 inches to 5 feet in width. The stibnite ore occurs in lenses encased in quartz and calcite. Arseno-pyrite is sometimes found associated with it.

Outcrops are also reported from Pike county, but no development has taken place there.

Alabama

Its association with arseno-pyrites suggests a liklihood of its being found in Clay and Randolph counties, Alabama, where this rock is found in abundance.

Mississippi

The Mississippi Development Company, some years ago, reported stibnite in Smith county, Mississippi. Its occurrence has recently been verified.

* * * * *

When we approach the titaniferous minerals, we find a large group of inter-related metals, occurring in close association.

Uses

Titanium is an infusible iron gray crystalline powder

found only in combined form. Titanite is a combination of lime, silica and titanium. It is a constituent of some igneous rocks, and is generally yellow or brown. Titanium resembles silicon in many respects, and is widely distributed, but in small quantities. It may be found in ilmenite, in sand, clay, granite, or mineral waters. Occasionally it occurs as yellow scales with a blue surface color. It is used as a ferro-alloy for bridge construction and steel rails, and when added to steel for tin plate, increases resistance to perforation and also increases the infusibility of slag and causes part of the iron to pass off in the slag.

Titanium alloys of copper are also made, and the ceramic, dyeing, and leather tanning industries use the salts of titanium.

Titanium tetrachloride, which was discovered after the war, is used to create smoke screens. In two minutes after its use an entire battleship may be hidden.

Titanium is also used for delicate shading in coloring false teeth.

Uses

Rutile is titanium dioxide, and is one of the chief sources of titanium. Dentists use it in the manufacture of artificial teeth. There have been four areas in the world where rutile and ilmenite have been commercially found. The first is Krageroe, off the southern coast of Norway. The second is Bay St. Paul, on the north side of the St. Lawrence River in Quebec. The third is near Adelaide, Australia, and the fourth comprises the various sources in the United States.

Uses

Ilmenite is iron-titanium oxide, or natural titanite of

iron. It is similar to hematite, opaque and slightly magnetic, and generally found with gneisses and schists, together with magnetite. The white pigment "titanox" has 2½ times the hiding power of the best white lead, and is made from ilmenite. Ilmenite is also used in the ceramics, for arc light electrodes, for a flux, and in various metallurgical processes. It enters into the manufacture of automobile tires, in imitation ivory, and piano keys. The difference between rutile and ilmenite being principally that of oxygen content, they may for practical purposes be considered as synonymous.

Monzonite is an igneous rock associated with ilmenite, and carrying from 46 to 73 per cent silica.

Uses

Zirconium, when occurring as a silicate, is clear and orange colored, and forms the gem hyacinth. It is an element of the titanium group, and occurs in both the amorphous and crystalline forms. Zirconium itself has no industrial importance, but its oxide is used in gas mantles, and zirconia, the dioxide, on account of its infusibility and brilliant luminosity when incandescent, is used as an ingredient of the Drummond light and for gas mantles, and to replace tin-oxide or antimony oxide for vitreous enamels on sanitary ware, as a mordant in dyeing, and in weighting silks. It is also very valuable for high temperature porcelains such as spark plugs, and electric fittings. Zirconium, when isolated, is a black powder.

The mineral **zircon,** is a natural silicate, and has been much discussed for crucibles and refractories. Commercial zircon now ranges in purity from 80 to 99 per cent, the general range being 90 to 96 per cent. It is remarkably resistant to carbon, and has great density and hardness, a lustre similar to the diamond, a low resistance to the ultra-violet ray, a low thermal conductivity, a remarkable pigmenting power when ground, an extremely low coefficient of expansion, and almost unique low electrical conductivity. When incandescant, an inertness to chemical action, exhibited by few substances, a high index of refraction, and other specific physical properties for which new terms must be created.

North Carolina

The **Zircon-Monazite** deposits of North Carolina are described in Bulletin 25 of the North Carolina Geological Survey.

Uses

In its various forms, it is used for refractories, abrasives, dyes, glazes, enamels, paints, colors, gas mantles, electric light filaments, cements, porcelains, papers, textiles, plastics, rubber, and pharmaceuticals.

Being absolutely non-poisonous, zirconia is especially in demand for paints and lacquers. As an abrasive, zirconium carbide is a substitute for the diamond in cutting glass.

Columbium occurs in black lustrous crystals, usually associated with tantalum.

Columbite is a variable of iron and manganese, grading into tantalite, in which tantalum predominates, and is used for electric light filaments.

Samarskite is a columbate and tantalate of uranium, found in pegmatites, and is a source of thoria for gas mantles, and a prospective source of radium.

Uses

Cerium is an element resembling iron, but is soft, malleable and ductile. It tarnishes readily in air, and is usually associated with monazite. Metallic cerium is combined 70 per cent with 30 per cent iron and used for cigar, gas, and carbide-lamp lighters. One to 2 per cent of cerium oxide added to a gas mantel gives it an exceedingly brilliant light. Ferrocerium up to 0.3 per cent is used as a desulphurizer in steel.

Monazite is phosphate of cerium and other rare-earth metals, including thorium, which gives it commercial value.

Thorium, when isolated, is an infusible grey metallic powder. It is found in gneisses and granites, and is used in incandescent gas mantles. It belongs to the titanium group, with monazite. It resembles nickel and has a very high melting point. When heated in air it takes fire and burns with a luminous flame. It dissolves readily in a mixture of nitric and hydrochloric acids (aqua regia) but is not attacked by alkaline solutions. It may be slowly dissolved in dilute hydrochloric acid. It may also be found in sands and gravels.

Thoria, the oxide of thorium, is prepared on a large scale from thorium. It is used in gas mantles, and is also radio-active, emitting Alpha, Beta and Gamma rays. Thoriated tungsten tubes, being radio-active, have made possible the development of long range, high-powered transmitters of compact type, strong, reliable, and simple, and of such efficiency that a number of filaments may be run from a set of dry batteries, without shortening the life of the battery. They are used by the U. S. Coast Guard in flashing ice patrol warnings, without interfering with commercial broadcasting.

Gadolinite, occurring as a brittle crystalline greenish

black or brown silicate in combination with iron and cerium in pegmatites, yields colorless soluable salts of little commercial importance.

Uses

Carnotite is a canary yellow mineral containing both uranium and vanadium, with either or both lime and potash. It is radio-active and used as a source of radium.

Uses

Uranium, in carnotite, samarskite, yttrialite, and several other combinations, is used not only as a radium-source, but as a deoxidizer in copper and other alloys; and in glass and pottery coloring.

Uses

Vanadium is similarly found in carnotite and eight other minerals, and is used in high speed tool steel, and as a deoxidizer in steels, bronzes, brasses, and bearing metals. It also occurs in iron ores, fire clays and granite. A minute quantity added to steel makes it harder, stronger, and more malleable. In the form of ammonium metavanavate, vanadium is a valuable drier for paint oils. Vanadium driers act twice as quickly as manganese driers, and five times as rapidly as lead driers, and only slightly less rapidly than cobalt driers, and have no tendency to the formation of surface films or skins.

There is a group known as the "oxygen-sulphur family," on the borderline between metals and non-metals, and which are found in small quantities with other ores. **Tellurium** is one of these, and is similar to sulphur and selenium, occurring occasionally in native crystal form. It is soluble in sulphuric and nitric acids, and in potassium hydroxide, but not in water. It is used in medicine and in the ceramics. It is very brittle and easily powdered, and not infrequently associated with gold ore. It is recovered as a by-product in the smelting and refining of copper.

Uses

No ores are known that are rich enough in tellurium to warrant operation for tellurium alone. Two-tenths of 1 per cent diethyl telluride in gasoline is a reliable antiknock compound and eliminates carbon deposits. Tellurium is used in high resistance alloys, in organic dyes, for staining art silver, in medicine, as a chemical reagent, as a glass and porcelain color, and dissolved in sodium sulphide as a toning bath for photograph prints. In combination with zincite crystals, it is used as a radio detector.

Uses

Selenium is usually associated with the copper ores and pyrites, and is chiefly recovered as a by-product in the electrolytic refining of copper. It was discovered in the deposits from sulphuric acid chambers, which are still a commercial source. It is used in glass manufacture to neutralize the green tint of glass, and to produce red and violet colors in glass and enamels. It burns in air with a bluish flame and disagreeable odor; and increases its electrical conductivity on exposure to light, which renders it of value in photometry, wireless telephony, and electrical experimental work. Selenium should not be confused with selenite (Chapter XXVI).

Uses

Strontium, when finely divided, ignites spontaneously in air, and takes fire under friction. When heated in oxygen it burns with a dazzling red flame. It tarnishes (oxidizes) rapidly when exposed. It is used in analytical chemistry, for refining sugar, as paint pigment, in medicine, for smokeless powder and in fire-works.

Reverting, now to the sources of these highly useful and little developed minerals in the South, we find the titaniferous group, rutile and ilmenite, the subject of a special Bulletin (No. III-A) by the late Dr. Thos. L. Watson, of the Virginia Geological Survey. The reader is referred to this volume for a broadly developed discussion of these minerals, and their world occurrence.

Virginia

The Virginia deposits are principally in Amherst and Nelson counties, with undeveloped prospects in Goochland, Hanover, Roanoke, Charlotte and Buckingham counties. The industry is prosperous in Virginia and the rapidly increasing uses for the product indicate an expanding market.

Ilmenite is also found in Nelson county, where with white apatite, it is mined with rutile as "Nelsonite."

North Carolina

In the pegmatite measures of Mitchell and Yancey counties, North Carolina, rutile is found along the Clinchfield Ry. Rutile and ilmenite in the Haysville section of Clay county extend into Towns county, Georgia. The deposit near Murphy, Cherokee county, was extensively mined during the war, to provide material for smoke screens and special paint pigments. Both these sections achieved an enviable reputation for the quality of their product. In Clay county they occur as placer gravel; in Macon, Alexander and Tredell counties, associated with corundum (vide Chap. XII). Ilmenite was also prospected in an iron ore deposit north of Lenoir, Caldwell county.

South Carolina

The gneisses of Newberry county, South Carolina, and the gold quartz veins (vide Chap. XIII) of Abbeville county carry rutile and ilmenite but have not been worked. Rutile crystals are found in Kershaw and Cherokee counties.

Georgia

Graves Mountain, Lincoln county, Georgia, is in the center of a highly mineralized zone. Rutile occurs here in a matrix of cyanite and hematite. Over $20,000 of rutile gems have been shipped from this locality. Difficulty was experienced in separating the crystals from the matrix, and little development work is now being done at this place.

Arkansas   Texas

Rutile was first mentioned in Arkansas in 1864, when it was discovered at Magnet Cove, Hot Spring county. No commercial development has been attempted. Two occurrences of ilmenite are reported from Mason county, Texas, and two from Llano county. Neither have attained prominence as a source of supply.

Florida

The discovery of large deposits of ilmenite in the beach sands of Florida, where it is separated by concentration, greatly reduced the consumption of rutile. Several thousand tons are now being produced annually. The mineral-bearing sands extend from Duval county to Palm

Beach county. At Riviera, Palm Beach county, the sand is almost black with ilmenite.

The recovery approximates 11 per cent, distributed in about 15 tons of zircon, 100 tons of ilmenite, 8 tons of rutile and 2 tons of monazite from 1100 tons of sand.

As this survey goes to press further beach sand deposits of ilmenite and rutile are reported between Venice and Sarasota on the west coast of Florida, but no definite information is available.

* * * * * *

Monzonite cannot be economically mined in North Carolina at current prices and cost of labor. It is found in Lincoln, Cleveland, Rutherford, Burke and Gaston counties.

* * * * * *

Zircon occurrences in Virginia are coincident with rutile and ilmenite (vide supra).

In North Carolina it is found in the pegmatites of Henderson and Iredell counties and is mined at Zirconia, Henderson county. In Burke, McDowell and Rutherford counties it occurs in certain gravels operated for other minerals. The Southern Railway also exhibits specimens from Murphy, Cherokee county.

Florida zirconiferous areas are the beach sands already referred to extending from Duvall county to Palm Beach county. These metalliferous sands seem to have been derived from concentration along the Atlantic coast of minerals carried in the debris of the Piedmont range now worn down into the Piedmont Plateau.

* * * * * *

Columbite and other radio-active minerals are found

in Mitchell and Yancey counties, North Carolina, along the Clinchfield Railway.

It also occurs in association with mica in Amelia county, Virginia.

* * * * * *

Samarskite is similarly found in North Carolina, along with Columbite.

* * * * * *

Cerium in its phosphate form as monazite, occurs with mica in Amelia county, Virginia, and also as sand in many stream beds.

It is extensively found in North Carolina, over an area of 3000 square miles. In Burke and Cleveland counties it is hydrauliced. Near Mars Hill, Madison county it occurs in boulder formation. Alexander, Catawba, Rutherford, Lincoln, Gaston and Iredell counties also furnish considerable quantities.

At Zion, Spartanburg county, South Carolina, is a 76-acre deposit of monazite, mica and graphite. Monazite is also mined at Gaffney, Cherokee county, and Greenville, Greenville county; and deposits have been prospected and found of commercial value in Anderson, Laurens, Oconee and Pickens counties.

* * * * * *

Thorium is associated with monazite, and is found in the gneisses, granites, sands and gravels of Virginia, North Carolina and South Carolina, mentioned above.

In Texas it is associated with yttrialite and gadolinite at Barranger Hill, eleven miles north of Kingsland, Llano county. This hill, like the Lincoln county area of Georgia, is highly mineralized, and carries uranium, vanadium, thorium, yttrium, molybdenite, fergusonite and gadolinite in commercial quantities and quality. This is the only known occurrence of gadolinite in the South.

* * * * * *

Tellurium is found in gold-bearing gangues near Fredericksburg, Spotsylvania county, Virginia, and King's Mountain, Cleveland county, North Carolina. Traces also occur in some of the copper ores of Georgia and East Tennessee.

* * * * * *

Selenium is recovered as a by-product of copper smelting and refining, and of the silver industry. The copper sulphide ores and pyrites deposits of the United States have not, as yet, been studied for the recovery of selenium, although its increasing use in the selenium cell has created an increased demand. The great gypsum, barytes, sodium sulphate, and sulphur deposits are also selenium bearing, and offer a field of research.

* * * * * *

Strontium, as "celestite" or strontium sulphate, is mined from the Trinity limestones in Pike, Howard and Sevier counties, Arkansas.

In Texas the carbonate form, known as "Strontianite" is mined for its chemical salts along the Colorado River, near Austin.

The sulphate "celestite" is found in extensive crystalline deposits in Burnet county; in lenticular formation, north of Lampasas, Lampasas county; and associated with topaz in Mason and San Saba counties.

The peculiar pyrotechnic qualities of strontium make it a valuable mineral product.

CHAPTER XI

MOLYBDENUM, TUNGSTEN, NICKEL, MAGNESIUM

The metallic element **molybdenum,** which constitutes 60 per cent of the ore molybdenite, has general efficiency as an alloy and has gained in popularity because of the ease with which it may be fabricated, and the consequent low shop cost. It has a low coefficient of expansion, and can be welded to pyrex glass.

The purpose of any ferro-alloy is to produce strength, toughness and resistance to wear. Before the introduction of molybdenum, the field for alloys was in high carbon steel rolls. Molybdenum is now used in low and high carbon, sand and chilled rolls. The results show as high as 12 times the maximum service previously obtained.

Uses

After smelting molybdenite, the concentrates are roasted and treated to produce a variety of chemicals of great technical and industrial value. Among them are molybdic acid, phosphomolybdic acid, sodium molybdate, and other salts used in dyes, medicine and chemistry. The molybdic acid is mixed with charcoal and heated in an atmosphere of hydrogen to produce pure molybden powder, which is compressed into billets, and rolled into sheets or drawn into wire and used in vacuum tube manufacture. The powder is also used as a blue pigment in making fine-grade porcelain.

Molybdenum steel is now used for shovels, plows, scrapers, ball mills, automobile frames and springs and elevator buckets. Molybdenum wires are used in windings for electric resistance furnaces. The metal oxidizes at about 1100° F. and it is therefore necessary to provide air insulation to protect these windings.

Molybdenum is substituted for platinum in jewelry, being cheaper and possessing the qualities of softness, malleability, ductility, silvery lustre, and freedom from tarnish. Gold and silver-plated molybdenum wires are used in dentistry. Sodium and potassium molybdates are used in textile dyeing and pottery glazes, and molybdenum tannate with extract of logwood to produce fast brown and black colors in leather, silk, wool and rubber goods.

Texas

The only known molybdenite deposits in the Southern states occur in Llano county, Texas, on the west slope of Packsaddle Mountain. This proposition was commercially opened up in 1918. Although not as yet prospected, there are intrusive igneous areas in Uvalde and Kinney counties which might logically carry molybdenite ore.

* * * * * *

Tungsten is a metallic element which in the Southern states occurs only as wolframite, a tungstate of iron and manganese. Tungsten does not unite with acid radicals to form salts like ordinary metals; but it combines with oxygen to form an acid oxide, giving rise to a series of compounds, called "tungstates." Its melting point is 6000° F. There is nothing in which tungsten can be melted. It has the smallest co-efficient of expansion, and in wire the highest tensile strength of any metal. Its heat conductivity is twice that of iron, and its electrical conductivity one-third that of copper.

The swords of the Middle Ages had tungsten in their composition. About 1875 its use began in the United

States. For economic reasons the ore should be concentrated to 60 per cent, or better, for shipment.

Uses

It is used as a substitute for platinum contact points, incandescent light filaments, in dentistry, for phonograph needles, shell steel, ferro-alloys, chemical dye-stuffs, and as a mordant in the cloth industry. It is especially valuable in dyeing crepe paper, and fireproofing theatrical goods, while as an element of high-speed steel it has no equal. About 1918 a method of welding a thin plate of high-speed steel to ordinary bar steel was developed to form the cutting edge of lathe tools, thus decreasing the consumption of high-speed steel for this purpose.

In the manufacture of vacuum tube thermocouples tungsten is alloyed with copper-nickel. A description of this process will be found under "Nickel" in this chapter.

North Carolina

Samples of wolframite and cuproscheelite have been reported from Cabarrus county, North Carolina, but no deposits in commercial quantity.

Arkansas

Tungsten was mined in association with manganese and other minerals, about 15 miles west of Little Rock, Pulaski county, Arkansas. A shaft 150 feet deep was sunk, and drifts extended for about 100 feet. The plant was closed during the war and has since been abandoned.

Texas

El Paso county, Texas, has been referred to as containing wolframite in combination with cassiterite, but no substantial ore bodies have been developed. On the north slope of the Baylor Mountains, in Culberson county, about 30 miles from Van Horn, wolframite has been found, and the samples submitted carried 15 per cent to 17 per cent of tungstic oxide. This is a promising field for further prospecting. The situation with regard to Tungsten prices is encouraging. There is a continuous demand for the ore, and available supplies are scarce.

* * * * * *

Nickel is a white metal of the iron group, chiefly valuable as an alloy. It has frequently been called "white copper" because of its ductility and malleability. It is slightly magnetic, has a high fusing point and resists oxidation.

Although refined in large quantities in the United States, the principal sources of supply are nickel matte from Sudbury, Ontario, and by-product nickel from American copper refineries. Hence, any local source in commercial quantity would find a ready market.

Virginia

Pyrrhotite has been mined for nickel in Floyd, Grayson, Carroll, and Amherst counties, Virginia. The largest operation is near Shawsville, in Floyd county.

North Carolina

Silicate of nickel, or genthite, is found at Bakersville, Mitchell county, and Democrat, Buncombe county, North Carolina, along the Clinchfield Railway. The latter deposit is also associated with chromite (qui vide, Chapter X) which offers an inducement for their joint operation. At Webster, Jackson county, is a deposit of genthite which has been for some time a source of experimentation.

South Carolina

Nickel, as a by-product of gold and copper, has been recovered in Saluda and Aiken counties, South Carolina.

Georgia

The United States Geological Survey reports combined millerite and genthite near the North Carolina line, in Towns county, Georgia, which have never been mined.

Tennessee

Nickel also occurs with cobalt in Hickman county, Tennessee, near Centerville.

Uses

The uses of nickel in its various alloys, are almost unlimited. As nickel steel it goes into automobile parts, bridges, railroad frogs, machine tools, band saws, ordnance, power plant equipment and die-blocks.

It is added to cast iron to improve the machining qualities through finer grain and greater hardness, and for its high-lustre finish. As ferro-nickel it is used for electric resistance wire, and rustless steel, invar and elinvar. The heat resisting and electric alloys are nichrome, chromel, calido, hardite, calite and a group known as the "Q-alloys."

Nickel (German) silver is used for jewelry, lamps, watch cases, restaurant and hospital equipment, tableware, keys and soda fountain accessories.

Copper-nickel becomes coinage, bullet jackets, pyrometer wire, valves and valve trim.

Malleable nickel is used for chemical and laboratory apparatus, cooking utensils, dairy equipment, electrical instruments, food products machinery, glass machinery, and spark-plug electrodes.

Monel metal is an alloy of nickel, copper and iron, made by direct reduction of the Canadian ore without separation of the metallic contents. It is used for high-pressure valves, acid pumps and wherever an acid resisting or steam corrosion-resisting strong metal is required.

Nickel anodes are used for plating; and various combinations of alloys, for armor plate, gun forgings, bayonet steel, and as a general substitute for brass, bronze and plated ware. The manufacture of nickel sheets and tubes has been so improved and their use so extended as to make nickel a strong competitor of aluminum for kitchen utensils.

Nickel is, because of its adsorptive action on hydrogen, a catalyzing agent in the hydrogenation of oils, and has made possible the production of edible saturated oils and fats from cheaper unsaturated ones. The nickel oxide-iron-alkaline storage battery, as developed by Edison in 1902, is another utilization.

The refined nickel is marketed as "shot" of varying carbon content for use in making alloys; as ingots or pigs used in the manufacture of open-hearth and electric furnace steel; as finely divided nickel oxides, both black and green, for decolorizing glass, for use in enamelling, and for chemical purposes; and as electrolytic nickel in 100 pound cathodes.

Thermocouples are required to adjust circuits in the vacuum tube repeaters on long-distance telephone lines. These tiny glass bulbs are used to measure small alternating currents in telephony and radio. The wires, made of copper-nickel alloys in fuses to protect the thermocouples, are passed through an electrolytic acid bath where they are eaten down to the size required, it being impracticable to draw wire through dies of sufficient fineness. Both copper-nickel and tungsten wires are used. They are invisible to the eye, and it is necessary to weld them together under the microscope for enclosure within the bulbs. The tungsten threads are the smallest of all, being only two hundred-millionths of an inch in diameter. One hundred of them are required to make one wire, the size of a human hair.

* * * * * *

In considering **magnesium** we must also include magnesite, dolomite, and brucite, which occur in associated groups.

Uses

Dolomite, or magnesium limestone, is referred to in Chapter XXV. It is a carbonate of lime and magnesium, much used in the sulphite process of paper manufacture from wood pulp. It is also the base from which carbonic acid is made.

Brucite is magnesium hydroxide, and is converted by calcining into magnesia, which is then used for paper pulp making, in medicine, and in the arts.

Magnesite is carbonate of magnesium, thus differing from dolomite principally in its freedom from lime, and is also used in wood pulp processes, for Sorel cement, plaster board and tiling, artificial marble, stucco, refractory bricks, fireproof and damp-proof paints, in making carbon dioxide, and in the rubber industry.

Magnesium, itself, is a silver-white metallic element, whose commercial oxide is magnesia. It is a raw material of fundamental importance in many industries. It is frequently associated with asbestos, talc, and serpentine. Other of its occurrences, as kainite and carnellite are worked for the recovery of their potash content. Magnesium sulphate is a medicine (epsom salts). The French call meerschaum clay by the name magnesite.

Metallic magnesium is used (1) for the deoxidation of other metals; (2) in the desulphurization of nickel at high temperatures; (3) as an alloy in high-strength aluminum metals where, up to 3 per cent of the content, it improves the quality of aluminum castings, sheets and forgings, and (4) in photography and pyrotechnics as a powder for actinic illumination.

Transportation rates for magnesium are double first class. The imported article carries the trade name of "electron."

The magnesite industry in the United States has centered around the states of California and Washington. Due to prohibitive freight rates, however, only a small amount reached consumers east of Chicago. The tariff of 1922 brought an increased production of 164 per cent in 1923, but was not sufficient to enable complete competition with foreign products, and compelled a considerable use of high magnesium dolomite as a substitute. A concession in rates on August 25, 1924, enabled California producers to reach Chicago all-rail for $10 per ton, or New York via Panama for $8 per ton. It is said that a tariff rate of $18.75 marks the point at which the industry could operate at a profit.

Magnesite as a refractory finds its principal market in the basic open-hearth process and in copper metallurgy. It is used as a lining in converters, kilns for sulphuric acid manufacture from pyrites burning, and in electric furnaces.

When mixed with the salt manufacturing by-product,

magnesium chloride and cork, talc, asbestos or similar materials, it reaches the flooring trade under many names, and is valued because of its lightness in construction and its greater resiliency.

The production of metallic magnesium from dolomite is a recent development and bids fair to become a substantial aluminum alloy, and in the future a light metal of importance on its own merits. The alloy is in favor for airplane and automobile construction.

Additional uses are as pipe and boiler coverings and lining of living quarters on board war vessels and transports, scientific instrument mountings, and artificial limbs. Dolomite is found in most of the Southern states, and notably in Arkansas and Georgia, and the deposits are described under "Limestone" in Chapter XXV.

Chapter XII

CORUNDUM, GEMS, DIAMONDS, GRAPHITE

Uses

Corundum in its purer form is known as sapphire, ruby, garnet, oriental emerald and topaz. Its granular impure form is sold as emery, and under various trade names, for abrasive purposes. Emery usually contains magnetic iron with the aluminous oxide of corundum. It is used as an abrasive agent on paper and cloth and also for built-up wheels. The nearer the product approaches pure corundum the higher its abrasive qualities. The domestic product meets with keen competition from Turkish and Grecian emery ores. The Turkish ore runs 60 per cent to 70 per cent aluminous oxide, with iron content below 20 per cent, and changes its quality under heat. The Greek ore runs above 20 per cent iron, and is more stable under extreme heat, hence it is favored for grinding-wheels. It is also more carefully prepared and graded. The ores are imported in lump and crushed and graded after arrival.

Artificial emery, or carborundum, is a product of the electric furnace, and has displaced emery for many abrasive purposes, especially grinding-wheels and fine grades where absolute uniformity is essential.

Bulletin 269 of the United States Geological Survey treats of the natural abrasives.

There are in operation at the present time but two domestic sources of these abrasives, New York and Virginia, the earlier Massachusetts deposit having been worked out. Four firms handle American corundum and emery, and four companies produce high-grade artificial abrasives in the United States.

Virginia

There are three operations along the main line of the Southern Railway in Virginia north of Danville and west of Chatham. The area covers twenty square miles, and its producers claim that Pittsylvania county corundum is the equivalent, by actual test, of the best imported Grecian emery. This is one of the large reserve areas in this country. It is not a true emery, however, but a combination of spinel and iron oxide.

Georgia—North Carolina

Until 1889 the deposits of Georgia and North Carolina supplied a major portion of the corundum used in this country. The introduction of artificial abrasives has, in recent years, so lowered the price of native corundums that, aside from true emery, a limited market has resulted. There still remain great reserves of high-grade natural abrasives, which with the extended transportation facilities of recent years, can again be produced at a profit. The cutting efficiency of an abrasive is measured entirely independent of its hardness, and is controlled by the manner in which its grains wear and break away under actual test.

* * * * *

The "gem minerals" are classified as (a) those of value for jewelry; (b) those which may be cut and polished for ornamental purposes, and (c) crystals of mineralogical value. The corundum gems are second only to the diamond in hardness. The North Carolina gems lead in richness of lustre and variety of color, while those of

Virginia and Georgia excel in cutting power. A large number of properties have been operated and there are many others available. The entire southwest corner of North Carolina, embracing the counties of Clay, Macon, Jackson, Franklin, Haywood, Transylvania, Buncombe, Madison, Yancey and Mitchell, is rich in gem minerals. East of the Blue Ridge they are also found in Guilford, Iredell, Alexander, Gaston, Burke and Cleveland counties. Agates are found in Cabarrus, Mecklenburg and Orange counties. Amethysts are found in Iredell, Lincoln, Macon, Wake and Warren counties; and aquamarines in Alexander, Burke, Jackson, Macon, Mitchell and Yancey counties. Beryl is found in Alexander, Burke, Clay, Iredell, Macon, Mitchell and Yancey counties.

These latter deposits extend into York, Spartanburg, Anderson, Laurens and Oconee counties, South Carolina. Many tons have been shipped from the region around Nannie's Mountain, in York county.

Corundum float, with mica scales, evidently derived from mica schist, may be picked up in the stream beds northwest of Gaffney, Cherokee county.

The Blue Ridge corundum belt of North Carolina continues southwestward into Rabun and Towns counties, Georgia, and extends over an area about forty miles wide, across the state, emerging from Troup county into Chambers, Tallapoosa and Coosa counties, Alabama. The quality of the Georgia product is high. All varieties except emery are found in the state. On account of its aluminum content corundum was at one time extensively used in the manufacture of that metal and for copper and iron alloys. It has been replaced in recent years by bauxite for this purpose.

The Alabama occurrences between Dadeville and Dudleyville in Tallapoosa county have supplied single crystals weighing as much as fifty pounds. The rubies and garnets of Tallapoosa and Coosa counties offer many felicitous opportunities for economic operation.

Gems of various kinds, including topaz, opal and agate, occur in the Big Bend district of Texas, in Presidio, Brewster and Culberson counties. Topaz is also found in the Llano River valley gravels of Mason county. Garnets occur in San Patricio county, along the Gulf coast, but their extent has not been prospected.

A particular species of gem-garnet occurring in North Carolina has been named Rhodolite. Standard grades sell for about $85 a ton. In Jackson county the gneissic rock carries 25 per cent to 30 per cent of rhodolite. Several operations have been opened up. The Macon county rhodolite is equally beautiful, but slightly softer.

Aside from the abrasive industries, corundum, or "gem metals," find a market for 20,000,000 watch jewels annually, and for use in electric meters. The wheel abrasives vary in size from small dental points to the largest grinding stones.

The electrical manufacturing companies are now experimenting with beryl for insulating purposes.

Beryl is also a source of beryllium ore, a metal one-third lighter than aluminum, and one-fourth more elastic than steel developed by electrolytic processes into airship frames, motor pistons, and as a competitor of duralumin. Beryllium is also used in the form of oxide by portrait painters to produce the olive complexion of the Latin-American type.

Deposits of the corundum type may be more easily identified by tests for hardness and specific gravity. When fragments are found in loose gravel, associated with talc or mica, they have traveled but a short distance from their source higher up.

* * * * * *

Diamonds have been found in sporadic instances in Virginia, Georgia, Alabama, North Carolina and Texas. The only field which has ever shown indications of promise is Arkansas. The Virginia stone was found in Tazewell county; the Alabama specimen came from St. Clair county; and the Texas diamond from Foard county. Reference is made in the "Mineral Resources of Georgia" to sixteen counties in that state which have furnished one or more stones each. Ten authentic diamonds have been found in North Carolina from Burke, Franklin, Lincoln, McDowell, Mecklenburg and Rutherford counties. While the genuineness of the discoveries and the quality of the diamonds seem undisputed, the source of the stones remains undisclosed. It was also suggested in 1888 that Elliott county, Kentucky, would be a second Kimberley. But the district remains like the others mentioned above, in statu quo.

The Murfreesboro field, in Pike county, Arkansas, has grown to considerable proportions with the completion of a million-dollar plant. Discovered in 1906, this field, intermittently operated until recently, has yielded over 5000 stones of marketable quality, up to 20¼ carats. The product runs 40 per cent white, 37 per cent brown, 22 per cent yellow, and 1 per cent bort. The white stones are of superior quality and of extreme hardness and brilliancy.

The diamond-bearing area covers about 90 acres, of which 85 acres represents the top of the "pipe" enclosing the peridotite formation.

* * * * *

Graphite is an iron-gray form of carbon. It differs but slightly in appearance from molybdenite. The latter, however, being a sulphite and the former being relatively pure carbon, a simple blow pipe test will serve to distinguish them. Because of its infusibility, chemical inertness, high conductivity, extreme softness and low specific gravity, it is of great economic value. It occurs in two forms; as amorphous graphite formed by the action of igneous intrusions on coal beds, and as crystalline or flake graphite, which occurs in veins, or in flakes disseminated through country rock. Artificial graphite, formed in the electric furnace, is of the amorphous type.

Recognized as an industry in 1896 graphite mining grew very rapidly for about ten years. North Carolina and Texas were large producers, Georgia and Arkansas became factors, and in 1914 the flake graphite industry was greatly augmented by the Alabama field, where over $4,000,000 was invested in graphite mines and mills. The Bureau of Mines after tests covering several years, determined that when American clays and flake graphite were properly prepared crucibles made from them gave superior results to those made from the best imported product.

Notwithstanding this, the Ceylon and Madagascar graphite continued to fill the market as soon as shipping became available after the war. The Tariff law of 1922 imposed a duty of 10 per cent ad valorem on amorphous graphite, 20 per cent ad valorem on crystalline lump, chip or dust, and 1½ cents a pound on crystalline flake. Imports increased over 50 per cent during the following year, however, and because of the inadequacy of this protection, American production has become very erratic and many of the fields have closed down and dismantled their mills. The diversity of American graphite deposits and the small margin of profit, when unprotected, make it impossible to compete with the cheap labor of Ceylon, which permits cheap mining, careful sorting, rubbing up and blending.

The graphite industry is a clear-cut case in which American labor, paid a standard wage, cannot compete with foreign labor paid a pauper wage. The quality and quantity of American graphite is adequate to supply a large part of the trade, when sufficient tariff is applied to equalize the wage rate and ocean freights on imported graphite. When the tariff is taken out of politics and considered as an economic problem, graphite mines in Alabama and other Southern states will be in active operation.

Virginia

The Southern Railway's Development Department reports graphite of commercial quality and quantity in Virginia at Culpeper, in Culpeper county; near and south of Riverton, Warren County; south of Orange, Orange county; west of Charlottesville, Albemarle county; and west of Keyesville, Charlotte county.

North Carolina

Graphite has been found in North Carolina, in Buncombe, McDowell, Catawba, Haywood, Wake, Yancey, Macon, Alexander and Cleveland counties. The Catawba county graphite is amorphous, and the deposits in Cleveland county are found in pockets. That of Macon county is in combination with a fine-grained clay. It is possible that when properly prepared this deposit may prove of value for crucibles. In some of the Macon county graphites, garnets are also found. The Buncombe county graphite operations have been closed down due to the excessive cost of separation.

South Carolina

At Zion, Spartanburg county, South Carolina, is a 76-acre deposit of graphite, mica and monazite.

Georgia

Both amorphous and crystalline varieties occur in Georgia, the former in Bartow county, and the latter in Bartow, Pickens, Elbert, Hall, Madison, Franklin, Douglas, Troup and Cobb counties. The Georgia product is much of it interbedded with slates and schists or occurring in gneissic pockets. It has, therefore, carried sufficient impurity to prevent its use as a refractory, and the principal consumption has been as an inert filler for commercial fertilizers. The Bartow county deposits, however, have never been thoroughly prospected, and with the railroad facilities of that county, offer an inviting field for both amorphous and crystalline varieties.

At Royston, on the line between Franklin and Hart counties, is a vein 60 feet wide and proven up to a depth of 60 feet, which extends for 2½ miles, and averages 48 per cent graphite. This deposit is now being actively developed.

Alabama

For many years Alabama was the principal American

source, and the price of Alabama graphite was slightly higher than the average for the country. Clay county was more extensively developed than Coosa, Chilton, Tallapoosa, Elmore or Pike counties. Not less than 30 well-defined veins have been noted. Much of this is the crystalline form. The Pike county deposit is about three miles from Troy, on the A. C. L. R. R. The showing at Jackson's Gap, Tallapoosa county, is a vein ten to twelve feet in width. In Elmore county, one mile below Tallasee, lenses up to two inches in diameter are found in garnetiferous schist.

Arkansas

Two outcrops of high-grade crystalline graphite occur in Arkansas. One is in the Trap Mountains in Hot Spring county, and the other at Buttermilk Springs, northeast of Caddo Gap, in Montgomery county. Other exposures in Pulaski, Garland and Montgomery counties are in shale, and are ground for paint pigment and dark brick. A third type, of amorphous graphite, is reported in northern Montgomery county.

Texas

The Texas deposits are principally in Llano and Burnet counties, in the "pack saddle schist." The Llano county properties were originally mined for gold. $400,000 was spent on equipment and about $50,000 of gold recovered from the graphitic schist. The companies then turned to graphite, which is being mined successfully. These schists run from 10 per cent to 12 per cent graphite. It is probable that as improved methods of separation are devised, this district will be mined for graphite, gold, silver and lead.

The latest developments near Burnet, Burnet county,

have proved very satisfactory. The product is hauled by motor trucks to Burnet and here loaded in cars for shipment to Houston.

The "pack saddle" formation extends into Mason, Blanco and Gillespie counties, and graphite occurrences are frequent.

It was stated in 1923, that as a result of extended tests, Texas graphite ranked first, and Alabama second, taking all factors into consideration. Ceylon and Madagascar products followed. In addition to longer life, the Texas and Alabama crucibles carbonized the steel to a lesser degree. Higher tariff protection, lower freight rates and the manufacture of graphite articles near the source of production is the solution of the American graphite problem. Given a fair and impartial entrance without discrimination into a reopened or expanded market, the graphite operators have no fear of results.

Uses

Graphite for crucibles, foundry facings, lead pencils, and lubrication, are the large fields for the product. Polishes, paints, dry battery fillers, boiler mixtures, as a glaze for tea leaves and coffee beans, fertilizer filler, pipe joint dope, dynamo brushes, steam packing, arc electrodes, preparations used in electro-plating and glazing and in steel cable making, case hardening and other processes constitute the remainder of the demand.

The increased use of the electric furnace has stimulated artificial graphite much of which is used for giant electrodes.

Artificial graphite is also used for graphite powders, electric furnace resistors, electrotypers' leads, manufacture of molded mechanical rubber goods, rope lubricant and special lubricants of deflocculated graphite. Solid forms of artificial graphite appear as electrodes, anodes, blocks and plates for casting non-machinable metals, laboratory crucibles, resistor units and contacts.

On account of its availability to the sources of hydro-electric power, anthracite coal dust and coke breeze are utilized for artificial graphite. In the South the vast supplies of sawdust and the plentiful supply of power open a possibility for the manufacture of giant electrodes near the point of consumption.

CHAPTER XIII

GOLD, SILVER, COPPER

The uses, market and value of **gold** need no exposition. Gold production has fallen off, and in many districts entirely ceased, due to the high cost of labor and materials. Unlike other metals with a fluctuating price, gold remains at $20.67 per ounce, so that when the cost of extracting an ounce of gold approximates or exceeds that value, gold mining must necessarily be confined to rich deposits or those which may be operated at minimum cost.

Virginia

The gold belt of Virginia starts in Montgomery county, extends through Fauquier, Prince William, Stafford, Spotsylvania, Orange, Louisa, Goochland, Fluvanna, Buckingham, Cumberland, Charlotte, Halifax and Pittsylvania counties.

In general, this deposit extends from the Virgilina district of Virginia, across North and South Carolina, east Tennessee, north Georgia and Alabama. A detailed description of the Appalachian Gold Belt may be found in the "Sixteenth Annual Report of the United States Geological Survey for 1894-95," part 3, pp. 251-331. Bulletin 7 of the Virginia Geological Survey also covers the James River deposits.

The ores are sulphides, associated with pyrites. The work must be confined to sulphurets below the ground water level. Many of them are high-grade ores and amenable to treatment, and if worked by practical mining men in an economic way will produce good profits. They are not, however, susceptible to operation by usual promotion methods.

At Mineral and Louisa, Louisa county, and near Fredericksburg, Spotsylvania county, mining operations are intermittently carried on. At the latter place a centrifugal separating machine is used to recover the nuggets and flour gold from the blue clay on a 700-acre tract. Some gold is recovered from cinders of pyritic ores shipped to smelters.

North Carolina

Little actual gold mining has been done in North Carolina, but there are large quantities of low-grade gravels which have been tested near Brindletown, Burke county, and which offer a good dredging field, with shale bed rock, and valleys wide enough for a dredge to swing, with plenty of water for flotation. Nuggets are found north of Morgantown, and around South Mountain, in the same county.

The Southern Railway has on exhibition gold-pyrite ores from Greensboro, Pine Hill, and Guilford Cove, Guilford county; and Salisbury, Rowan county. Promising gold deposits are now being developed near Rockingham, in Richmond county, along the S. A. L. Railway.

Gold-bearing quartz occurs along the Norfolk Southern R. R. between Starr and Aberdeen, in Montgomery county. Deep mining is carried on at Eldorado, Montgomery county, and development tunnels are being driven in Moore, Catawba, Davidson and Rowan counties. Caldwell, Randolph, Person and McDowell counties have had examinations, reports and some prospecting. Stanly and Cabarrus counties joined the producers in 1923. Much of this ore is complex and the recovery includes copper-lead.

South Carolina

South Carolina production is confined to hydraulic operations around Blacksburg, Cherokee county, and scattering plants in York county. A generation ago over a million dollars in gold was taken out at the Dorn mine at McCormick, McCormick county, on the C. & W. C. R. R. No work has been done there in recent years. There is a large mineralized section extending from north of McCormick across the Savannah River, into Lincoln, Wilkes and Columbia counties, Georgia. Thirty-five years ago some twelve mines were hand operated by pick, and the gold recovered in "Long Toms," with amalgam. The gold is found in pockets which became coarser and more frequent at increased depth. The veins are disarranged through seismic conditions, and few of the operators had engineering skill to extend their workings. One of the mines reached a depth of five hundred feet and another over three hundred. Copper, lead and silver were also recovered from the quartz gangue. In the light of present-day metallurgy it is probable that these complex ores might be operated at a good profit.

The Haile mine near Kershaw, Lancaster county, ran .065 oz. gold per ton, or about $1.36, by the cyanide process. Production since 1913 has been negligible, due to prohibitive labor costs. Nuggets continue to be found in creeks and gullies of Spartanburg county.

Georgia

Gold production in Georgia reached its maximum in 1845, when over a half million dollars came from the Dahlonega field. Although most of the production has been from placer methods, there are many rich veins similar to and including those discussed above (South Carolina-Georgia) which need only intelligent engineering and metallurgical application to show a profit. Gold was mined in Georgia 20 years before its discovery in California on Duke's Creek, Habersham county. The entire area between the Chestatee and Etowah Rivers was productive in the small stream gravels. A branch mint was established at Dahlonega in 1838 and continued until 1861. Over $6,000,000 of Georgia gold was coined there, during that time. Much of the present production is by-product from copper and other metals.

The various operations and fields are described in detail in the "Mines Report on Gold, Silver, Copper, Lead and Zinc in the Eastern States" for 1922 and 1923, by J. P. Dunlop, United States Geological Survey.

The Southern Railway exhibits gold ore from Lumpkin county. If this should prove of workable extent, it would add to the present production of that county, which is largely placer.

Tennessee

Gold in Tennessee is derived from two sources, the placer operations at Coker Creek, Monroe county, and as a by-product of the Ducktown mines in Polk county. The Coker Creek area, similar to the Dahlonega field in Georgia, had its climax in the 50's, when a negro slave took out $80,000 in free gold. There are five veins in the surrounding hills, which have broken down into the meadows. Part of these show sulphide ore and part free gold. They range from 1 inch to 18 inches in width, and are apparently true fissure veins. They have never been adequately prospected. The valley carries sufficient water for dredging and is now being operated by steam shovel and washer, the recovery being by the amalgam method, the fines being cyanided. There are indications of former stream beds along the foot hills, and it is not unlikely that a "white gravel channel," similar to that on Bonanza Creek and the Klondyke River in the Yukon Territory, may be developed for hydraulicing.

Bed rock in the valley lies at 2 to 6 feet and values are found up to grass roots. Only coarse gold was extracted in the early days, and a mechanical process for handling and recovering a large yardage per day would make it worth while to re-work the old tailing piles.

Alabama

The gold bearing area of Alabama has for convenience been divided into an upper and lower gold belt. The dividing line between them is the boundary between Talledega, Clay and Randolph counties on the north, and Coosa, Tallapoosa and Chambers counties on the south.

At Arbacootchee, Cleburne county, on the headwaters of Dime Creek, gold has been continuously mined since 1835. There were 2000 inhabitants in this valley when the California goldfields were announced. Over at least one square mile, the stream bed has been turned, again and again, by hand shovels. In 1905 a small dredge re-worked the area. Considerable nugget gold has been recovered, and sluicing and hydraulicing are still carried on.

Another historical area extends from northeast to southwest, across Goldville, New Site, and Cowpens in Tallapoosa and Randolph counties. Near Hog Mountain are several narrow quartz veins showing good assays. This belt extends entirely across Tallapoosa county and offers an inviting opportunity for prospecting. The Hog Mountain region was worked and the gangue cyanided for several years, but due to high operating costs, the work was stopped. As much as $5000 was recovered one season. Five miles west of Dadeville, Tallapoosa county, is a quartz gangue with free milling gold which would work well with a stamp mill.

In the western part of Coosa county this same type of quartz and gold is found again. Coosa and Tallapoosa counties are sufficiently rich in varied metallic minerals to warrant properly financed prospecting. A little prospecting has been done in Chilton county and some creek values found. The Central of Georgia Ry. reports gold in Chambers, Coosa, Randolph and Tallapoosa counties. Values up to $16.00 per ton are being recovered at some of the Tallapoosa operations.

Arkansas

Gold, silver and platinum have been found associated at Sulphur Rock, Independence county, Arkansas. Their successful operation is dependent upon large scale production and adequate metallurgical facilities.

Texas

Texas gold is found in the graphitic schists of Llano county. Originally mined for gold, the principal output is now graphite, and gold a by-product. The old Heath mine in Llano county has been the principal source. Low assays of gold have been reported from the black sands in central west Texas and in recent formations on the coast.

* * * * * *

Silver has always been a favorite for its adaptability in manufacturing jewelry, and its utility in tableware.

With the growth of photography and moving pictures, increased demand has in a measure offset its post-war decreased use in coinage.

Virginia

Virginia has no known silver deposits. The copper-gold ores of the Virgilina district yield a small amount of by-product silver. Silver-lead ore is found at Drake's branch, Charlotte county.

North Carolina

Dr. Joseph Hyde Pratt predicts that the mines at Silver Valley and Silver Hill, Davidson county, North Carolina, have a prospect of long life and rich silver ore. The gangues are mixed sulphites, sphalerites, galena, chalcopyrites, pyrite, argentite and decomposed minerals. As long as the operations were confined to the decomposed areas, mining was profitable, and as high as $500 and $600 per ton were realized. When the work reached the 700 foot level and the sulphites were reached, work stopped on account of metallurgical conditions. As improved methods of separation are devised, increased development will result. This is a field for metallurgical research. Silver-lead ores are found at Asheboro, Franklin county.

South Carolina

Gaffney, Cherokee county, South Carolina, exhibits silver-gold and silver-lead ore, but no strong deposits recoverable for silver.

Tennessee

Like gold, in Tennessee silver is a matter of by-product recovery from the Ducktown copper operations. A silver-lead ore is exhibited by the Southern Railway, from Sevierville, Sevier county.

Alabama

The Tallapoosa county gold ores of Alabama also carry a recoverable value in silver.

Texas

The Shafter silver mine, in Presidio county, Texas has been in operation for over 65 years. The ore is argentite which has infiltrated into limestone caverns, and is associated with varying quantities of galena.

The Hazel mine, in Culberson county, carries a copper-silver gangue with intrusions of silver-lead.

North of Allamore, Culberson county, and in El Paso county, north of El Paso, are similar Permian limestones which are worth investigation. Various points in Brewster county, and operations south of the Quitman Mountains along the Rio Grande in Hudspeth county, have shipped some very rich silver ore. Approximately $8,000,000 in silver has been produced in Texas since 1882. Brewster, Culberson and Hudspeth counties may well be further prospected.

Uses

The uses of silver are principally for coinage, jewelry, photography, medicine, the dental trade, and the electrical industry.

* * * * * *

Copper is probably the first metal which was utilized by man, because of the ease with which it can be smelted, refined and worked. It occurs in three principal forms; as sulphide ore, as native copper found only in large amounts in the Lake Superior region of Michigan, and as oxide ores.

The products of the sulphide and oxide ores are extracted by fire or electro-metallurgy and are known as blister and black copper. The effect of fire refining is to volatilize the sulphur, arsenic and other impurities and to reduce to slag the manganese, iron, antimony and other metallics. Electrolytic refining utilizes anodes of raw copper which are subjected to the action of sulphuric acid and copper sulphate, and re-deposited in cathode sheets. These cathodes are re-melted into wire bars, slabs, and ingots, in a reverberatory furnace. The final cathode copper is the purest commercial form.

No industry has shown a more orderly growth or closer application of science to the improvement of the product. The absorption of re-melt, or secondary copper, after the war, caused a temporary depression in the industry, but as the supply of war copper has gone into commerce, the raw material situation has improved. The world's annual consumption approximates 1,500,000 tons, of which over one-half is consumed in the United States. Sixty per cent of this is used in the electrical industry; 20 per cent in vehicles, transportation and building accessories; and 20 per cent in industries and arts.

The natural gravitation of copper from all sources of the United States is toward the northeastern seaboard. It would be logical for much of the Southern ore, as from Utah, reaching Gulf points by water or rail, to be refined at some point along the Inland Waterway System, or on the coast, as at the mouth of the Warrior River, where coal, coke, and flux are available at low transportation costs.

The copper deposits of the Appalachian States were described in 1911, in Bulletin 455 of the U. S. Geological Survey. Many developments have since been made.

Virginia

The native or elementary copper ore reserves of Virginia are found in Page, Warren, Fauquier, Greene and Madison counties, along the Blue Ridge. These ores are all low grade, but are amenable to recovery by improved metallurgy. They are not a steam shovel proposition because they occur in basalt of the Precambrian formation.

The Virgilina district, 40 miles east of Danville, in the Piedmont region, has produced some copper. Halifax and Charlotte counties have also produced. Deposits are found in Mecklenburg county which have never been operated. Many of the mines have been worked to a depth of 500 to 600 feet. The ore is a chalco-bornite mixture without pyrites or chalcopyrites. Bulletin 14 of the Virginia Geological Survey has been issued to describe these ores in detail.

In Carroll, Grayson and Floyd counties, but chiefly in Carroll county, is a pyrrhotite body of gossan. Before the Civil War, black (secondary enrichment) copper was gophered for a distance of 18 miles, and hauled by wagon to Baltimore, and there marketed. It occurs at the base of the gossan and the upper surface of the fresh pyrrhotite. The pyrrhotite mass below water carries irregular stringers of chalcopyrite averaging better than ½ per cent metallic copper. In the utilization of these ores in manufacturing sulphuric acid, the copper is saved as a by-product.

North Carolina

The copper ores of Rowan and the Virgilina district of North Carolina have suffered much at the hands of promoters. They must be handled like the Catoctin ores of the Blue Ridge in Virginia, on a large scale, and their development will depend upon active metallurgical research.

The Ore Knob Mine was worked for copper in Ashe county before the railroad was within 75 miles. This deposit runs from 3 to 3½ per cent metallic copper, and is a low-grade proposition to be worked on a large scale. The Jackson county ores are chalcopyrite. The Swain county deposits are similar to the Ducktown, Tennessee, ores. In Guilford county, near Greensboro, the chalcopyrite originally worked for gold, proved to be a better copper proposition, with gold as a by-product.

Near Asheboro, Randolph county, is a good showing of copper, formerly operated, but suffering for engineering management. At Fontana, Swain county, a vein showing 9 feet in width at the outcrop, and widening as the 60-foot drift advanced, shows 6½ to 8 per cent metallic copper. The company is shipping ore running 6½ per cent or better, and stocking lower grade for mill development. The property is three miles from the railroad, and the cover rises at about 45°. A lumber road operates across the property. Back of this lies a second, carrying the Fontana vein. Across the Little Tennessee River at Marcus, Graham county, the same vein outcrops 12 feet in width. It would appear that Swain and Graham counties offer unusual promise for copper development.

Cabarrus and Granville counties also have deposits from which ore specimens have been exhibited.

South Carolina

One copper mine was operated at Saluda, Saluda county, South Carolina, but has been closed for some years. The ore is lean, and complex.

Georgia

Georgia copper is found principally in Fannin, Cherokee and Haralson counties. As a by-product of gold-silver-lead, it occurs in Lincoln, Wilkes, Lumpkin and Fulton counties. In strike and dip, the veins conform to the country rock, and the surface zone is usually gossan, or brown iron ore. Below this the black oxides and green-blue carbonates are found, in lenticular irregularity, with leaves of native copper and below this, at 80 to 100 feet from the surface, occur the pyrrhotite and chalcopyrites.

Tennessee

Tennessee copper is produced in the Ducktown district. There are many other deposits of apparently the same formation, but they are of lower grade, and become beneficiation problems. There is also a pyrrhotite deposit showing 1½ per cent copper, 1 per cent zinc, with traces of recoverable gold and silver. The chemical problem in connection with sulphuric acid has been solved. The zinc has so far been wasted. This field is receiving concentrated research along metallurgical lines and considerable advance may be expected.

Alabama

At Stone Hill, on the line between Cleburne and Randolph counties, Alabama, are two copper properties which were worked on the surface for many years, where the chalcopyrite-sulphide ore leached out and concentrated. The first marketings yielded fine concentrates, which were sacked and shipped to Baltimore, and smelted at a profit. The lower ores were less concentrated and needed a mill to concentrate the product before shipment. These lower ores run from 5 to 6 per cent metallic copper and could be easily concentrated. At one of these properties a shaft was sunk and 8 per cent ore taken out. They have not been worked for 40 years. The ore on the dump is still leaching.

Fifteen miles from the A. B. & C. and the Central of Georgia R. Rs. in Randolph county are other properties yielding 7 to 8 per cent copper. This is a vast unprospected area which holds promise of some day serving the growing needs of the copper industry.

Arkansas

Seventeen miles west of Little Rock, Arkansas, a copper property was opened up in a manganiferous shale, which carried as high as $130 per ton in leached copper. A shaft and tunnel were driven and considerable ore taken out until the panic of 1907 caused a cessation. The ore on the dump has the appearance of chalcocite, with the manganiferous stain. It is unfortunate that the shaft has caved in, thus preventing further examination. The ore in evidence assays high copper content. So far as known, this is the only copper operation in the state which has actually produced profitable ore.

Native copper, widely disseminated, has been exposed near Olsen, Arkansas, and at a point four miles east of Harrison, Arkansas.

Hydrous copper carbonate (malachite) was found in

small quantities in Searcy county and in Pulaski county. It is probable that such copper recoveries in Arkansas as may prove profitable will be those associated as by-products of lead and zinc.

Texas

Copper in Texas is a by-product proposition at present. A number of outcrops in green clay have been noted by Udden in Foard, Knox, Stonewall, Baylor, Archer, Haskell, Clay and Taylor counties. It is not thought that they are sufficiently valuable under existing conditions to warrant attention. They are leached concretions from clay, originally sea sediments.

The Van Horn copper-silver deposits referred to under "Silver" above are an entirely different formation.

There are five copper refining centers in the United States: Baltimore, New York, Tacoma, Anaconda and the Michigan Lake District. One of the great consumers of copper is the photo-engraving and electrotyping industry, which uses more than 4,000,000 pounds annually.

Uses

Among the unusual and newer uses of copper are horseshoes alloyed with tin, to prevent sparks in dry forests. Its easy fabrication and non-corrosive qualities have earned a wide field in the chemical industry. Milk evaporators, laundry machines, condensing equipment, kettles of all kinds for candy, cooking, and heating in the various food industries; ducts for corrosive fumes and ventilating systems, bath tub linings, automobile radiators and tanks, and in a wide range of alloys.

In building, for pipes, cornices, eaves, doors, flashings, gutters, roofs, frames, trim and ventilators.

The electrical industry surpasses all others in its consumption and application of copper, and its alloys brass and bronze. It occurs as anodes, cables, conductors, reflectors, switches, motor brushes, fans, fuses, electric stoves, dish washers, carpet sweepers, telephone and telegraph wires, locomotive fire box plates, and the myriad applications of electric power.

In candy, glue, paint, preserving, soup and varnish manufacture, in refrigerator lining and tanks, in boilers, reservoirs, floats, linings, gaskets, sterilizers, thermostats, chafing dishes, funnels, ladles, measures, molds, pails, pans, percolators, roasters, skillets, strainers, fire extinguishers, kettle drums, mail boxes, nails, nuts, sinks, plates, railway car roofs, soda fountain fixtures, stationary signs, show cases, tacks, washers and rivets, we find copper an indispensible material.

As brass and bronze it is an integral part of adding and calculating machines, bells, gongs, automobile parts, bicycles, bedsteads, candle sticks, cash registers, jewelry, clocks, dental and surgical instruments, desk and office accessories, dictaphones, drafting instruments, fans and fittings, emblems, novelties, checks, engine and fire room fixtures, fire arms, fire extinguishers, lanterns, flashlight equipment, lighting fixtures, lamps, locks, miscellaneous hardware, medals, badges, buttons, motor cycles, trucks, musical, nautical and optical instruments, organs, phonographs, pianos, picture frames, plumbing supplies and fixtures, railings, scales, signs, store fixtures, surveying instruments, typewriters, wire screen and pipe.

The copper nickel alloys are used for brazing solder, cutlery and knife stock, jewelers' wire, keystock, spoon and fork stock, and platers' bars and cores.

One of the valuable features in the use of copper is its factor of safety. When subjected to high pressures, copper does not "let go" at once, but gives warning and time.

The fields of copper research at present are:

(1) To perfect a suitable joint which will be leak and wind proof, allow expansion, and be easily put together.

(2) To produce new and artistic finishes in oxidized reds, greens and browns, through varying exposures to nitric solutions of differing grades.

Chapter XIV

PYRITES, GOSSAN, COPPERAS, SULPHUR, SALT

The primary development of **pyrites** in the United States, was as a source of sulphur in the manufacture of sulphuric acid. Prior to 1918 the annual consumption of imported Spanish pyrites was approximately one million tons. For the acid process, arsenic in excess of 1 per cent is objectionable; but for the manufacture of calcium arsenate (vide Chap. XXV) as developed at Tuscaloosa, Ala., by Dr. Stewart J. Lloyd, high arsenical ores would find a ready market.

The development of a vast quantity of high-grade sulphur in Texas and Louisiana has in recent years greatly decreased the pyrites importations and their incident freight charges. Virginia was formerly a large producer of pyrites, as was Georgia; North Carolina and Alabama also have large reserves. In Tennessee the gangue carries sufficient copper and by-products to warrant operations.

The late Dr. Thomas L. Watson, State Geologist of Virginia, expressed the opinion shortly before his death that the manufacture of acid and of iron would so increase that pyrites would ultimately "come back," both for sulphur and gossan.

Uses

No pyrite under 52 per cent sulphur is sold for acid making. One ton of sulphur is roughly equivalent to two tons of high-grade pyrites. As long as sulphur continues abundant and at its present cost, the development of pyrites will be dependent on its relation to the point of consumption, and its other constituent parts, such as arsenic or gossan, which may find available markets equally contiguous.

A new use for pyrites is as an anode in an alkaline solution for electric energy.

Virginia

The principal pyrites belt of Virginia is in Prince William, Stafford and Louisa counties, where the most extensive pyrites operations on the North American continent were once in full blast. In Carroll county the pyrites occur with pyrrhotite, the magnetic form, in which nickel is usually associated (vide Chap. XI). This ore is still operated, and is the only deposit in the South still supplying the sulphuric acid manufacturers as primary consumers.

North Carolina

The pyrites deposits of North Carolina, when mined for gold or copper have been described in Chapter XIII. North of Bessemer City, Gaston county, a pyrites deposit was mined until recently. The pyrrhotite deposits have been listed also in Chap. XIII.

South Carolina

Similarly, the pyrites and pyrrhotites of South Carolina, in York, Chesterfield, Lancaster, Spartanburg and Union counties, have been operated for gold.

Georgia

The change in basic practice in the sulphuric acid industry has seriously affected the pyrites mines of Georgia, all of whose product was mined for that industry. Carroll, Haralson, Paulding, Cobb, Cherokee, Lumpkin, Fulton and Harris counties have all been producers. The ores are usually pure, but are handpicked, crushed and concentrated before shipping. Other occurrences are reported in Bartow, Dawson, Greene, McDuffie, Murray, Oglethorpe and White counties. All these deposits lie north of the "Fall Line," in the Piedmont Plateau.

Alabama

The Clay and Randolph county deposits in Alabama are the subject of a special report by the Alabama Geological Survey. These beds lie along the A. B. & C. R. R., and near the power plant of the Alabama Power Co. on the Tallapoosa River. Transportation, water and power are therefore available. The ores are arseno-pyrites, carrying both gold and white arsenic. They were originally operated for gold only, and as soon as the oxidized ore passed into the unaltered arsenic ore, below water level, development was halted. The gold recoveries have averaged from $16.50 to $18 per ton over a 20-foot stratum of quartzite and decomposed slate, and are therefore worthy of consideration in estimating operating costs.

The arseno-pyrites belt is approximately two miles in width, and extends for at least 1½ miles northeast and southwest. The gangue carries gold, lead, iron and arsenic. Frequent "chimneys" occur in this area, from vein intersections. The metallic arsenic content runs from 16 to 18 per cent, or around 23 per cent of arsenic trioxide. Much of the deposit is above water level and susceptible of steam shovel operation.

This area is of especial economic value to the South because of the work of Dr. Lloyd, referred to above, and also discussed under "Calcium Arsenate," in Chap. XXV.

Arkansas

The only commercial deposit noted in Arkansas is on the southern slope of West Mountain, near Hot Springs.

Texas

Pyrite is found in Brewster county, Texas, associated with cinnabar, and bituminous shales, but never in commercial quantities.

* * * * * *

Gossan, as described in Chapter IX under iron ores, was the pre-Revolutionary source of iron. "Bluebilly" is the trade name of the iron by-product obtained from the sulphuric acid process. The reader is referred to Chapter IX for further discussion of the gossan ores.

* * * * * *

The generic term **"copperas"** is somewhat loosely used to include melanterite which is hydrous ferrous sulphate and also chalcanthite which is hydrous copper sulphate. The former is a green crystalline astringent used in dyeing, ink-making, photography, sulphuric acid processes and in the form of red iron peroxide is used as rouge in plate glass polishing, while the latter is principally known in veterinary medicine as an antiseptic.

Mississippi—North Carolina—Tennessee

A deposit of melanterite some four feet in thickness has recently been discovered on Leaf River, near the Smith-Jasper county line in Mississippi. Chalcanthite is reported as a secondary mineral associated with gold in

Cleveland county, North Carolina, and associated with the Ducktown ores in Polk county, Tennessee.

* * * * * *

The **sulphur** industry in the southern states is confined to Louisiana and Texas. Recently, on account of the high cost of operation at excessive depth, the major operations in Calcasieu parish, near St. Charles, La., have been dismantled and the company has moved its activities to the shallower Texas field.

Sulphur plays a basic role in the chemical industry. Until the war, Spanish pyrites was the source of most of the sulphur used in making sulphuric acid. This process, however, entails the handling of a large quantity of material with slow combustion in expensive roasters, and the disposal of a large amount of cinder, while one-half the same weight of sulphur burns without residue, in inexpensive equipment, and is free from arsenic and other impurities which would affect the quality of the acid.

The average annual consumption approximates one million tons. The producers today guarantee a product 99.7 per cent pure on a moisture free basis. Run-of-mine sulphur should pass at least 95 per cent through a 100 mesh screen. The 100 per cent pure product, through a 200 mesh screen is the medical form called flowers of sulphur.

When vaporized and caught in a molten state and cast into sticks it is called roll sulphur. For the rubber industry, which requires a finely ground product with a minimum of impurities, and a maximum solubility in bisulphide of carbon, the sulphur is cooled slowly in large receptacles, so that the crystals will assume orthorhombic form to meet the requirements of solubility.

To the development of the Frasch process of injecting large quantities of hot water under pressure and thus bringing the sulphur to the surface, is due the rapid rise of the sulphur industry.

The use of sulphur as a fertilizer is of recent growth. Finely pulverized sulphur when added to an alkali soil, creates an acid reaction, thus neutralizing the soil. Or if sulphur is composted with ground raw phosphate rock, the phosphate is rendered available within a short time. Bacteria in the soil oxidizes the sulphur to sulphuric acid which acts on the raw phosphate to give available plant food. Similarly when sulphur is mixed with glauconite or green sand marl, the oxidation of the sulphur makes available the water-soluble potash.

The New Jersey State Agricultural Experiment Station reports that sulphur when properly applied to the soil will control and check potato scab, sugar beet scab, eel worms, and many other plant diseases, and used around barns and stables prevents the spreading of animal diseases and insect pests.

Texas

The Texas deposits occur in association with gypsum and salt domes. Large operations are found in Matagorda and Brazoria counties. Pecos and Smith counties are being developed. The bulk of the product is mined by three large companies.

Uses

Seventy-five per cent of the country's production goes into the sulphuric acid, paper-pulp, chemical, and fertilizer industries. The balance goes principally into rubber insecticides and explosives. Because of its die-electric strength (like mica), its low fusability, and its acid and water resisting properties, many new industrial uses are being found.

Diatomaceous earth, fibre board and similar porous materials are easily impregnated by immersion in a sulphur bath. Cured Portland cement concrete will absorb 17 per cent by weight, of molten sulphur, greatly increasing its strength, waterproofing it, and making the surface less susceptible to abrasion. Although the tensile strength of sulphur is only about 200 pounds per square inch, a lean mixture of cement and sand, breaking under a tension of 150 to 200 pounds, when given a sulphur treatment, increases its tension limit to from 1200 to 2000 pounds, per square inch. The weaker the cement mixture, the greater the proportionate increase in strength by this treatment.

When pulp and paper products are bathed in molten sulphur, they become acid resistant and weatherproof, more rigid, and if thin, more brittle. It is necessary therefore to shape them before processing. Window boxes, flush tanks, acid carboys, textile cones, phonograph horns, caskets, bee hives and artificial deer heads are among the products so treated.

Practically all dried fruits are subjected to sulphur fumes. Nuts, broom corn, cotton felt, feathers, fur, hair, hemp, jute, paper, rattan, straw, wool, wicker furniture and many other products are bleached with sulphur dioxide. Heavy machinery is cemented to its foundation by sulphur. Ammonia leakages are discovered by burning sulphur, which produces a white cloud in the presence of ammonia. Florists bleach flowers by burning sulphur candles. Drinking water is purified with copper sulphate.

Gunmetal, oxidized metal finish, and irridescent bronze all derive their individualities from immersion in liquid sulphur, alternately cool and hot, rinsing, buffing, etc.

Acid proof pipe is made by treating fibre conduit with sulphur. The fibrous material absorbs 380 to 390 per cent of sulphur, and a three-inch pipe after treatment will easily support the weight of a man, although the walls are only 3/16 of an inch thick. This material, under the trade name of "fibresul" is used for battery cases, electroplating tanks, chemical pails, etc. Many other combinations of sulphur, fibre, coke breeze, etc., are on the market.

Among the other uses of sulphur are in the manufacture of dyestuffs, artificial silk, belting, celluloid, ebonite, elastics, films, fire extinguishers, fungicides, gasoline refining, galvanized iron, glue, glycerine, rubber and canvas hose, leather tanning, matches, medicine, paints, chemical reagents, shoe polish, soap, sodium thiosulphate, pickling steel, refining sugar, automobile tires, and as weed killer.

* * * * * *

Salt contributes more to the health and welfare of both man and beast than any other mineral. Its sources, however, are limited in number. Its principal uses are obvious. In addition to the preparation of food, it is a source of soda and soda compounds, of chlorine, of hydrochloric acid, and is used to form a glaze on pottery, in enamelling, in refrigerating, for curing and preserving hides, fish, meat, butter and vegetables, and for clearing oleomargerine. It thaws switches in winter and affords non-freezing solutions for fire pails.

In the chemical industry it is used in the manufacture of soda ash, caustic soda, and soda bicarbonate. These and the various bleaching powders and alkalis, may be considered as by-products of the salt industry.

There are three methods of salt mining—evaporating salt water; dissolving salt in water, out of other materials, and then evaporating it; and mining rock salt. To render table salt moisture proof, about 1 per cent of magnesium or calcium carbonate is added to coat the grains.

Where rock salt is mined, it is necessary to remove the salt powder after the crystals have been ground to the required size. This dust covers everything in the mill, and its deliquescent nature makes it exceedingly difficult to preserve metals from corrosion. Machinery is continually slushed with oil, and motors and delicate mechanisms must operate in sealed boxings.

West Virginia

The salt fields on Gauley River, West Virginia, from Kanawha Falls down to Point Pleasant and up the Ohio River to Pomeroy Bend, are still active, and using the evaporative process. Around Mason City and Hartford, in Mason county, and Malden, in Kanawha county, the salt carries bromine and certain magnesium salts, which are of value in medicine and in the arts.

Uses

For over 50 years these operations produced table salt, until the Michigan evaporators opened up, using slab sawmill waste for fuel. Then the heat distillation and condensation processes were added for the production of bromine, chlorine, soda carbonate or "soda ash," and soda sulphate or "salt cake," magnesium salts, and other chemical by-products, and the profits on these valuable materials made it possible to continue operations. These soda salts are extensively used in the glass industry, window glass, making salt cake, and bottle glass using soda ash. Manganese is added to counteract iron discoloration in the silica sand.

Well drilling around Huntington, Cabell county, has shown salt deposits under that region. This would be an excellent location for a by-product chemical plant, on account of oil, gas, coal, coke, glass sand, and rail, and water transportation. Bromine is also used in the preparation of tetraethyl lead with which gasoline is treated to prevent knocking and carbon formation.

Virginia

The Virginia deposits occur in Smyth and Washington counties in the valley of the north fork of Holston River. They are associated with gypsum, and the product of the numerous wells near Saltville, goes into caustic soda and other soda processes. The necessary limestone, which must be of exceptional purity, is much of it shipped into Saltville from Marion, Smyth county.

Tennessee

These measures continue westward across Scott county, Virginia, and are found in similar occurrence at Waycross, Hawkins county, Tennessee, on the Clinchfield railroad, along the south side of Clinch Mountain.

Louisiana

Louisiana ranks first in the production of salt. Brine wells and salt springs had long been the source, until in 1862 a brine well intersected a rock salt bed at Avery Island, Iberia parish, and the present operations are at the 500-foot level. Over 400 feet above, and thousands of feet below, as far as drills have gone, is salt of the purest quality, so pure that it needs only to be crushed and ground, and it is ready for use.

In 1896 oil drillers discovered salt cores in the dome formation on Jefferson Island, and a year later at Belle Isle, La. Both sulphur and oil have been found to carry an intimate association with these domes. Many theories have appeared regarding their origin, and their interrelation makes them of great economic importance. There are at least 60 such domes in Louisiana and Texas, more than 20 of which are oil producers.

A revolutionary process for the manufacture of salt cake is being evolved in Louisiana, by heating salt to fusion, treating it with sulphur dioxide instead of sulphuric acid, and producing sodium sulphite instead of sodium sulphate. This method gives a vast quantity of hydrochloric acid with which to treat calcium carbonate.

The old reactions are:

(a) $2NaCl + H_2SO_4 = Na_2SO_4 + 2HCl$
(b) $CaCO_3 + HCl = CaCl_2 + CO_2 + H_2O$
(c) $CaCl_2 + Na_2CO_3 = CaCO_3 + 52NaCl$

The new process gives:

$2NaCl + SO_2 = Na_2SO_3 + 2HCl$, etc.

Texas

In 1901 deep oil drilling near Saratoga, Hardin county, Texas, disclosed salt in the dome formation at this and other points in the county.

Seven miles southwest of Houston, Harris county, is a salt dome-oil area. The salt here, is within 1100 feet of the surface, and extraction is obtained by dissolving the salt in water forced down through wells. Gas and oil are available for evaporation, and the finished product is shipped through the port of Houston.

Small deposits are operated in southern Brooks and northern Hidalgo counties. A dry salt lake of 45 acres extent, has been worked for many years in the basin of the Trans-Pecos region in western Texas. The Salt Fork of Red River, and the Salt Fork of Brazos River both leave evaporative crusts of salt along their banks. The evaporative process is used on the brines of Young county, and rock salt occurs at Colorado City, Mitchell county, Grand Saline, Van Zandt county, and Palestine, Anderson county.

Chapter XV

ZINC, LEAD, TIN

Zinc and **lead** are so usually associated, we may consider them in combination. The ability to volatilize these metals in complex ores, and to recapture them from the fumes has marked an advance in metallurgy and has reduced the earlier smelter penalties on zinc.

Zinc occurs as calamine and as blende. The former term is used in America to distinguish the oxidized ores of zinc from the sulphide ores or blendes. The silicate ore is usually designated smithsonite.

Lead is usually found in the form of galena, or associated with zinc blende and pyrites.

The principal markets are New York and St. Louis. Recent research has made possible the utilization of low-grade zinc ores, which were hitherto unworkable, so that today 150 tons of pure zinc are daily produced from these ores, at the same time liberating 8 tons of copper and 12 to 15 tons of lead, with considerable amounts of precious metals.

The application of electric smelting to the brass and bronze industries has eliminated a large number of graphite crucibles and at least 75,000 tons of anthracite coal per year. Over one-half of the brass and bronze smelting in the United States is now done in the electric furnace.

Virginia

In many counties in Virginia, lead occurs associated with zinc ores, especially in Wythe county, but these are essentially zinc deposits. Occasionally pockets of sufficient lead are found, to warrant saving them. The chief lead deposits are in the Piedmont region. The area developed by one operator in Albemarle county near the Nelson county line, contains galena and blende, with a gangue of quartz and feldspar.

Another important lead-zinc area is in Louisa and Spotsylvania counties, where the ore is a complex sulphide, mainly galena and blende, with chalcopyrite, pyrite, pyrrhotite, and low values in gold and silver. One of the largest bodies of undeveloped sulphide ore in the East is the pyrrhotite bed in Carroll county. This deposit is similar to that of the Ducktown, Tennessee, district. Many of these areas can be profitably operated by experienced men, but the complexity of the ores precludes neophytic operation.

North Carolina

The Southern Railway's Development Department exhibits samples of zinc ore from Silver Hill, Davidson county, and of galena from Gold Hill, Rowan county, Asheboro, Randolph county, Silver Hill, Davidson county, and Paint Rock and Marshall in Madison county, North Carolina. The Randolph county deposit was worked for several years, but had insufficient capital for equipment. The others need prospecting.

Zinc blende is also found in Cabarrus county with lead and silver ore; in Cleveland county with gold; in McDowell county in limestone formation; at numerous places with gold ore in Union county, and smaller quantities in Alleghany, Gaston, Macon and Montgomery counties. Galena is also found in Cabarrus, Cherokee, Cleveland, Davidson, Gaston, Randolph, Rowan, Union, Watauga and Wilkes counties in commercial quantities. Other localities have been reported as carrying commercial deposits in Alleghany, Burke, Caldwell, Chatham, Macon, Montgomery, Surry, Swain and Union counties. Lead carbonate or cerusite is found in Caldwell, Cherokee, Davidson and Rowan counties, usually in combination with galena and silver.

South Carolina

An alleged galena deposit southwest of Gaffney, Cherokee county, South Carolina, consists of float ore in small quantities. Some lead has also been recovered from that state as a by-product of gold.

Kentucky

While lead and zinc occur in Kentucky, they are always in association with barytes and fluorspar, and have been mined as by-products of these industries in central and western Kentucky.

Tennessee

The zinc industry in Tennessee has grown remarkably within the past ten years. The only sulphide operation is at Mascot, Knox county. Carbonate ore is mined at Embreeville, Washington county. The zinc ores at Mascot, which average $3\frac{1}{4}$ zinc content, are typical of all the east Tennessee ores. It is evident that the only successful method of handling such ores is by large operations capable of a stupendous tonnage. The oxidized ores are localized and pocketed in clay, and occur at shallow depths. At Embreeville, Washington county, the rich ore streaks extend up rather than down. The method of working is to sink shafts to the point where the ore pinches out or becomes of minimum value, tunnels are then driven under the saddles, and the workings extended horizontally and the ore stoped. Transportation conditions are good, and while no ore pinnacle offers long life, continued prospecting produces new areas. The Hancock county field lies 20 miles from the railroad and has suffered from loose financing, and lack of engineering, such machinery as has been installed, being unsuited to local conditions. It is probable that there are large deposits of 3½ per cent ore in eastern Tennessee. The blende occurs in the Knox dolomite, which gives the key to prospecting. The horizons are intensely brecciated layers. The formation is 2500 feet thick and the ores occur in 5 to 10-foot strata. The Polk county area around Copper Hill is very promising. From Roane, Loudon, Anderson and Knox counties, the deposit continues northeast to Virginia.

Lead is being mined at Lead Mine Bend, 20 miles southeast of Tazewell, Union county. It occurs in little veins in middle Tennessee, and at Nolensville, Williamson county, 12 miles east of Nashville, is a deposit 18 inches thick which was mined during the Civil War.

Ruby zinc, or transparent blende, is mined in Johnson county, and Bradley and Monroe counties have unprospected lead-zinc areas. A galena deposit is reported by the Southern Railway three-quarters of a mile southeast of Cleveland, Bradley county. This was operated some years ago, but was never properly financed.

Five miles from Sevierville, Sevier county, is a mountain of zinc blende, which has been opened up, showing veins 4 feet and 5 feet in thickness, and 10 feet apart at the surface, dipping 41° and 43°, and therefore presumably coming together below. Nine hundred feet higher up is another vein which is perpendicular and which assays 14 per cent metallic content. Zinc-blende is also found near Jefferson City, and New Market, Jefferson county; and Mountain City, Johnson county.

Arkansas

In several of the northern counties of Arkansas there are extensive deposits of zinc ores. The first attempt was made to develop these in 1857, when a smelter was erected at Calamine, Sharp county. This was closed in 1861. About 1886 prospectors began to develop the deposits in a small way, and by 1899 several large companies had invested heavily in Marion county. With the revival of zinc, came a revival also of lead mining. In 1920 there were 71 companies in active operation in the state. Marion, Searcy, Boone, Baxter, Benton, Carroll, Newton and Washington counties all have many available properties of high grade. The average percentage of concentrates recovered from mine-run ores in the White River Valley is double that from many other districts. The blende is free from iron, and runs over 60 per cent metallic; the carbonate ores from 40 to 48 per cent.

At Havana, Yell county, a lead-gold ore has been uncovered, but not developed, and near Black Rock, Lawrence county, a zinc-lead deposit is being prospected.

Texas

Zinc operations in Texas are confined to Hudspeth, El Paso, Presidio, Culberson and Jeff Davis counties. The Hudspeth county plant at Sierra Blanca was burned and has not been re-built. The shaft was 700 feet deep. These plants shipped their product to the smelter at El Paso.

The only galena mined in Texas has come from the

silver mined at Shafter in Presidio county. Prospect shipments have been made from the Quitman Mountains in Hudspeth county, from Altuda and other points in Brewster county, on Silver Creek in Burnet county, and various points in El Paso county.

Uses

An enumeration of the uses of zinc would cover many pages. Lithopone, which is a mixture of zinc sulphide and barium sulphate, is used extensively as a paint pigment, and in the manufacture of linoleum, printers' ink, and in all industries using rubber goods. It requires about 400 tons of raw materials such as zinc, barytes, coal, sulphuric acid, and chemicals, to make 100 tons of lithopone. As a substitute for white lead, it requires less grinding in oil, is more easily mixed, spreads evenly, and does not yellow, check, or chalk off.

Zinc chloride is used as a wood preservative.

Zinc oxide links up with the by-products of coke, in the production of an almost infinite range of coal tar dyes.

Rolled zinc, zinc sheets, zinc dust, zinc strip, and ribbon zinc all appear in a thousand forms. For a comprehensive list of established uses, the reader is referred to "Make it of Zinc," for April, 1923, and June-July, 1924, published by the American Zinc Institute, 27 Cedar Street, New York. Another exhaustive list is to be found in the Mining Congress Journal for September, 1926, entitled, "Zinc in American Industry," by A. P. Cobb.

Among the more unusual uses, is the attaching of zinc slabs to stern posts and rudders of vessels using bronze propellors, to protect steel near the propellers from corrosion by electrolytic action. Zinc slabs are also placed in boilers to prevent corrosion of the tubes.

Zinc is used for letter boxes, armored cable, and metallic galvanizing of all kinds.

When used as an interlocking shingle, of pure oxidized zinc and properly grounded, protection is afforded against lightning.

Germanium is extracted from crude zinc oxide. In crystalline form it is a glossy, flaky substance, resembling zinc, hard and brittle. It is worth many dollars a gram, and is obtained by heating crude zinc oxide with strong acid. A highly volatile compound of germanium distills over, and is decomposed by water to produce pure germanium oxide in the form of a white powder. Ingots of the pure metal are obtained by fusion of the powder with common salt.

One pound of zinc will yield one gram of germanium powder. Chemists are still puzzled by the element, which resembles silicon and carbon in some respects, and tin in others. At Cornell University germanium dioxide has been used as a substitute for sand in the manufacture of optical glass. The product is said to have rare refractive qualities. Research is also being carried on to determine whether the element has medicinal properties. The development of an extended use for germanium would provide an increased market for zinc.

Lead is finding a rapidly expanding market in the storage battery industry. It is used for fuses, artificial diamonds, linoleum, watches, dentistry, the manufacture of lake colors, for vulcanizing rubber, in medicine and the arts, for sheet lead, lead pipe, plumbing supplies, shot, Babbitt metal, type metal, paint pigment, foil, solder, caulking, counter-weights, in glass manufacture, rubber vulcanizing, ammunition, and miscellaneous metallic alloys.

Litharge, which is made by heating lead moderately in a current of air, is straw-yellow and is used in flint glass and assaying work, and also as a paint pigment.

In addition to white and red lead, sublimed white lead and lead acetate-chromate-lactate-oleate-resinate-arsenate-nitrate-linoleate and peroxide, all enter into industry.

* * * * * *

It is estimated that the annual tin requirements of the United States are 70,000 tons. At the present time practically all of this is imported, save only that which is recovered by de-tinning processes. Substitution, elimination, and reclamation are urged in the interest of industrial preparedness and commercial efficiency.

In 1916 the smelting of imported tin concentrate in the United States was begun. In 1921 there were five smelters and in 1922 two smelters on the Atlantic Coast handling tin. In 1924 but one American smelter handled any tin, English competition having supplanted American plants in this industry. The smelter at Perth Amboy, N. J., produced electrolytic tin.

There is no reason why any American smelter should not be able to handle domestic cassiterite however, provided a sufficient quantity were offered. The Chinese smelt tin ore in a small clay furnace, using charcoal as a reducing agent. The European companies use large reverberatory furnaces with coal, and a small amount of lime.

Uses

Tin enters into combination with lead and antimony,

in varying proportions to make what are known as "white metals." These include Babbitt and other antifriction alloys, and solder. The best solder is composed of equal parts of new tin and new lead. Other combinations are printer's metals, pewter, Britannia metal, die-casting metals, toy and mould metals, and special alloys used for castings in chemical works, battery plates, bullets and collapsible tubes.

High-grade bearings for high-powered automobiles and airplane engines contain from 20 to 93 per cent tin, $3\frac{1}{2}$ to 15 per cent antimony, and $1\frac{1}{2}$ to $3\frac{1}{2}$ per cent copper, zero to $63\frac{1}{2}$ per cent lead, in varying combinations.

Tin foil wraps the working man's tobacco and the school girl's chocolates; tin imparts rustle and lustre to silk, and its use in church organ pipes offers inspiration. No complete substitute has been found. Its great commercial use is in tin cans and boxes, as a mordant in dyeing, for silvering mirrors, and as tin oxide in the form of polishing paste for sharpening fine cutting instruments, and for enamels. In sheet form it enters into roofing, and the automobile industry.

Virginia—North Carolina—South Carolina

On account of its value, it is possible to work very low grade ores, if they are in quantity. Tin ore was discovered near King's Mountain, Cleveland county, North Carolina, in 1883. In 1886 systematic prospecting was begun and in 1888 a stamp mill was erected. Due to litigation, no development was accomplished, and the subject was dropped, while in 1903 a similar deposit was found at Gaffney, Cherokee county, South Carolina. This deposit is a pegmatite carrying cassiterite. The vein or dyke broadened out as it went down, but contained no higher amount of tin, hence less recovery per ton of gangue mined. Similar deposits were found at Blacksburg, Cherokee county, South Carolina, and Lincolnton, Lincoln county, North Carolina.

A recent attempt has been made to operate the Lincolnton deposit. Five shafts have been sunk in an area one-half by two miles square and several tons of concentrates were made.

The entire Appalachian tin belt apparently reaches its maximum in a distance of eleven miles north and eleven miles south of Lincolnton and at a point about three and a half miles southeast of that place, along the Seaboard Air Line Ry. southward to Ross, S. C.

The vein is three and a half to four feet of tin in a ten foot wide gangue, running $1\frac{1}{4}$ per cent metallic tin.

Rockfish, Nelson county, and the eastern end of Rockbridge county, Virginia, show veins from 8 to 12 inches, widening at intervals to several feet. Several test shipments have been made from the district, but the ore was improperly cleaned, considerable quantities of ilmenite and arseno-pyrite being present, so that the concentrate recovered was 43 per cent metallic tin.

It is evident that this tin belt extends from Rockbridge county, Virginia, southwesterly across North Carolina and into Cherokee county, South Carolina. The Gaston, Cleveland and Lincoln county, North Carolina, deposits have been intermittently worked for tin, by attempting to hydraulic the material and remove the clay in a log washer. If this process were reversed, and the white plastic clay produced for paper filler or white face-brick, the cassiterite nodules would become a profitable by-product. The 5 or 6 feet of overburden is a high-grade lime marl which could also be utilized.

Reference is made to Bulletin 19 of the North Carolina Geological Survey on "The Tin Deposits of the Carolinas," and the Virginia Geological Survey Bulletin on "The Tin Deposits of Irish Creek."

Alabama

Continuing the line of deposits from Virginia and the Carolinas, to Cleburne, Clay and Coosa counties, Alabama, we find a belt extending from Rockford, Coosa county, past Hollins in Clay county, to Heflin, Cleburne county. No systematic prospecting has been done in the pegmatites where these crystals are found. With electric power and electric furnaces available in Alabama, an interesting opportunity is presented for useful prospecting.

Texas

On the eastern flank of the Franklin Mountains, about 12 miles north of El Paso, Texas, are found three well defined veins of tin ore, which have been prospected in a number of places, and upon which several favorable reports have been made. About $5000 worth of ore has been shipped. Cassiterite and stannite are also found along the North fork of the Llano River in Mason county.

It is to be hoped that renewed interest will finance systematic prospecting of American tin resources. If an ore contained but 1 per cent of metallic tin at 40 cents a pound the product would be worth $8 a ton, which would make a profitable proposition, especially for a plant prepared to handle several hundred tons daily. Many of these gangues carry from 3 to 5 per cent tin, so that with adequate provision for water supply, an experienced hydraulic miner should be able to develop a tin industry in the "Virgilina" district which would be of great economic value.

Reference was made earlier in this chapter to reclamation by de-tinning. There are three of these processes in use, the electrolytic alkali, the chlorine, and the alkali-chemical. Of these, the latter two have, since 1907, achieved distinction. By the chlorine process the recovery is 100 per cent in the form of tetrachloride of tin, which is used extensively in the silk dyeing industry. In the alkali-chemical process the tin is recovered in oxide form, which is used extensively as coloring matter in enamels, and smelted in reverberatory furnaces to form pig tin of very high quality. About 2000 tons per year is reclaimed in this manner.

Chapter XVI

KAOLIN, CLAYS, CYANITE, SILLIMANITE

The clays of the South constitute a major portion of the mineral production, exclusive of coal, oil and gas.

Their general classification as used by the U. S. Geological Survey, is as follows:

"High-grade clays:
    White-ware clays (non-plastic and plastic).
        Kaolin, porcelain, or china clay.
        Ball clay.
        Paper clay.
    Refractory or fire clays:
        Glass-pot clay.
        Flint clay.
        Plastic fire clay and shales.
        Graphitic fire clay.
    Pottery or stoneware clays.
    Medicinal clay, bentonite, Denver mud.
Low-grade clays:
    Vitrifying clays and shales:
        Terra-cotta clays and shales.
        Sewer-pipe clay and shale.
        Roofing-tile clay and shale.
    Brick clays and shales:
        Loess clay.
        Glacial clay.
        Pressed-brick clay and shale.
        Paving-brick clay and shale.
        Adobe clay.
    Gumbo.
    Slip clays.
    Fullers' earth."

Of these, bentonite is discussed in Chap. V, and Fullers' earth in Chap. II. Locally, the general classification is as follows:

      1. Flint clays
      2. Hard clays
      3. Semi-hard clays
      4. Soft clays
      5. Bauxitic clays
      6. Bauxite.

They vary in color from white and cream, to gray and blue, with red, brown and yellow pigment clays as described in Chap. IV, and bauxite in Chap. III.

In general it may be said that flint, hard and semi-hard clays are used for refractories, are light in color, fine in texture, free from grit, plastic when softened in water, and strong when dry. The soft clays are used for filler and in the ceramic trades, but require washing. They are plastic and of low bonding strength, suitable for wall tile, electric insulators and floor composition. In the bauxites, 56 per cent alumina is the point between low and high grade. "Chimney Rock" lies on the border between bauxite and bauxitic clay.

The hard clays are frequently in lenses overlain by Fullers' earth. Sewer-pipe may be manufactured from plastic surface or alluvial clay, of the present day; from buff burning stratified clay with poor cleavage, laid down in an earlier age; or from red burning shales with marked cleavage of still earlier formation. These clays are usually selected after careful balancing and consideration of chemical analysis, location of the material with reference to point of fabrication or consumption, and mining methods to be employed. It must be borne in mind that the extra cost of underground clay mining is usually more than outweighed by the better quality of product.

Clay veins usually conform to surface conditions, and drainage becomes an important feature. More timbering is also required than in metal or coal mines, which usually operate under hard rock conditions. These features require the highest type of engineering skill and managerial ability, yet many clay pits are veritable "holes in the ground," and their failure is due to lack of foresight rather than to quality of product.

White ware is a porous body covered with a brilliant transparent glaze. It is usually 52 per cent clay, 34 per cent ground flint (quartz) and 14 per cent feldspar (vide Chap. XX). The clay content is non-plastic white-burning kaolin and plastic buff-burning ball clay, giving whiteness and strength respectively. Flint reduces shrinkage and feldspar acts as a flux, dissolving some of the quartz and cementing the mass. The principal distinction between whiteware and porcelain is that more feldspar is used to eliminate voids in the latter.

Mineral fillers, such as clay, barytes (Chap. IV), mica (Chap. XVII), talc (Chap. XVII), whiting (Chap. V), ochre (Chap. IV), silica (Chap. XXIII), graphite (Chap. XII), and slate (Chap. XVIII), are ground, milled, and washed or otherwise purified, without undergoing any chemical change, or exerting any chemical action on the basic material. These fillers are consumed largely in the large manufacturing centers of the eastern and northern states. The filler clays are principally those of sedimentary origin, white, and susceptible of economic washing. The residual kaolins go into ceramics. Uniform fineness, approximating 300 mesh is usually essential.

Porcelain for spark plugs is required to withstand sudden changes in temperature without cracking, and must maintain its insulating qualities. It must be extremely low in iron; and the raw materials, clay, flint, feldspar and whiting, are ground very fine in porcelain lined mills, and when combined, must have a low coefficient of expansion. A special glaze is applied before burning. While sillimanite is the ideal material for this purpose, its scarcity has induced sufficient research to produce a finished porcelain nearly or quite its equal from certain high-grade kaolins and cyanite (vide sequi), found in the South.

Wormser states that there are at least 25 varieties of high-grade clay, whose physical characteristics are of greater importance than their chemical analyses. Ball clay, having good plasticity and bonding power, is mixed with kaolins to give them adaptability and strength. Color is an important item. Many black or slate gray clays burn white. Porosity regulates the sale of wares for certain limited uses. Shrinkage is a significant characteristic which looms large in the question of imported vs. domestic clays. American clay deposits are the most extensive in the world. The lack of uniformity in preparation, and the complete absence of standardization in the product, however, which obtained for many years in the American clay industry, militated against the ready acceptance of domestic supplies, particularly ball-clay.

"Off-color" clays are sold for saggers, which must be refractory. On account of the scarcity of skilled labor, the casting of sanitary ware by pouring into plaster of

Paris molds is a growing phase of the industry. Clays which give casting mixes their fluidity, as well as contributing to the vitrification of the body, are a development in ceramics and are much sought.

The potter has never been forced, and does not feel safe in making changes in mixture, although unquestionably he could do so if compelled.

Little by little, however, potters are introducing as much North Carolina and Florida kaolin as they dare. Tennessee and Kentucky ball-clays are slowly supplanting English ball-clay. Georgia clays, because of their colloidal nature have necessitated special research for ceramic purposes.

The best clays have been imported from England, France, Germany, Austria and Japan. Japanese clays are rock and must be ground, but they are vitreous, and when mixed with other clays make a high-grade of dinner and hotel ware, which due to cheap Japanese labor, is being imported and sold at attractive prices.

Up to 14 years ago the American potter was secure, but at the present time, foreign competition necessitates a higher tariff on finished ware. English ball-clay is getting poorer and poorer, and carries much lignite and other impurities.

American clays are usually shipped in bulk in box cars, loaded by mechanical loaders, except the highest grade pulverized clays which are sacked. There is an abundance of flint and feldspar, and it is only a matter of time, until the ball-clays and kaolins of the South will be adequately prospected, carefully classified and extensively utilized.

Kaolin is said to be a Chinese word meaning "a white hill." It applies to decomposed feldspar, which occurs in combination with quartz and mica. These latter materials must be washed from the decomposed mass to produce clean clay. The high-grade clays of the Eastern United States are discussed in Bulletin 708 of the U. S. Geological Survey. Many of the State Surveys also, have issued monographs on their respective clays. The reader is therefore referred to these publications for analyses and similar data. "Clays, their Occurrence, Properties and Uses," by Dr. H. Ries, may be considered an encyclopedia of American clays.

Virginia

The clays of Virginia are described in Bulletins I, II, IV, XIII and XX of the Virginia Geological Survey. These clays are widely distributed over the coastal plain, and are sedimentary. Common brick clay is abundant. Materials for face and building brick, drain tile, hollow ware and cheap pottery are found in many locations, but have received little attention. These deposits are usually in lenses, and are red- or buff-burning. In the region around Alexandria the various grades are carefully separated and a diversely colored product is obtained. The counties of Alexandria, Henrico, Chesterfield and Nansemond produce over 80 per cent of the state's clay products.

A high-grade kaolin deposit is found at Cold Spring, Augusta county, whose product is used for whiteware and paper filler. High-grade kaolin is also shipped from Buena Vista, Rockbridge county, on the Norfolk and Western Railroad. At Moneta, Bedford county, is a clay (kaolin?) which is used in putty manufacture. In the same county is a red clay which is calcined for paint pigment (vide Chap. IV). A superior red clay for pipe, tile and face brick is found at Bermuda Hundred, in Chesterfield county, about one mile from James River and three miles from the Atlantic Coast Line Ry. It is plastic, of great tensile strength, occurs to a depth of 49½ feet with an overburden of only a few inches, and burns to a cherry red at 2100° F. It shows 9 per cent shrinkage and 8½ per cent loss in weight or burning. At Toshe's, Pittsylvania county, a high-grade kaolin deposit has been exposed. Unfortunately it lies about 10 miles from the railroad. North Mountain, four miles north of Staunton, Augusta county, is a solid mountain of refractory clay and shale.

West Virginia

West Virginia contains no known deposits of porcelain clay. Vol. 3 of the West Virginia Geological Survey treats of the other clay deposits.

Berkeley county has stoneware clays which would support a large plant, but not a pound of stoneware is made in the state from native material. These deposits are at Tabler, south of Martinsburg. Two plants were formerly in operation at Parkersburg, Wood county, and Bridgeport, Harrison county, but were abandoned, due to city development. There are other deposits on Opequon Creek, in Berkeley county. The clay is found in pockets, and takes a good salt glaze.

Although not technically in the range of this immediate survey, reference might well be made here, to a half million ton deposit of exceptionally high-grade refractory clay, operated in a small way at Leslie, Cecil county, Maryland, on the Baltimore and Ohio Railroad. This material has a fusing point of 3300° F., and is used wherever a load test is required. In Mineral county, opposite Cumberland, Md. are good brick clays.

Just east of Piedmont, in the same county, is the Mt. Savage fire clay. The location affords a gravity supply to the plant, and a quantity sufficient to support a much greater output.

These fire clays extend westward into Preston county where they are in evidence at Cascade Station on the Morgantown and Kingwood Railroad. Also into Taylor county, where they are mined at Thornton, and in Marion county, at Hammond.

Brick clays are found along the Monongahela River in Monongalia county, and around Clarksburg, Harrison county.

The yellow nodular clays of Hardy county are not easily susceptible of beneficiation.

North Carolina

Kaolin and clay products offer a bigger field in North Carolina than ony other one mineral possibility, and they are well distributed. The western North Carolina clays are residual and are widely shipped to East Liverpool, Ohio, Beaver Falls, Pa., and Trenton, N. J., for spark plugs, porcelains, etc.

The production comes from Mitchell, Yancey, Avery, Macon, Clay and Rutherford counties. Undeveloped deposits are in Buncombe, Macon, Clay, Lincoln, Yancey and Jackson counties.

The clays of Mitchell county are used to make tableware at the Irvin pottery. Motor transportation is making many of these deposits valuable.

There are many deposits of clay which might be

utilized for hollow tile and pressed brick. In frequent instances better workmanship would assist in establishing a market.

The large beds of clay for light buff and white brick in Rockingham county are now under investigation. Outcrops of similar clay which offer promising inducement for prospecting, occur in Montgomery, Anson, Rutherford, Lincoln, Cleveland and Buncombe counties. Along the valley of the French Broad River, in Henderson county, a soft fire clay occurs, suitable for buff or gray brick.

Excellent building brick clays are found in Madison, Buncombe, Jackson, McDowell, Catawba, Wilkes, Davidson, Guilford, Forsyth, Yadkin, Alamance, Moore, Rockingham, Wilson, Wayne, Pamlico, Pitt and Beaufort counties. Some of these also produce a high-grade face brick.

So general are these deposits that thriving brick or tile industries may be operated along the lines of every railroad in the state.

In Lee county, under the Cumnock coal, is an 8-foot stratum of fire clay, while above the coal is a shale bed. This combination of raw material and fuel offers an opportunity for the manufacture of refractory brick.

The Omar Khayyam Pottery uses clay from near Luther, Buncombe county. After costly experiments this clay has been processed until it is recognized as of a distinct class. Earthenware is being made from the same clay by other potters.

Just out of Asheville, Buncombe county, on the Murphy branch of the Southern Railway, is a deposit of kaolin 30 feet thick, over an area of ten acres. Farther down the branch, on the north side of the railroad, one mile from Hazlewood, Haywood county, is a similar deposit.

In Jackson county, in the neighborhood of Sylva, are many deposits, which it is necessary to wash. Farther down, near Bryson City, Swain county, are many others, some of which are working, and others which have never been opened up.

China clay from Hayesville, Clay county; White clay from Hot Springs, Madison county; brick clay from Bridgewater, Burke county; and kaolin from Franklin, Macon county; Dillsboro, Jackson county, and Topton, Cherokee county, are exhibited by the Southern Railway.

Clay county is now being developed on an extensive scale and the latest type of clay machinery, washers, and conveyors is being installed. The kaolin produced at these operations is said to be of unusual whiteness, high in plasticity, low in shrinkage, highly refractory, and remarkably free from foreign substances. Such material as is washed out is principally silica sand, which is sold for road purposes.

Near Troy, Montgomery county, along the Norfolk Southern R. R., a filler clay is being developed. Reference has previously been made to the Deep River Shales near Cumnock, Lee county, overlying the coal. At Colon, in the same county, face brick are being made from these shales, which give a metallic ring at 1750° F.

At Jugtown and Blackburn, Catawba county, English and Holland Dutch potters and their descendants have operated small potteries for generations.

North Carolina kaolin is mostly shipped out of the state and repurchased at a great enhancement in price.

Just as the demand of the cotton field led to the textile mill, so the potteries and clay deposits of North Carolina should bring the ceramic industry closer to the source of raw material.

South Carolina

The clays of South Carolina are likewise among the greatest assets of that state. They are structurally and geologically similar to those of North Carolina. Commercially, they may be classified as (1) brick clay and (2) sedimentary kaolins. A white burning clay has been found north of Columbia, Richland county, along the Seaboard Air Line Ry. Around Abbeville, Abbeville county, on the upper Savannah River, are a number of clay deposits sufficiently pure for a cheap grade of insulating porcelains. The veins are wide, and mixed with quartz.

The sedimentary kaolins around Aiken, Aiken county, are good for fillers of all kinds and for crockery. There are large tracts in this county awaiting development. These sedimentary clays are usually found in ravines and must be carefully opened up to avoid contamination after development by flooding of surface soil.

Indications have been noted in Oconee, Pickens, Greenville and Anderson counties, of white porcelain clays, but no attempt has been made to follow them up. The northwest part of the state, lying as it does at the foot of the Saluda and Chatooga ranges, in the Piedmont Plateau, offers a favorable section for investigation.

The preparation of white clays for market, in the vicinity of Langley, Aiken county, is described in Serial 2382, of the U. S. Bureau of Mines. These clays are sufficiently pure in many instances to be shipped to Trenton without washing. The overburden runs from 0 to 30 feet. They compete favorably with the English clays. Other operations have recently been reported in the vicinity of Bath and in Lexington county.

Denmark, Bamberg county, is a railroad center served by the Southern, Atlantic Coast Line and the Seaboard Air Line R. Rs. The entire district around Denmark is underlain with an excellent plastic fire clay, topped with a good brick clay.

A good grade of building brick is made at Sumter, Sumter county, and many other points listed in Bulletin 624 of the U. S. Geological Survey.

At Killian, Richland county, north of Columbia is a fire clay deposit, intermittently operated. In the same county about 13 miles from James' Crossing is an 80-acre kaolin deposit, partially developed.

Kaolin is also mined at Dunbarton, Barnwell county; between St. Paul and Summerton, Clarendon county; and at Congaree, Richland county.

From Augusta, Ga., to Charleston, S. C., along the Charleston and Western Carolina R. R. are 14 different clay industries. The material is very fine, being silt from prehistoric overflow of the Savannah River. Much of this goes into face and building brick. Two plants make floor and wall tile, and one plant makes jugs and flower pots. There are vast deposits and a wide diversity of materials. At Kathwood, Aiken county, is a clay which burns to great tensile strength. At Scotia, Hampton county, on the Southern and Seaboard Air Line Rys. is a 50-acre clay bed, extending to great depth, and carrying three different types of clay, superimposed. All are fire burning, adaptable to many uses, and undeveloped.

One of the great handicaps to the establishment of a

great clay industry in South Carolina has been the attempted operation of many deposits on too small a financial scale, with inadequate equipment and lack of experience. The product has failed to meet competition, and many excellent clays have thus lost recognition.

Georgia

The efforts of the Central of Georgia Ry. and the recent establishment of a ceramic school in the state, have served to focus attention on the great clay deposits of Georgia.

The white clays may be said to follow the "Fall Line," across the state, from Augusta, Richmond county, to Butler, Taylor county, on the margin of the Coastal plain, covering an area of about 10,000 square miles. These clays appear to have been derived from the disintegrated and decomposed rocks of the Piedmont Plateau above, and were laid down as in deltas or as islands. All deep wells in Georgia are warm, and it is probable that the alteration of high-grade kaolins has been induced by hot springs carrying H_2S.

The deposits are exceptionally pure, and the clay lenses have a matrix of sand. These lenses vary greatly in extent, from a few yards to several miles. East of the Ocmulgee River, the deposits thicken, reaching their maximum in Twiggs and Wilkinson counties. In Wilkinson and Washington counties, the upper part of the deposit is frequently bauxite.

At Phillip, Adams Park, and Reids, in Twiggs county, several thousand acres of kaolin and refractory clays are being developed, while adjoining areas await prospecting. Brick made from these clays are said to test up to 3000° F. Georgia kaolin brick have proven very successful for lining open-hearth ladles. Much of the kaolin shows less than 1 per cent impurity.

Wilkinson county produces 65 per cent of the clays mined in Georgia. From a single mine, 14 years ago, there has been developed a prosperous group of mines, refineries, potteries and brick plants.

The reader is referred to the *Mineral Directory of the Central of Georgia Ry.* for much valuable information about the brick, tile, china and refractory clays along its lines in both Georgia and Alabama.

In Warren county, Georgia, there is an industrial plant which manufactures paints and enamels from local clays.

Between Thomasville, Thomas county and Albany, Dougherty county are found excellent brick clays. Sand lime brick are made at Albany.

At Lumpkin, Stewart county, and Americus, Sumter county, are deposits of bauxitic clay, high in silica. Wherever the silica content does not exceed 10 per cent, this would be suitable for alumina cement. With the limestones and coal which lie to the north, an opportunity is seen for the development of a great industry.

Georgia produces more paper clays than the balance of the United States. At Ludowici, Long county, roofing tile are made from clay in the Altamaha River. There are also deposits of building brick clay in the same neighborhood.

At Hepzibah, Richmond county, is a clay which is shipped for linoleum filler and pottery stock. Below this is a good fire brick clay, which in turn rests on 10 feet of molding sand.

Dallas, Paulding county, and Gaillard, Crawford

county, have kaolin beds, and Gibson, Glasscock county, flint clays, which have not been developed.

Volume production is the only way in which the clay producer can be efficient to the consumer. It is said that it does not pay to operate on less than 50,000 tons per year as a minimum. The originators and first shippers of high-grade washed clays in America were the Edgar Brothers, who, operating in Georgia and Florida, first proved the value of American clays.

It is probable that in gross tonnage, there is at present an over-production of Georgia washed filler clays. To rectify this condition, the improperly prepared product should be withdrawn from the market, in order that the industry may not suffer unjust criticism. On the other hand, there is ample opportunity for the building up of an enormous consumption from this section, by concerted effort to produce a uniform quality and to educate the consumer to an appreciation of this quality.

The question of freight rates is intimately associated with the functioning of the industry in Georgia. If more manufacturing were done near the source of supply, the railroads would receive a higher return through the increase in rates on finished brick and tile, while the manufacturer would gain through the saving on transportation of raw material. Coal is available from both Tennessee and Alabama, with producer gas a possibility from the southern Alabama lignites, and Gulf Coast and Mexican oil by water routes.

Seasonal movements of fruit and vegetables, cotton and fertilizer, tend to interrupt car supply for regular clay shipments. Differential rail rates on imported clays also have an important bearing on the economic situation in the industry.

Many common brick plants, as at Calhoun, Gordon county, and Adairsville, Bartow county, supply the local building trade.

Much Georgia clay goes to the linoleum and oil cloth plants of the north. A substantial saving could be effected in this industry by manufacture near the source of the filler. The refractory clays of Georgia are superior to the best Pennsylvania clays. Some of these are not white enough for fillers or pottery use, but are admirable for white face brick. The deposits are convenient to the port of Savannah, and the great Central and South American markets are thus accessible. It is said that South America alone, imports 30 million refractory brick annually. Most of the Georgia clays may be operated as open-cut propositions the year round. Production costs are therefore a minimum.

Light face brick sells in Atlanta at $55 to $60 per thousand, and all comes from north of the Ohio and Potomac Rivers. Equal or superior brick can be made from Georgia clays, shales and sand, all occurring within 10 to 25 miles from the clay deposits, at not exceeding $25 per thousand. Pennsylvania clays take eleven days to burn and five days to cool. Georgia clay takes 36 to 50 hours to burn, and 36 hours to cool. A kiln of 75,000 brick of this type could be burned in 72 hours. On account of difficulty from discoloration from coal ash, oil is preferable for burning. It can be laid down in the East Macon, Bibb county, district for approximately 7 cents per gallon, while coals costs $5 to $6 per ton.

The manufacture of Mission Tiles for roofing, from

Georgia shales has become an established industry, which not only ships to twenty different states east of the Rocky Mountains, and to Mexico, but also exports considerable quantities to the Bahamas.

For rubber filling, the clay must be from 400-700 mesh. The whirlpool method of refining Georgia filler clays has created a steady and rapidly increasing market for clays of this fineness.

Florida

While many of the clay resources of Florida have not been adequately prospected, Lake and Putnam counties were among the first to be developed. The ball clay production is principally confined to four companies, and is shipped to Ohio, Pennsylvania, New York and New Jersey. The extra high grades are used for porcelains, but are too plastic to be used in the original state, and are mixed with less plastic Georgia and northern material. There are several deposits around Leesburg and Yalaha, in Lake county, and at San Antonio and Dade City, Pasco county, not yet developed. All of these are in commercial quantity, and near the railroad.

Three potteries in Florida produce vases and artistic furnishings. At Orlando, Orange county, Bradentown, Manatee county, and St. Petersburg, Penellas county, are kaolin deposits of excellent grade.

There are about 15 common brick plants in the state, and several others making face brick, hollow building tile, and drain tiles. Most of the brick are of good quality, but there is room for improvement in handling and preparing the clay. The state has no known material for vitrified brick. Road building is becoming standardized with either concrete, or limestone base and asphalt surface. Such paving brick as are used, come from Georgia and Alabama.

Building brick are made along the northern tier of counties and the west bank of the Chattahoochee River above its junction with the Apalachicola. Palm Island, in Florida Bay, between Miami and Key West, has a calcareous clay which is reported to make a good sand-lime brick without further treatment.

Florida clay is very peculiar in that it is highly plastic, yet burns as white as the best English china clay, and is therefore a partial substitute, but must be used carefully, on account of shrinkage, and stresses at certain temperatures.

Where the Lake and Putnam county clays are recovered by dredging, about 100 tons of washed clay are recovered to every 400 tons of pure silica sand, which latter was for many years allowed to accumulate in great tailing piles. Of recent years, however, this sand has become valuable for concrete construction and road building, on account of its purity, sharpness, and low iron content. Florida backwoods sand is high in titaniferous material and unsuited for use with cement.

The glass industry might well consider this as a source of supply, with cheap oil available at Tampa, for a much-needed bottle plant.

Florida clays are also achieving recognition as fillers, as the producers have reached a standard of quality which is more uniform than the imported article.

Taxation difficulties have militated against the industry. The creation of road districts, drainage districts, bridge districts, etc., has caused erratic bond issues, covering overlapping areas. The co-ordination of all necessary public enterprises and improvements through a wisely constituted statewide authority, whereby such projects may be intelligently authorized and financed under a unified and simplified system of tax assessment is a prerequisite to efficient administration.

Seasonal shipments of fruits and vegetables affect car supply as in Georgia. This situation is slowly being improved, however, through the creation of a branch car service bureau in the southeast.

Kentucky

Suitable clays for brick making occur widely distributed throughout Kentucky, with the exception of the more remote sections of the eastern coal field.

Clays used in the manufacture of pottery, tiling, etc., occur particularly in that portion of the state lying west of the Tennessee River; and at a few isolated points in the southeastern portion of the bluegrass section, near Bybee and Moberly, Madison county. These deposits are not large. Suitable brines for soap making in connection with the bentonite deposits extending south from High Bridge, Jessamine county (vide Chap. V) are found in Clay county, within 75 miles of the eastern coal field.

The Kentucky Geological Survey in Vol. VIII, Series VI, by H. Ries, publishes a detailed description and analysis of many Kentucky clays.

The fire clay of Kentucky is considered to be first grade. It extends along the C. & O. R. R. from a point 15 miles west of Ashland, Boyd county, to Morehead, Rowan county, through Greenup and Carter counties, and is commercially known as the "Olive Hill District." It occurs in two forms, as "No. 1, Flint," and "No. 2, Refractory." Fire clay is also found in Ballard, Graves,

Elliott, Fulton, Jackson, Jefferson, Kenton, Covington, Laurel, Lewis, Powell, Pulaski, Rockcastle and Wolfe counties. The flint fire clay deposits of the northeastern Kentucky coal field are among the best in the world.

Molding sand-clay is found from Mentor, Campbell county, east to Ashland, Boyd county. The most important district is that around Augusta, Bracken county; the second is four miles west of Maysville, at Ausauba, Macon county; the third is not developed to Maysville, but is potential.

The best ball clay in America comes from around Mayfield, Graves county, along the Ill. Cen. R. R. It is used for high tension insulators and does not require the addition of any English clay.

At Clay switch, in Graves county, white, ball and sagger clay are mined. Building tile are made in Kenton county, south of Covington.

Tennessee

The state of Tennessee has brick and tile clays in nearly every county, and in over 50 counties brick plants have been actually operated. Fire clay is also of common occurrence, especially in the central portion of the state lying east of the Tennessee River.

Deposits of ball clay are found in Henry, Carroll, Carter and Stewart counties. That of Henry and Carroll counties compares favorably with the Graves county deposits of Kentucky. The industry has not yet reached its growth in Tennessee. Most of the product is shipped to East Liverpool, Ohio. Several virgin deposits are available for prospecting. The material occurs in lenses which must be carefully mined to avoid contamination by matrix and overburden. In the vicinity of Whitlock and

Puryear, Henry county, are clays especially adapted to the manufacture of high tension insulators. Raw material is estimated at 5 per cent of the cost of the finished article, while labor and freight constitute the bulk of the remainder. Freight rates on finished clay products are high. Cheap pottery finds its market in the southwest; the higher grades sell in the North. The pottery industry has a very close union and the apprenticeship list is said to be based on conditions at East Liverpool, Ohio.

A logical place for a plant would be at Memphis, available to both rail and water as a distributing center. The freight differential on finished articles at Memphis is equivalent to 5 cents on close competitors in Evansville, Indiana.

At Erwin, Unicoi county, and other points along the Clinchfield Railroad, a high-grade tableware pottery is operated. Feldspar from North Carolina and kaolin from Georgia and Florida are also ground at Erwin. At Knoxville, Knox county, is a plant for electrical porcelains.

At Newcomb and Jellico, Campbell county is a very high-grade fire clay used for refractory brick, which is in great demand. Several undeveloped properties remain available.

At Cleveland, Bradley county, is a white clay deposit of some 200 acres, very fine and smooth in texture which has aroused much local interest, but of which no tests have been made.

Bulletin No. 50 of the Tennessee Geological Survey refers to the clays around Milan, Gibson county, bordering on Carroll county. These have been drilled and found to carry to a depth of 20 feet over a considerable area.

Bauxite clays available for alumina cement are found contiguous to the East Tennessee limestones in large quantities in Campbell county. The Southern Railway shows samples of kaolin from Del Rio, Cocke county; of ball and porcelain clay from Knoxville, Knox county; and Bulls Gap, Hawkins county; and fire clay from Newcomb, Campbell county.

Plastic clay occurs along the Mobile & Ohio and N. C. & St. L. R. Rs. near Jackson, Madison county.

Twenty-two miles south of Jackson, Madison county, between Pinetop and Silerton, Hardeman county, on the Gulf, Mobile & Northern R. R., is a refractory clay which makes excellent vitrified brick. It is topped by 35 feet of sandstone and a blue plastic clay overburden.

A building brick plant with a capacity of 20,000 brick per day is in operation at Bruceton, Carroll county, on the N. C. and St. L. R. R. On the same line at Paris, Henry county, is a face brick plant; and two miles south of Paris at Hancock Spur is a shale from which a special grade of light-weight brick is made. A standard brick of this material weighs only three pounds, and will stand all freezing, acid and strength tests. This brick should meet with a ready market in competition with gypsum, tile, etc., for partitions and structures where weight is an important item. On account of this feature and its strength, it can also take shipment to more remote points, in direct competition with other building materials.

Alabama

Many of the clays of Alabama are described in the

Mineral Directory of the Central of Georgia Railway. A number of years ago a State Clay Report was prepared by Dr. H. Ries. The primary kaolins occur wherever mica is found. Bulletin 740 of the United States Geological Survey will be found helpful in locating these deposits. The secondary, or china clays are found in Colbert and Franklin counties. In general it may be said that the clay belt of Alabama crosses from Georgia, along the east central border and extends up to the northern end of the boundary between Alabama and Mississippi. The clays are derived from decomposed crystalline rocks lying to the northeast, and in the northwest part of the state, and from Montgomery, Montgomery county, eastward to Columbus, Ga. Bulletin No. 28 of the Alabama Geological Survey contains much detailed information about the local deposits of that state.

Northwest of Fort Payne, De Kalb county, and Gadsden, Etowah county, the white clays are associated with sub-carboniferous fire clays and bauxite. In Randolph county, primary kaolin, gold and mica are found associated. The entire De Kalb county area is a field for the manufacture of bauxite brick, with coal, labor and transportation conditions good.

Macon county has a peculiar red clay whose coloring is vegetable and not mineral. It is not, therefore, a brick clay, but has been utilized by Dr. Geo. W. Carver, the Tuskegee chemist, for dyes, paints and pigments. In Tallapoosa county the decomposed feldspar is free from iron, the potash has leached out, and a snow-white kaolin remains.

The common brick industry in Alabama is a large one. Firebrick are made in many counties. Flint clay occurs in Choctaw, Clarke, Conecuh, Monroe and Washington counties. The kaolins have been shown to be extensive. It is within the province of Alabama to manufacture all her necessary clay products and to supply the local markets with their requirements. A new type of paving brick has been experimentally made at Gadsden by pouring hot furnace slag direct into molds. 40,000 brick can be made from one run. These brick withstand a pressure of 18 tons per square inch. The utilization of slag for this purpose adds to the economic resources of the state.

Mississippi

Mississippi is rich in clays of all kinds. Bulletin No. 4, "The Clays of Mississippi," and Bulletin No. 6, "The Pottery Clays of Mississippi," by the State Geological Survey afford the reader a wealth of detailed information.

In Grenada and Carroll counties, and a part of Holmes county, are extensive deposits of good quality white and gray clay, well located about a half mile from the railroad, and above it, so that it may be handled by gravity. In Grenada county, is also found a pink clay.

Tallahatchee county, however, is the banner clay county of the state. Around Charleston, and for ten to twelve miles north, is a large outcrop of white clays of high plasticity and very refractory. They have been noted in earlier Governmental reports as remarkable, both in quality and quantity. The zone extends northward through Panola, Tate and De Soto counties into Tennessee.

In the central tier, Marshall, La Fayette, Yalabusha and Webster counties carry extensive deposits of pottery clays. From the west edge of Tippah county, south through Union and Pontotoc counties to Chickasaw county is a region of gray clay outcrops. This is a nuisance wherever it occurs in the public roads, although it is not a fire clay, but it is refractory, and makes a fine light brick, burning almost white.

On the northeast, overlying the Paleozoic formation in Tishomingo county, are the snow-white tripolitic clays, weathered out with free silica.

The best brick clays are found in Lincoln county, around Brookhaven, although many other localities have excellent material, but use poor methods and slipshod workmanship, thus turning out an inferior product. In east Lauderdale county are brick and tile and terra cotta clays. The porcelain clays are confined to Panola and Tallahatchee counties.

In Smith county are white and red clays. At Gulfport, Harrison county, are clay and sand, which extend north toward Hattiesburg, Forrest county. A combination of the two makes an excellent paving brick.

At Leesdale, Franklin county, two miles from the railroad, are several fine grades of white clay. Extending eastward from Leesdale more or less across the state are a number of brick and bentonitic clays which, upon experimentation, have yielded a wide diversity in color of superior brick and tile.

Pottery, slip and tile clays of exceptional quality, and at least one deposit of filler clay have been proven up in Winston county, around Louisville.

The brick industry in Mississippi should develop as the forests are disappearing and brick and concrete must ultimately replace timber.

Louisiana

Bulletin 660-E of the United States Geological Survey refers wholly to Louisiana clays. In it will be found the record of elaborate tests of 26 different clays from that state. The Avery Island clay in Iberia parish is said to be suitable for fine art tiles. Many of the pure white kaolin deposits have been locally called "chalk" and attention thus diverted. These deposits occur in Caddo, Catahoula and La Salle parishes. White potter's clay is found near Lena, Rapids parish, and also in Sabine and St. Tammany parishes. The Southern Pacific R. R. burns a local clay, found in Iberia parish, between Jeanerett and New Iberia, for ballast purposes. Silica brick are made in New Orleans for building purposes.

Arkansas

The clays of Arkansas are the subject of Bulletin 351 of the United States Geological Survey. They are also detailed and classified at length with a complete bibliography on pages 99-104 of "Outlines of Arkansas' Mineral Resources"—1927, by the Arkansas Geological Survey. The southeastern third of the state lies within the Coastal Plain, and contains a wide diversity of clays for tile, drain pipe, terra cotta, etc. These are at their best in Saline, Hot Spring, Dallas, Ouachita and Nevada counties. There are some high temperature porcelain clays in western Pike county.

The "Niloak" pottery ware comes from Saline county. It is made of natural clays, mixed and burned. Materials are available for all colors and grades of bricks, from white face to vitrified paving brick. The Paleozoic clays, around Fort Smith, Sebastian county, are especially suitable for the latter.

At Piggott, Clay county, is a yellow pigment clay. The entire region between Camden, Ouachita county, and Texarkana, Miller county, supplies material for sewer pipe and firebrick. From Pine Bluff, Jefferson county, southwestward is also a good brick clay belt.

Nine miles north of Paragould is a deposit of very plastic, fine-grained, buff-burning clay, and near Harrisburg, Arkansas, a 4-foot bed of plastic fire clay overlies a 5-foot lignite vein. A pipe clay deposit along the St. L.-S. F. Railway at Jonesboro, Arkansas, has recently been discovered.

For paper filler the Pike county clay ranks high. In general, it may be said that Arkansas can supply any grade of clay needed for industry. Around Batesville, Independence county, is a polishing clay to which the trade name of "Saponite" has been supplied. It runs 11 per cent aluminum, and has the appearance of kaolin.

Texas

The best Texas refractory clays are from the Pennsylvanian in the north central part of the State. Many vitrified brick are made there, particularly just west of Rock Island, Colorado county. The Dallas clays are from the Cretaceous. In Austin, Travis county, brick are made from alluvial clay found along the river. At Bastrop, Bastrop county, the Tertiary clays are used.

Under the lignite deposits of Milam, Lee, Bastrop, Fayette and Caldwell counties are excellent deposits of fire clay; also pockets of tile and face brick clay. Near Muldoon, Fayette county, is a bed of hydrous magnesium silicate, known as meerschaum clay. At Leakey, Real county, are apparently extensive clay beds, which have never been adequately prospected. This is a new county, just north of Uvalde county, and the Leakey kaolin, pure white with only a trace of iron, which is easily washed out, is shipped to England and other export markets for special porcelains. Microscopic examination shows it to consist of exceedingly small crystals of kaolinite, too small to be defined. It takes 300-400 magnifications to see the oblong crystals. It was shipped at a profit, even before the railroad was built and it was necessary to haul it 60 miles by wagon. These deposits are found along the Uvalde and Northern Railroad.

A similar kaolin, for fine chinaware, occurs at La Grange and Plum, Fayette county, along the M-K-T R. R. and in Nueces county. Most of the kaolins in southeast Texas are plastic.

On the Live Oak Peninsula, on the Copano Bay side, north of Corpus Christi, is a heavy blue clay which has been tested for paving brick and found well suited to this purpose. Brick and tile clay are also found near Portland, San Patricio county, on Corpus Christi Bay.

The same clay which the Southern Pacific Railroad is burning in Iberia parish, Louisiana, for ballast, is burned for brick and tile at Rosenberg, Fort Bend county, Texas.

All the Coastal Plain clays carry lime. When they occur in nodular form they are no good. When well distributed, they are usually workable. At Winnsboro, Wood county, is a potter's clay which is shipped to the potteries at Dallas, Athens and Fort Worth. The Dallas pottery is the largest and makes all varieties of jugs, pots, vases, dishes, chinaware, door stops and ornamental pieces.

Milam county is the center of oil, lignite and clays. It should have a big future for power distribution and the general manufacture of ceramics. At Milano, Milam county, on the Santa Fe Railroad, is a 2100-acre kaolin bed.

United States Bureau of Standard tests on Texas clays show that they take a good glaze, but require finer grinding.

Brewster county clays are the source of refractory brick used in the quicksilver furnaces of the Terlingua district. Slip clays are widely mined in Bexar, Wise, Polk and Grimes counties. Proportional to its great area, therefore, it will be seen that Texas is rich in ceramic material of many kinds, distributed over many counties and on every railroad line in the state. The products of the Texas clay industry amount to over three million dollars annually.

Uses

The uses to which the various clays are put are extremely varied and widely comprehensive. A poor grade of one type of clay may be admirably adapted to first-class use in combination with another grade. As paper filler the principal markets are in the north and east. Trenton, N. J., and East Liverpool, Ohio, are the principal pottery centers. High voltage insulators and glass refractories come principally from Western Kentucky, although many of the Florida, Tennessee and North Carolina kaolins are also used for that purpose. Talc, mica and similar materials are competitors of clay for all grades of filler. Clay products, with a few exceptions, do not bring high prices at the point of origin, so that freight rates play an important part in the development of the industry in any state and in controlling the source of supply for any given market. Clay is also used for cold-water paint, kalsomine and wallpaper.

Brick may be classified as common or building brick with the various grades known as pressed or face brick, vitrified brick, sometimes called paving brick, and firebrick and general molded refractories.

Ballast clay is used as a sound deadener in floors and as road material with sand. Cement clay, as its name would indicate, is an ingredient of cement (vide Chapter XXV).

China clay is used not only for chinaware and porcelains, but for graniteware, basins, sinks, lavatories and all whiteware. Earthenware clay is made into flower pots, filters, drain tile, etc., while a more porous grade is made into chimney flues, ventilators, and inside partition blocks. Stone ware clay goes into the manufacture of jugs, churns, crocks, pitchers, jars, urns, jardiniers, and sewer pipe, while tile clay is used for drains, irrigation ditches, roofs, floors, walls and fireplaces.

When unburned, some of the finest clays are used as adulterants for white lead in fulling cloth, decolorizing oil and forming a body for soap fats.

Toys, marbles, smoking pipes, retorts, thread guides and many miscellaneous articles are made from various combinations of clay. Chemical evaporating dishes, pestles and mortars, ovens and crucibles, gas retorts, glass pots, saggers, electric insulating tubes, door knobs, fire kindlers, fence posts, copings, tombstones, ink bottles, vases, pedestals, match safes, tea sets, candle sticks, umbrella stands, calendars, clock cases, picture frames and fern dishes are all dependent upon clay for their raw material.

It is also used to temper molding sand, as an absorbent for medicinal purposes, relief modeling, artists' molding materials, and puddling in reservoirs.

The term "faience" is usually used to denote all classes of permeable wares covered with a glaze.

The writer has already called attention to the necessity for the development of ceramics in the South. Although the South furnishes much of the material from which these great industries receive their being, nevertheless, it buys its tableware, its porcelains, its insulators, its spark plugs, its linoleums, and its paper in great measure from Northern plants.

A new phase in the use of clay which has recently come to the front is the teaching of clay modeling in public schools. The ethical value of clay modeling, like its analogy, free-hand drawing, lies in raising the standard of artistic appreciation and in the development of self-expression.

Although Pennsylvania at present produces about 40 per cent of the refractory clays of the United States, the writer has already called attention, in an earlier portion of this chapter, to the very high grade of refractory brick which have been and can be made from certain Southern clays. In addition to the fire clay and hard-flint clay, there are also in lesser measure deposits of ganister rock which is a pure white quartzite occurring as massive bedded sandstone. The value of raw and finished clay products in the United States per year is exceeded only in the mineral industry by coal and petroleum.

So many variations of potteryware, tableware, sanitaryware and decorative articles are made from clay that the foregoing only serves to indicate in general the various classes into which they may be divided.

A special type of ware for gas lighting and heating and

for electric ranges and heaters is also made from combinations of the various clays. It is logical to anticipate that continued tariff protection and the work recently undertaken by the ceramic schools at the various universities, will tend more and more to establish definite standards of fineness, of color, of texture, of plasticity, and to obtain for American clays adequate recognition and independence for the industry from any substantial quantity of imported clay.

* * * * * *

Cyanite is identical in composition with sillimanite, but differs in physical properties.

Cyanite is triclinic and may be blue, gray, green or brown, and a specific gravity of 3.3 to 3.7, while sillimanite is orthorhombic, and white, gray, green or brown, with a specific gravity of 3.2 to 3.3; thus they may be distinguished by microscope or by specific gravity.

The value of these minerals was deduced from a study of porcelains, and the segregation of synthetic sillimanite created by high temperature combinations of clay, silica and feldspar.

It was learned by the United States Bureau of Standards that porcelain bodies containing high percentages of this material possessed great tensile strength, high dielectric properties and low thermal expansion. It at once became evident that such a substance would be ideal for electric porcelains, spark plugs, and similar articles subjected to great heat and vibration.

Both cyanite and its associate, andalusite, when fired at a temperature of approximately 2500° F., invert into sillimanite. The group, as occurring in nature, is usually associated with corundum, garnet, beryl or barytes.

Beryl is commercially found as a by-product of feldspar and mica (vide Chapter XII), and when substituted up to 45 per cent for feldspar in the manufacture of porcelain, gives high electrical resistance and low thermal expansion. Thus a new field is open for research in porcelain materials and for prospecting in the search for these minerals in commercial quantities. Likewise, an opportunity for chemical experimentation in synthesis of mineral products.

Crystals of cyanite are found near Charlotte Court House, Charlotte county, Virginia, and at numerous points in North Carolina, notably at Chubb's and Crowder's mountains, on the road to Cooper's Gap, in Gaston and Rutherford counties, and at Swannanoa Gap in Buncombe county. Around Yellow Mountain, Mitchell county, isolated crystals of blue and moss-green color have been found, but their source has never been traced. An extensive deposit of high-grade cyanite has recently been proven at Black Mountain and Old Fort in North Carolina, as well as at Burnsville, Yancey county.

The mica and hornblende schists of Macon, Haywood, Transylvania, Yancey, Caldwell and Catawba counties are likely locations for prospecting. Green cyanite is known to exist at the north end of Black Mountain, Yancey county.

This group of minerals is valuable not only for porcelain manufacture, but for refractory cements, and as a component with other refractories, of firebrick, and special high-temperature furnace linings.

It has been found necessary by experiment to mix some material with pure cyanite to counteract its initial expansion. Diaspore (aluminum hydroxide) is commonly used for this purpose in proportions of 20 to 30 per cent cyanite and 80 to 70 per cent diaspore. One of the problems in the development of the cyanite industry has been its concentration by flotation or otherwise since the other minerals with which it is commonly associated are of practically the same specific gravity and it is essential that these minerals should be removed on account of their lower fusing point.

CHAPTER XVII

MICA, CHLORITE, SERICITE, TALC, SOAPSTONE

Mica occurs usually, as muscovite or biotite. The former is potash bearing, white mica; the latter is the magnesium-iron form, or black mica. Variations of these are lepidolite, a vari-colored lithium bearing mica, and phlogopite, which is biotite with a minimum of iron. Sericite is mica in massive form, with the appearance of talc. It is hydrous muscovite occurring in schistose rocks.

The color of mica is determined by the rock with which it is associated. One of the properties of true mica is that it can be indefinitely subdivided into thin sheets. When first blocked out it is split by rubbing the edge against a file to break the laminations loose.

Its specific gravity varies from 2.7 to 3.2; 8 pounds of sheets split per day, is a good day's work. Because of its non-absorptivity of water, it is especially valuable as an electrical insulator. Its resistance to rupture by high voltage, called its "di-electric property," also surpasses that of any other known material.

Stocks of mica never accumulate, and once used, it is never salvaged. The phenomenal growth of radio has caused a rapid increase in the demand for mica, so that the total consumption in the United States is four times the domestic production, the deficit coming principally from Canada, India, Africa and South America. In 1890 the total production in the United States only amounted to $250,000, while in 1923 the value of this mineral handled in the markets of this country exceeded $2,800,000, or over one-half the world product.

Mica is usually associated with feldspathic rocks, and frequently the pegmatite dykes carry other minerals or gems. In some cases properties originally opened for mica, revert to feldspar or kaolin mines, with mica as a by-product. Not infrequently the mica is quarried or operated by open-cut, in which case it becomes a seasonal operation. Its crystals vary from a fraction of an inch to several feet in diameter, but the usual product rarely exceeds 6 inches across.

These crystals usually have irregular adherences of rock on the edges, which must be cobbed with a hammer before they can be split into 1/16 inch sheets. These are then graded for quality and color, split into the required laminations, and trimmed to standard size or pattern. The trimmings are also utilized. The United States Geological Survey estimates that 3 per cent of cut sheet and 8 per cent of cut discs and washers are obtainable from mine-run mica, the balance being waste or scrap.

For use in condensers for wireless, the sheets must be 1/1000 of an inch thick, and free from impurities, cracks, holes or wrinkles and must have di-electric strength to withstand a voltage of 20,000. One of these sheets, 1/1000 of an inch thick, if of grade 1 quality, can readily be bent into a cylinder ¼-inch in diameter, without showing any cracking.

Any mica to be classed as sheet must cut at least 1½ by 2 inches and be clean and uniform and free from spots or cracks. Large sheets meeting this requirement command an extra price and a ready market. Trimmings and small sheets are made into built-up mica by pressure, with a shellac binder, and used in various electrical goods.

Phlogopite is comparatively soft and offers about the same frictional resistance as copper; hence it finds a market as insulation between copper segments in dynamos, motors and electrical machinery where the edge of the mica lies even with that of the copper, so that both wear down together.

There is no satisfactory substitute for sheet mica in electrical insulation, which, in turn, utilizes 86 per cent of the total sheet production. It is obvious, therefore, that the mica resources of the United States offer a strategic commercial value to the prospector.

Much of the mica bearing area is in agricultural regions, and the operations have been erratically conducted on small capital. The operators have not only lacked engineering knowledge, but have little idea of the rapidly increasing value as the sheets increase in size and have sacrificed profits to avoid intelligent timbering, pumping and handling. Also led by war-time enthusiasm and stimulated by promotion promises of radio development, many properties were sacrificed to stock-selling schemes, and still remain inactive.

Bulletin 740 of the United States Geological Survey on "Mica Deposits of the United States" will prove of interest. Circular No. 7044, June, 1927 on, "Mica," by W. W. Myers, and published by the United States Bureau of Mines, contains much recent data.

Virginia

Virginia mica is widely distributed over the entire Piedmont region. The principal districts are the Amelia county area; the Ridgeway area in Henry county; and the Chestnut Ridge area in Franklin county. Each has produced much and is capable of producing more.

The Amelia county product is in large sheets of good quality. The deposit in Henry county operates a good portion of the year, and ground mica is produced in Henrico county.

North Carolina

Mica in North Carolina antedates historical records. Stone implements unearthed in old mica deposits show that older even than Indian tradition, a race of men valued and mined for mica. The product of the state today is trimmed and graded and the scrap mica ground by local labor. At Spruce Pine, Mitchell county, are three mills producing ground mica from both muscovite and biotite. At Micaville, Yancey county and Isinglass Hill, Rutherford county, are mills working old deposits, grinding schist or scrap mica.

Since 1903 North Carolina has supplied more than one-half the total mica production of the United States. The mica belt covers twenty counties in Western North Carolina and extends northeast and southwest across the state, reaching an extreme width of 100 miles.

The Cowee-Black Mountain belt lies west of the Blue Ridge; the Blue Ridge belt, as its name indicates, follows the summit of these mountains; and the Piedmont belt, parallel to the other two, lies to the east.

Most of the mica from the first and last of these belts is clear and rum-colored, while that of the central belt is usually speckled and smoky or greenish-brown in color.

Mica is associated in highly metamorphic rocks, with the abrasives and gems discussed in Chapter XII, and with hornblende, gneisses and schists.

The market is affected by foreign importations. Mica is an essential war mineral. The present tariff, being inadequate to prevent the importation of Indian mica, reserves are being accumulated from importations mined by cheap labor. The American mica producer under present conditions can only compete by mining his highest grade ore and abandoning the medium and low-grade portion of his deposit.

Of special interest in North Carolina are the mica deposits in the Toxaway district, upon which special survey reports have been issued. Near Sapphire Lake is a combination deposit of mica and garnet. At Willets, Jackson county, the ore is crushed to recover the abrasives from the matrix of granite and the black flake mica is recovered and shipped to Chicago for foundry facing. The Black Mountain deposits are supplying high-grade sheet mica. The Southern Railway exhibits mica from Buncombe and Macon counties.

Beds of mica, associated with feldspar, have recently been disclosed along Reddie's and Mulberry rivers in northern Wilkes county.

South Carolina

But little mica has been proved up in South Carolina. A deposit at Abbeville, Abbeville county, is of considerable extent, but its quality is unknown. The Oconee county deposits are probably a continuation of the North Carolina beds and are worth investigation. Pegmatites in Anderson and Greenville counties also carry mica and their value and extent are undetermined. It is also found in combination with graphite and monazite in a 76-acre deposit at Zion, Spartanburg county.

Georgia

Most of the product from Georgia is sold crude to Asheville, North Carolina plants. Valuable deposits exist in Upson, Oconee, Cherokee, Lumpkin, Union, Hall, Rabun, Haralson and Monroe counties. Many undeveloped properties are still available. Mica is also found associated with feldspar in Talbot and Harris counties. There is opportunity for a mica grinding plant at several locations throughout the state.

Alabama

The mica areas of Alabama include Randolph, Clay, Tallapoosa, Coosa, Cleburne, Chambers, Elmore, Talladega and Lee counties. For the most part the deposits carry very little overburden and offer available drainage. A peculiarity of the Tallapoosa county product is the occurrence of clear muscovite in proximity to specked and spotted mica with mineral inclusions. The particular spotted mica appears unaffected for electrical purposes by these inclusions and brings a high price.

Splitting, cutting and boxing mica is an established rural industry. The sheets go to the electrical manufacturers and the trimmings and flake are shipped largely to North Carolina for fabrication.

Arkansas

It is commonly stated that no mica occurs in Arkansas, although a deposit of gypsum in Drew county has several times been mistaken for mica. Biotite is reported in Garland county at Potash, Sulphur Springs and Magnet Cove. The industrial department of the C. R. I. & P. R. R. reports undeveloped mica at Forrest City, St. Francis county.

Texas

The only Texas mica of known value is a deposit in the Van Horn Mountains on the southern limit of Culberson county and about midway between the Texas Pacific and the Southern Pacific R. Rs.

Uses

Two-thirds of the total production of ground mica is required in the manufacture of roofing. High-grade sheet mica is used for electrical purposes, glazing, stove fronts, motor goggles, diving helmets, compass cards, windows in war ships, smelting furnace sight holes, optical lanterns, military lanterns, lining chimneys and canopies, gage fronts, phonograph diaphragms and other sound producing devices, washers and disks, electric light sockets, spark plugs, insulators, fuse boxes, guards in rheostats, telephones, lantern slides, radio apparatus, heat screens, submarine detectors, inlaid tiles, painters' placques, and ornaments.

Scale and ground mica are used with oil as a lubricant, as a coating for tar and other roofing papers to prevent sticking, as a possible source of potash, mixed with shellac and molded into sheets as built-up mica, and in this form as a substitute for hard fibre, glass, porcelain, hard rubber, rawhides and various other molded compounds for use in commutators, bushings, brush holders, noiseless gear blanks, wiring conduits, spools for spark coils, and magnet windings, separators, meter disks, etc. These compounds have various trade names, such as micanite, micarta, balkalite, micamina, tungash, etc.

Other uses of the finer grades are in railroad car axle packings, pipe and boiler covers, fireproof paints, rubber tires, annealing steel, as an absorbent of nitro-glycerine, in calico printing, tinsel decorations, artificial snow, wall paper decorations, flexible mica cloth and tape. Ground mica gives lustre to wallpaper and cloth and to fancy paints, ornamental tiles and concrete. It is an excellent dry lubricant for wooden bearings. Considerable quantities are also consumed as medicine. When coarsely ground and mixed with other ingredients it makes concrete facing material, giving the effect of natural rock.

* * * * * *

Chlorite is a term applied to a group of greenish minerals resembling mica and consisting of hydrous silicates of magnesium, aluminum and ferrous iron. It is used for many of the purposes to which talc is assigned. Chloritic schist is frequently found in the presence of mica, talc and soapstone. Georgia is the principal source of high-grade chlorite, which is shipped to Pittsburgh and Chicago and sold at a high figure for insulating purposes. Much of this manufactured product returns to the source of the raw material, with freight and manufacturing costs and handling profits added, to be repurchased by the original producers.

* * * * * *

Sericite is a variety of muscovite (white mica) with silky lustre, frequently associated with schists and gneisses, in the metamorphic rocks. Its occurrence coincides with that of muscovite, recorded earlier in this chapter.

* * * * * *

Talc is a white, gray or greenish mineral, soft and greasy to the touch. It is a silicate of magnesia, resistant to heat and unaffected by ordinary acids. Soapstone is a massive schistose form of talc, usually impure.

Pyrophyllite is a form of chlorite (qui vide) and is used for slate pencils and marking crayon.

Talc varies in weight from 31 to 46 pounds per cubic foot. When prepared for the market it must pass 95 per cent through a 200-mesh screen. In recent years French and Italian talc have offered serious competition, while the new tariff slightly raised the competitive price, it was not sufficient to stimulate domestic industry or to encourage expansion. Talc is shipped principally to points north and east. It is sold under various trade names, as "steatite," "potstone," "talc-clay," "agilite," "asbestine," and "verdolite." In general, however, the term talc should be applied to the pure white, gray or green varieties having a hardness of 1 in the established scale, while steatite or soapstone may be yellow, red or brown, massive and impure with a hardness up to 3 or 4.

On account of its general distribution, transportation and freight rates play an important part in its development.

Lava-grade talc, used for tips of gas jets, however, is so rare that a deposit of this grade would probably offer inducement for development no matter where located.

As a mineral filler, talc competes with clay, mica, graphite, asbestos, tripoli and similar non-metallics. The cost of installing a grinding mill is such that a deposit should show at least 15 years life to warrant construction. Royalties paid owners range from 25 cents per ton to $4 on lava grade talc selling at a much higher price.

Talc is usually obtained by underground mining. Soapstone is quarried, and the general processes used are analogous to those of the marble industry.

Virginia

The principal sources of talc and soapstone in Virginia have been in Albemarle, Fairfax, Nelson and Orange counties until recent years. Fairfax, Franklin and Nelson counties are now opening up several places for both the ground and quarried product. The largest soapstone plant in the world is at Schuyler, Albemarle county. The "Alberine" belt of Nelson county is very active and its product is shipped to every civilized country.

The Franklin soapstone is ground and used for red and brown mortar coloring. It is also mixed and dyed black. The "Virgilina" district also has highly-colored soapstone which is available for the same purpose. Undeveloped deposits of both talc and soapstone are found near Emporia, Greensville county, Keysville, Charlotte county, and in Amelia county.

North Carolina

The talc industry is being revived in North Carolina. In Moore county, a strip of land from two to five miles wide and twenty miles in length carries pyrophillite, whose aluminum base (vide chlorite) is exceptionally fine grained. It is being ground and put on the market in competition with magnesium-base talc.

True talc occurs in Cherokee, Swain, Graham, Jackson, Ashe, Buncombe, Alleghany, Madison, Mitchell and Yancey counties, all in the western part of the state. The pyrophillite deposits are found in Moore and Chatham counties, in the east-central part of the state, associated with slate. Talc is also reported from Franklin, Mason county, and soapstone at Sapo, Ashe county. Onyx and kaolin and marble are also found in the latter. Fibrous talc is mined in Avery county.

South Carolina

Soapstone is quarried at numerous points in South Carolina. The principal deposits are at Gaffney, Cherokee county; Chester, Chester county; Laurens, Laurens county; Fair View and Soapstone Hill, Oconee county; Central, Pickens county; Cedar Springs, Spartanburg county; and Nation Ford, York county.

Georgia

Georgia talc is found in combination with chlorite, referred to earlier in this chapter, as well as pure, and in soapstone form. The Central of Georgia Railway lists it in Carrol, Harris, Jasper and Merriweather counties, and soapstone in these and Monroe and Morgan counties. The Fannin, Murray and Gilmer county talcs are an extension of the North Carolina deposits. In the region around Mineral Bluff in Cherokee county are several deposits contiguous to the L. & N. R. R.

The soapstones occur from Towns and Union counties southwest to Harris county. The Southern Railway reports talc at Cohutta, Whitfield county and Laurel Creek, Dawson county.

Alabama

Alabama has never been a material producer of talc. It occurs in Chambers and Tallapoosa counties, but frequently impure. Near Talladega, Talladega county, is a deposit of actinolite, a light green calcium-magnesium-iron- silicate, which is often mistaken for pyrophillite.

Arkansas

What is said to be the only soapstone deposit west of the Mississippi River occurs twelve miles northeast of Benton, Saline county, Arkansas. It is favorably situated for operation. Talcose shales and schists (chlorite?)

are found in Montgomery, Hot Spring and Saline counties.

Texas

Texas talc is usually associated with serpentine or in the pack-saddle schist of Llano county, where it has been opened up about nine miles west of Llano.

Uses

The uses of talc and soapstone are very many. The reader is referred to Bulletin 213 of the Bureau of Mines, by Ladoo, where on pages 66-70 a complete list is given. These may be summarized as follows: *Powered form:* paper manufacture, roofing paper, textiles, rubber, paint, soap, foundry-facing, toilet preparations, wire-insulating compounds, lubricants, linoleum, oil cloth, pipe-covering compounds, pottery, porcelain manufacture and glaze, electrical insulation, rope and twine manufacture, leather dressing, cork, oil filtering, glass polishing, special cements, wall plaster, asbestos roofing, crayons, placques, preservative coatings for stonework, polishing coffee beans and other foodstuffs, bleaching grains of inferior color, in rubber stamp manufacture, composition flooring, insulated flooring and switchboards, imitation stone, boot and shoe powder, glove powder, dermatology, absorbent base for colors, in veterinary surgery, for purifying and de-greasing waste water, filters, conserving fruits, vegetables and eggs, sugar refining, contact material for catalytic reactions, absorbent for nitroglycerins, packing material for chemicals and acid, for fireproofing wood, for fireproof packing for pipe, automobile polish, fertilizer filler, insecticide filler, shoe polish and polish in yarn and thread manufacture, in pharmaceutics, for colored crayons, stove polish, imitation amber, cleaning hair and bristles, floor wax, as a substitute for oil in laying terrazzo flooring, to prevent candy and chewing gum from sticking, to opaque window shades, and as putty filler. *Massive form:* Lava blanks for electrical insulation, gas burner tips and spark plugs, crayons and pencils, tailors' chalk, glass molds, metallurgical molds, refractories, polishing wood handles, polishing and lubricating wire nails, oriental carvings, cooking utensils, electric switchboards, acid-proof tables, laundry tubs and sinks, fireless cooker stoves, foot warmers and griddles.

In recent years talc has also found a market as a filler in ready-mixed paints, for water proofing concrete, and also in the manufacture of fireproof paints. In sheet asphalt under certain climatic conditions it is of value in regulating expansion and contraction.

Chapter XVIII

SHALES, SLATE

Shale is fine-grained clay, high in aluminum silicates, which was carried in suspension and ultimately deposited in still water. Shales may be hard or soft and represent the intermediate stage between clay and slate. Slate is shale, burned in Nature's laboratory. Shale tiles and roofing are artificial slate, and shale products are the aristocrats of the brick and tile industry.

Shales naturally grade into those used for (a) cement; (b) brick; (c) paint pigment; (d) tiling and roofing; (e) oil shales. The first of these is discussed in Chapter XXV under "Limestones and Cement." The third is combined with "Pigment Clays" in Chapter IV. The second and fourth are logical adjuncts of brick clay and have been amplified in Chapter XVI. Oil shales are covered in Chapter VII.

Virginia

The diversity of shales in southwestern Virginia affords opportunity for the manufacture of any product of which shale is a component.

West Virginia

There are many good brick shales in Monongalia county and in southern Morgan county, West Virginia, and around Martinsburg, Berkeley county. Some of these are suitable for paving brick, but the Eastern states prefer asphalt or macadam, and the Ohio paving brick industry is strongly competitive.

North Carolina

The valuable shale area of North Carolina is composed

of Stanly and Union counties, and part of Anson, Montgomery and Rowan counties. Sanford, Lee county, and Madison, Rockingham county are centers of smaller beds. Around Hot Springs, Madison county, on the Tennessee border, is an unprospected area of promising appearance. Northwest of Goldsboro, in Wayne and Johnston counties, near Selma, Johnston county; around Nashville and Spring Hope, Nash county; and at Weldon, Northampton county, as well as in the Deep River coal field, overlying the Cumnock coal, are good brick shales of varying qualities.

These areas all have good transportation facilities. The shales would make high-grade face brick, hollow tile, sewer pipe and floor and roofing tile.

At Colon, Lee county, a face brick which will "ring" is produced at a temperature of 1750° F., as compared to the usual temperature of 2400° required for most vitrified brick. This represents a fuel saving of more than 50 per cent.

South Carolina

In McCormick county, South Carolina, near Modoc, is a 600-acre deposit of shale suitable for vitrified brick.

Tennessee

The entire Cumberland Plateau of Tennessee is underlain with shale beds. At Jellico and Newcombe, Campbell county, and Bull's Gap, Hawkins county, in East Tennessee; at Donovan, Anderson county, and at Rockwood, Roane county, and a few other locations around the rim of the central basin, these shales have been worked for brick, paving block and wood-fibre plaster materials.

Face brick and light-weight shale brick are made at Paris, Henry county.

Georgia

The shales of Georgia range from pre-Cambrian to carboniferous, and in thickness from 500 to 3000 feet. The ten counties comprising the northwest part of the state all supply accessible deposits. For the most part, they are low in plasticity, with low shrinkage and low vitrifying points, highly siliceous and red burning.

By mixing with various local clays, a wide variety of product is manufactured.

Alabama

The Alabama shale products come principally from Fayette, Blount, Jefferson and Marion counties. Along the Central of Georgia Railway are many undeveloped shales which special tests have shown to be of more than ordinary value in Catoosa, St. Clair and Shelby counties.

* * * * * *

Slate is a sedimentary rock in which numerous crystals, such as quartz, feldspar, chlorite, tourmaline and biotite are embedded in a matrix consisting, in the case of mica slate, of muscovite or sericite; or in clay slates the matrix is kaolin oriented in such a manner that the long optical axis of the crystal is always parallel to the line of cleavage, or at right angles to the direction of pressure which formed the rock, giving the rock cleavage and fissility. Slate varies in color from green to purple and is of fine texture.

It is the most workable of all enduring stones, and is susceptible of a greater number of uses than any other natural rock. It has great density and strength; it is sanitary and insoluble; it does not stain; it is impervious to oil or chemicals; and it does not absorb odors. Unlike many building materials, it may be salvaged and used over and over. Because of its non-conductivity, it is of great value in the electrical industry.

It was first used for roofing. The necessity for conserving rain water has led to its extensive use in New Orleans. The principal market for blackboard slate is abroad. Structural and roofing slate are seasonal, while the demand for electrical slate is uniform.

The centers of slate consumption are New York, Boston, Philadelphia, Schenectady, Pittsburgh, Chicago and St. Louis. Freight rates are an important factor since, until recently, the best obtainable rating on slate was sixth class. On this account there is not as much building or roofing slate used west of the Mississippi River or south of the Carolinas as there could be, except where water transportation is available to offer lower competitive rates.

As a result of the decision of the I. C. C. in reducing rates in 1922, and the efforts of the National Slate Assotion, and co-operation of railroad traffic men, some relief has been secured and the whole slate freight rate structure is being reworked to bring rates on slate products on a parity with other quarried or competitive materials. Pending conclusion of this rate investigation, progress on all individual commodity adjustments is retarded.

Slate flour, or pulverized slate, is a comparatively new filler material, ground from scrap, and used in roofing mastic, mechanical rubber goods, road asphalt mixtures, linoleum, oilcloth, paint and other industrial processes.

Virginia

The Arvonia district of Virginia, in northern Buckingham county, and Fluvanna county, on both sides of the James River is the principal slate-producing region of the South. It is extensively operated, and supplies high-grade, blue-gray, non-fading, roofing slate. This material was used on the old State Capitol building in Richmond in 1775, and stands today unimpaired and unfaded. It was also used on the early buildings of the University of Virginia, and is still in service over 100 years later. Recently a slate crushing mill has been located at Dutch Gap in this district to furnish blue-black granules and flour.

Another district is at Snowden, Amherst county, west of Lynchburg. It closed down during the war and probably will never be re-opened as it is too far from the railroad.

There is also the Esmont slate belt in Albemarle county, which supplies blue granules for artificial roofing and slate dust, or flour, for industrial processes. It is suitable for milling stock, panels, billiard table tops, etc., but has never been developed, although roofing slate production is now under way at this point.

Other minor areas are in Fauquier county, south of Warrenton, and the Quantico belt in Spotsylvania county. But there are no developments known in these areas.

West Virginia

East of Martinsburg, Berkeley county, West Virginia, there is reported a medium-grade roofing slate which has been quarried intermittently for local consumption.

Tennessee

The Tennessee slate deposits around Tellico Plains,

Monroe county, are operated for artificial roofing supplies. At Unicoi, Unicoi county, a red slate has been exposed, but never exploited.

Previous to 1910 there were many slate quarries operated along the Little Tennessee River, in Knox county. Other occurrences are in Blount, Cocke, McMinn, Polk, Sevier, Sullivan and Washington counties.

Georgia

Slate quarrying in Georgia might have been one of the leading industries. The largest area is in Polk and Bartow counties around Cartersville, Rockmart and Cedartown. The slate is dark blue to black, and of very fine texture. The Gordon and Murray county deposits are green, and could furnish a large amount of roofing slate. Occasional beds, more highly calcareous than others, are easily detected by the application of cold dilute hydrochloric acid. The Richardson Company are actively operating a granite quarry and mill at Rockmart, but there are no other quarries operating in Georgia at present.

Alabama

No extensive slate operations have been carried on in Alabama for the last sixty years, although promising beds are found along the Central of Georgia Railway in Talladega county; and former operations at Anniston, Calhoun county, and in Coosa, Cleburne and Chilton counties.

Arkansas

Considering the abundance, quality and diverse coloring of the Arkansas slates, it is remarkable that no greater development has taken place in that state. The slate area is in the Ouachita Mountains, south of the Arkansas

River, from Little Rock, Pulaski county, westward to Mena, Polk county, and includes the greater part of Saline, Garland and Montgomery counties, a district 100 miles long and 15 to 20 miles wide. However, this district is at too great a distance from the railroads to make economical operation possible. The slate measures are over 8000 feet in thickness. Large deposits of black, red and green slates, suitable for preparing roofing material, are found near Caddo Gap.

The colors vary from deep black, through blue, dark red, light red, greenish-gray, sea-green, light green, light gray and dark gray, the latter spangled with minute scales of mica.

Uses

The uses of slate are so varied that there is hardly a building that does not contain slate in some form. It is used as roofing, and as an ingredient of prepared roofings; as filler, and in plastic compositions; for all sorts of insulation, bases and panel boards; monuments, grave stones, vault lining, cabinets, work benches, table tops, counters, shelving, billiard table surfaces, flagging; hotel trim and general inside building finish for baseboards, wainscoting, fire places, mantels, garden seats, and benches and all decorative designs; coping, plinths for columns; tanks, lavatories and bath room trim; blackboards, score boards, bulletin boards, and general antiseptic, sanitary, damp-and-chemical proof finish. The grave yards in Arvonia or Ore Bank, Virginia, in the Buckingham field have many attractive slate monuments and markers carved by a man who learned his trade in London.

Chapter XIX

FLUORSPAR, LITHOGRAPHIC STONE

The distribution of **fluorspar** is general, but only a few of the known deposits are of commercial value. Even war requirements failed to develop any material ore bodies. Like anthracite coal mining, the exhaustion of shallow deposits, the added cost of deeper mining, de-watering, and exploration have all made fluorspar mining an increasingly expensive operation.

Eighty-five per cent of the production is used in basic open hearth and electric furnaces as a flux and deterent. Prior to the war 35 per cent of the steel furnaces were open hearth. Today 80 per cent are of that type. The consumption ranges from 8 to 19 pounds of fluorspar per ton of steel. No known substitute has been found, although the use of alumina has been advocated. Twenty per cent of the total domestic production comes from Crittenden county, Kentucky, and 70 per cent from north of the Ohio River.

Many of the operations are remote from the railroads; most of them lying from 4 to 15 miles from the shipping point, with dirt roads impassable in winter.

Fluorspar occurs in lenses in vertical fissure veins up to 30 feet in thickness. Below two feet in width the chutes do not pay to work. The deposits rarely extend deeper than 500 feet, the ore either pinching out or being replaced by calcite. Water and fuel are also important problems. It was stated in "Iron Trade Review," in 1922 that 164 tons of water are pumped for each ton of fluorspar produced, and that one ton of coal, costing $3.11 including freight, produced only two tons of fluorspar.

In view of the frequent occurrence of fluorspar, there is no doubt that the discovery of new commercial deposits would result from sufficient inducement to prospectors. As the consumption per ton of steel is slight, an increased profit of $5 per ton on the raw fluorspar would mean only two or three cents per ton of finished steel. Diamond drilling is not a satisfactory method of prospecting because of the lenticular nature of the ore bodies.

The Tariff Act of 1922 placed the duty at $5.60 per ton. This has materially cut down the German, English and Canadian importations, and has resulted in the proving up of commercial bodies of ore in New Mexico and elsewhere.

The distribution of the product is as follows:

```
Steel ingots and castings............................ 80%—85%
Glass and enameling.................................7½%—10%
Hydrofluoric acid ....................................  5%— 6%
Foundries ...........................................  1%— 2%
Miscellaneous ......................................       2%
```

The highest grade fluorspar which runs 98 per cent or better, calcium fluoride, sells at $45 to $50 per ton, for the manufacture of hydrofluoric acid. This may be either lump or ground.

The next grade, running 95 to 98 per cent calcium fluoride, goes to the glass and enamel trades. Clear flawless crystals of fluorspar are in demand for optical instruments. This grade is ground and washed before shipment.

The next two grades, running from 93 to 96 per cent, and from 88 to 92 per cent, sell at from $20 to $30 per ton, and are used for cheaper grades of glass and enamel, while the gravel spar, constituting 80 per cent of the production, and containing 85 per cent or better of calcium fluoride, goes to furnace and foundry.

The silica content runs from 1 to 5 per cent in the higher to lower grades. The ore must be free from lead and zinc sulphides. The ground ore passing 24 mesh goes to the enamel, glass and porcelain trades, while that through 55 mesh is used in the chemical industry.

Virginia

The most promising deposits in Virginia are in Albemarle county where fluorspar occurs as a gangue with lead and zinc. It is also found in Smyth and Wythe counties as a zinc gangue, but of questionable commercial value.

Georgia

It occurs in crystal form in the Knox dolomite near Graysville, Catoosa county, and Ranger, Gordon county, Georgia.

Kentucky

Large undeveloped deposits of fluorspar in Kentucky center about Marion and Mexico, Crittenden county; Salem and Smithland, Livingston county, and Princeton, Caldwell county. The Kentucky Geological Survey has prepared a fluorspar report on this area. It has been found that fluorspar is more widely distributed in this field than previously believed. It occurs in some sandstone regions at a considerable depth in the Chester series and adjoining the Chester limestones. The extent of the field can only be determined by adequate prospecting. There is also a deposit in Jessamine county, near High Bridge. The Illinois Central R. R. has recently built a three-mile spur to the Crittenden county field, at an expense of $200,000, to assist in developing the district.

Tennessee

The Tennessee deposits are found along the Tenn. Central R. R. in Smith, Wilson and Putnam counties. They are reported as being of good quality and available to rail transportation.

Texas

To the south and east of the recently developed New Mexico deposits, fluorspar is found in Texas, on the line between El Paso and Culberson counties, in eastern Mason county, northeastern Gillespie county, northwestern Blanco county, western Burnet county, and in various locations in Llano county.

Uses

In addition to the basic open-hearth smelters referred to, fluorspar is used in electric smelting of both ferrous and non-ferrous metals. Its advantages are reduction of required coke, cleaner and stronger castings, greater freedom from slag, more liquid slag, and less iron lost. A small amount is used in smelting gold, silver and copper ores, in refining copper, and in the electrolytic refining of antimony and lead.

It is also used in the recovery of by-product potash from Portland cement kilns. Sodium fluoride is a valuable wood preservative considered by many to be superior to coal tar, zinc chloride or creosote for this purpose.

Fluorspar is a valuable adjunct in the manufacture of aluminum from bauxite, and is indispensable in the production of hydrofluoric acid, sodium fluoride, high-grade optical glass and certain porcelain enamels. It also enters into the manufacture of calcium carbide.

* * * * * *

Lithographic printing depends basically on the antipathy between grease and water, which prevents a printing ink containing oil from adhering to wetted parts of the stone not covered by the design.

In the latest advances of color work, several photographs of the subject are taken on plates sensitized to the various colors. They are then developed and printed on a bichromated gelatine film on the stone and such parts of the film as have not been affected by the light are dissolved in hot water. The various stones are then inked in their respective colors, and the impressions transferred one over another, thus giving the finished print.

The stone used is a compact fine-grained limestone, gray, drab or yellow in color, and of high specific gravity. The greasy lithographic ink contains tallow, wax, soap and coloring matter, and the design is etched on the stone by treatment with dilute acid and gum water, which renders the fatty matter insoluble and enables the blank portions to retain their moisture.

The principal source of **lithographic stone** until about 1900 was Bavaria. Since that time it has been increasingly difficult to secure good stone or large sizes from abroad, and the increased demand for color plate work has led to many experimental substitutions of zinc, aluminum plates, etc. In "Mineral Resources of the United States," 1914, G. S. Loughlin states: "There are in the United States deposits of lithographic stone that have been proved to be of good quality, and it is reasonable to expect that the country's demand can finally be supplied from them."

Samples of stone for test must be 2 inches thick and at least 12 inches square, and polished on both sides. The usual trade sizes are 28 inches by 40 inches, and 44 inches by 64 inches, all 2 inches thick and polished. Many lithographers erase the old engravings and use the stone again. During and since the war prices have continued to climb, and substitute processes fail to meet requirements for maps and other high-grade work on hard papers.

Kentucky

In 1916 a lithograph stone quarry was opened up at Brandenburg, Meade county, Kentucky. About one-fifth of the product is available for this purpose, the balance going into the crushed stone trade. This production stopped, however, about 1917 when the owners went into the army.

Available deposits are reported in Hardin, Estill, Kenton, Clinton, Rowan and Wayne counties, Kentucky, but no development has been attempted.

Tennessee

Clay and Overton counties, Tennessee, were said by the U. S. Geological Survey in 1888 to contain the best lithographic stone in the country, but these similarly have been neglected. The best deposit which has come to the writer's attention is in Putnam county, Tennessee, along the Tenn. Cen. R. R., where a deposit of sufficient size to supply the world, has been proved up. This is a perfect lithographic stone and when sawn into 2-inch slabs and polished is valued at $1 a pound.

Alabama

Near Scottsboro, Jackson county, Alabama, is another deposit of good quality, but difficult to quarry. In Talledega county lithographic stone is reported, but has never been sufficiently prospected to qualify it. Other samples from Alabama have shown excellent grain, but were slightly "off color."

Virginia

The Virginian Railway reports a deposit of available lithographic stone near Ellett, Montgomery county, Virginia. This deposit has never been adequately opened up.

Arkansas

On West Lafferty Creek, Izard county, Arkansas, numerous attempts have been made to place a lithographic stone on the market. Difficulty seems to have been encountered with fine crystalline particles which break with ragged edges under the engraver's tool. Whether this, and similar deposits in Marion, Baxter and Searcy counties will show improvement at greater depth has not been ascertained.

Texas

Burnet county, Texas, carries Ordovician limestones, some of which have been pronounced of high specific gravity and fine texture, suitable for lithographic purposes. They likewise await development.

Chapter XX

POTASH, FELDSPAR, CINNABAR

Potash is an essential plant food, and aside from its other chemical and industrial uses, as an ingredient of fertilizer alone, is of great economic importance. An acre of land growing 25 bushels of wheat loses 80 pounds of nitrogen, phosphoric acid and potash, of which 21 pounds is potash. Thus we export 25,000 tons of potash in the form of wheat, from the United States annually.

Nitrogen is recoverable from by-product coke ovens and organic waste, from clover, cowpeas and similar plants which store in their roots nitrogen taken from the air, from various artificial processes of atmospheric nitrogen fixation, and augmented by Chilean importations.

The better grades of soap and glass, matches and explosives use potash in large quantities. As long ago as 1905, Mr. Edward Atkinson, a statistician of Boston, said:

> "The man who finds a potash mine corresponding to the Stassfurt deposits of Germany, will add more to the resources of this country, than by the discovery of gold, silver, copper or iron."

Not until the cutting off of potash importations by the war, did Americans realize the importance of a domestic supply. Much publicity under the guise of an appeal for "cheap fertilizer," has been broadcast, adverse to the protection necessary to develop a real American potash industry on a large scale in California, Texas and elsewhere. Since ordinary fertilizer contains not exceeding 3 per cent of potash, it is evident that any adequate tariff would still amount to an insignificant sum when allocated to the commercial product.

The lake bed deposits of Nebraska and California were opened up during the war, and their operators have now perfected their reduction process and in California at least, have become factors in the domestic market. Experimental work by the scientific bureaus developed by-product and waste recoveries, and attention has been directed to the reserves of west Texas and southeast New Mexico, whose extent is as yet but imperfectly determined.

Due to the dumping of German and French potash since the war, many of the new plants were unable to compete, and the wartime production of 54,000 tons in 1918 dropped to 12,000 tons in 1923. The annual consumption in the United States is 270,000 tons, of which over 90 per cent goes into fertilizer.

Glauconite sands and feldspar offer limited supplies of potash, but it is evident that the great mass must come from the major deposits of whose existence we have only recently taken cognizance.

Through the arid and semi-arid belt between the Mississippi River and the Rocky Mountains are many potash springs. These must receive their mineral from subterranean sources. It is believed by many who have studied the field that the great deposits of salt which underlie parts of central Kansas, Oklahoma, New Mexico and Texas, are indicative of similar potash beds at from 800 to 2,300 feet in depth. Such a formation has been found in a number of oil drillings, and would be analogous to the Stassfurt formation. This will be discussed later in the chapter, under deposits in Texas. What is needed is a source of natural salts which may be sold for direct application to the soil, without chemical treatment, or which could be readily refined to more concentrated form for cheaper transportation. It is believed that the Texas polyhalite will meet this requirement. Next in importance to the saline lake deposits, is the recovery of potash from cement kilns and iron blast furnaces.

About three pounds of potash is recoverable on an average per barrel of cement, by the Cottrell precipitation apparatus. Many plants, however, do not have sufficient potash in the raw mix to make its recovery profitable. Assuming that one-half of the cement operations in this country should put in recovery plants, the total available potash which could be recovered without any change in charges or operation would be about 40,000 tons. There is also a wet method of recovery by which the potash is leached out of the sludge, and converted into high-grade water soluble salt.

The average blast furnace charge producing pig iron from domestic ores and fluxes will yield about 12 pounds of potash per ton of pig iron. A portion of this is lost in the slag, but about 60 per cent is carried off in flue gases. The manganese ores run much higher in potash. The potential available recovery from these sources is estimated at 100,000 tons per year.

To encourage the installation of any process the operators would need the assurance of tariff protection for four or five years, by which time the industry would have become stable and self supporting. The by-product potash industry should be developed just as ammonium sulphate was developed as a by-product of the coking industry.

The extraction of potash from silicate rocks, on a commercial basis, is still embryonic. The principal sources in the South are from feldspar, from sericite, and from glauconite.

The feldspar deposits will be discussed later in this chapter. Potash is recovered from feldspar by smelting in a blast furnace with lime and coke. The slag is available for a special slow setting cement. Sixty-five per cent of the potash may be volatilized and recovered. The Georgia sericites are referred to in Chapter XVII. When a mixture composed of 70 per cent sericitic slate, 20 per cent limestone and 10 per cent salt is heated to approximately 1900° F., the potash content of the sericite is rendered soluble. It is leached out, dissolved as a chloride, and crystallized. This sericite is a hydrous silicate, which decomposes much more readily than orthoclase feldspar, and an assured market would result in rapid development of this source.

A new process for "breaking down" feldspar, and recovering potash alumina and silica has been proposed, and is reported as being installed to operate on the high potash feldspar of North Carolina.

Glauconite, or green sand marl, referred to in Chap. XXV, contains not only potash, but calcium phosphate and carbonate. High-grade glauconite carries up to 7 per cent potash. The sand is ground in ball mills to 200 mesh, and digested with milk of lime and live steam for one hour. The material is then filtered and evaporated with excess steam from the digestion operation. The residue makes an excellent brick. By developing a market for the by-product brick, this process would be able to operate against keener competition than any of the others. In addition to the glauconite marls, glauconite sand is found in Caddo parish, Louisiana, adjacent to the lignites, described in Chapter VI.

Recovery of potash from leucite and alunite is not discussed here because these materials do not occur in the Southern states. The other sources are molasses distillery waste, waste liquors from beet sugar manufacture, wool washings and other industrial wastes, wood ashes, and kelp.

Texas

The commercial possibilities of potash in West Texas have been voluminously treated in the press. Special bulletins to which the reader is referred for detailed information have been issued by the U. S. Geological Survey on the subject. The proximity of this potash to the proposed intercoastal canal on the Gulf border, makes possible a cheap barge haul to the entire Mississippi basin area.

The oil drilling which has so far located the beds, gives no information as to their thickness. A systematic core drilling of the area will be necessary to determine their extent and value. In certain counties, as Crane, the potash is encountered some 200 feet nearer the surface than in Regan, Ward, Loving, and other adjacent counties. There are now 48 potash wells in Texas and two in New Mexico. Of 217 quantitative samples taken, 117 yielded more than 1.5 per cent of potash, and 11, more than 5 per cent. The richest sample, containing 13.6 per cent of potash, equivalent to 21.3 per cent of soluble salts was from Regan county.

To quote from Dr. David White, Chief Geologist of the U. S. Geological Survey:

"The present trend of enormous increase in the consuming population which so rapidly swells our cities; of arrested growth of agricultural population and production, and of faltering, if not actually doubtful recuperation of our worn out or rapidly exhausting soils, constitute a menace to this nation of which the disastrous and far-reaching significance is not realized by a public habitually optimistic and blindly complacent. This is the most important economic problem of the United States. Beside it our war debts are trifling and ephemeral. Times have changed and are still changing. Either we must shift our economic basis back to the exportation of replaceable foodstuffs in larger amounts to maintain our trade balance or we must gravitate insensibly into the manufacture of raw materials, imported as well as domestic, on a plane of competition gradually approximating that of the Old World nations. The latter course will inevitably entail not only a continuous stern struggle for commercial prestige and independence, but a sacrifice of our standards of living as well. The productivity of American soils must be restored by every practicable means. Nothing that will lessen the cost of fertilizers or promote their wider and wise use on our lands can be overlooked or allowed to stand in the way.

"The interests of the public demand early and reliable information as to the exact thickness, extent, composition, centers of richness, availability, and possible utilization of the potash deposits in the Southwest. If these questions are not soon solved through private initiative, they should be pushed to adequate conclusion by the state or the Federal Government. Carefully distributed core drilling is imperatively needed."

Uses

The uses of potash in its various forms are as fertilizer, in soaps, cut glass, optical glass, incandescent light bulbs, explosives, fireworks, matches, medicine, meat packing, leather tanning, electroplating, photography, chemical industries, dyes, textile printing, disinfectants, and bleaches.

* * * * * *

Feldspar is a hard silicate, usually white or pink, occasionally blue or green, and much used in the manufacture of porcelain. When decomposed it becomes kaolin and is one of the principal sources of high-grade china clay. It is also of value for its potash content, as noted previously in this chapter.

In mining feldspar each lump is prepared by hand, and cobbed with a hammer, similar to the preparation of mica. It is frequently necessary to mine five tons of gangue to secure one ton of clean feldspar. Mica is a common associate of feldspathic rock, and the two are often allied products of the same operation. For white burning feldspar used in pottery, mica is objectionable. Iron is the most objectionable impurity; it being necessary to use granite buhrstones for grinding, to avoid introducing iron particles.

First-grade feldspar is practically pure. Second-grade

is 75 per cent pure, and more than 25 per cent quartz or other impurity is third grade. The feldspars are also classified according to their alkali constituents, as potash feldspar, soda feldspar, lime feldspar, and barium feldspar. In none of them does lime ever replace potash. When both lime and potash are present, an equal amount of soda is also in evidence.

Dental feldspar is specially hand picked, perfectly clear crystals free from all foreign material, which are then barrelled and sold to manufacturers of artificial teeth.

While there is no shortage of production in the United States, the big problem is standardizing the product. No two china formulas are alike. Freight rates also control available markets. A company making white ware from North Carolina or Maine or Canadian feldspar will take spar from another mine and say it is no good; yet after the chemist has analyzed it and corrected his formula, he may produce a finer grade of ware than before. Each particular spar has its own best combination. Selected North Carolina spar carries less silica and is purer. It is not soft enough for a glaze. Electrostatic separation has been tried for eliminating the mica which so persistently appears in the pegmatite dykes.

Uses

There appears no unanimity of opinion as to the proper size for grinding. One uses 60 mesh, another 90, and a third pays for extra grinding to 140 mesh. Specifications should be worked out for china, whiteware, pottery, porcelain, etc., with limits set, so that the various grades may be produced and prepared to meet these requirements. Certain of the high silica spars are used in glass manufacture. As an "onyx" glaze, feldspar finished slabs form table tops, counters, push buttons, mantels, pilasters, newel posts, and fancy stairways.

Virginia

Such feldspar as comes from Virginia is usually a co-product with mica, and goes into the pottery and scouring soap trade. At Moneta, Bedford county, about a car a day is shipped for these purposes. In Henry county is a similar deposit. At Amelia Court House, Amelia county, is a bed of soda spar, and several adjoining deposits of potash spar.

North Carolina

North Carolina produces two-thirds of the feldspar mined in the United States. There are many deposits not yet prospected, due to poor facilities for transportation. The great spar resources of the state lie in Madison, Buncombe, Jackson, Caswell, Macon, Cherokee, Clay, Yancey, Avery and Mitchell counties.

The northern half of Wilkes county has been found to carry large deposits of feldspar, on the upper waters of Reddie's and Mulberry Rivers, and the state geologist calls attention to high-grade potash spar five miles west of Waynesville, Haywood county.

The Black Mountain deposit near Asheville goes in large quantities to the scouring soap manufacturers. Near Bryson City, Swain county, is a 3500-acre deposit. Yellow Mountain, along Honey Suckle Ridge; Mitchell county, near Spruce Pine, on the Clinchfield Railway, is almost a solid mass of clear spar. This is located in the center of the producing district. Only one concern grinds the product, which it does not produce itself. The entire district from Black Mountain to Altapass, Mitchell county, is rich in potash spar.

A mill at Bristol, Virginia-Tennessee, brings its own spar in for grinding and shipment to the great pottery and ceramic centers of East Liverpool, Ohio, and Trenton, New Jersey. In fact, Bristol is a central receiving, sorting and shipping point.

Tennessee

At Del Rio and Burnett, in Cocke county, Tennessee, are spar deposits of high potash content. Aside from these and a few scattering deposits along the North Carolina line, there are no commercial deposits in Tennesse.

Georgia

The feldspars are widely distributed in Georgia, in association with mica and quartz. The principal production has so far been near Hiram, Paulding county, and in White and Rabun counties, for potash purposes. A large deposit, as yet unopened, is at McDonough, Henry county. The Central of Georgia Ry. lists commercial deposits of feldspar in 17 additional counties of Georgia along its lines.

Alabama

Feldspar has only been produced in a limited way in Clay county, Alabama, where it occurs at a considerable distance from the A. B. & C. R. R. In Chambers and Randolph counties along the Central of Georgia Ry. it occurs unaltered below water level and as kaolin on the surface.

Arkansas

Arkansas feldspar in Pulaski and Saline counties has never been developed.

Texas

There has recently been found along the M-K-T R. R.

in Texas a deposit of feldspar in the vicinity of Lagrange, Fayette county.

Uses

The basic use of feldspar is as a flux, to bind the clay and flint together, in the manufacture of porcelain. It is a principal ingredient, in the glaze of high-grade chinaware and tiling. It has been used in phonograph records, vulcanized rubber, and radio equipment. It goes into wood filler and heat resisting cooking utensils, high-grade glass, glazes and enamels; scouring soaps, stucco dash, dentistry, poultry grit, roofing material, and artificial marble. It is also used for surfacing interior concrete, and as a binder for emery and corundum wheels.

* * * * * *

Cinnabar, the ore of mercury, or quicksilver, occurs principally in the United States in Arizona, California, Idaho, Nevada, Oregon and Texas. California and Texas form the principal producers.

Unlike most other metals which must be smelted, cinnabar is treated at its source. Quicksilver may be decomposed and vaporized at a moderate heat. The process is exceedingly simple.

All that is necessary is the retort, an ample supply of ore, a tank of cold water, and plenty of good fuel. The ore is mined and crushed to one-quarter inch size. It is heated in the retort to 900° F., which breaks down the crystallization and releases the mercury in the form of a vapor which is drawn into the water-cooled condenser. It is then drawn off in liquid form into 75-pound flasks and transported to market.

Texas

The Texas deposits are distributed from the Mariscal

Mountains on the east to the Lajitas Mountains on the west, and from the Mexican boundary on the south to the Christmas Mountains on the north. The source of quicksilver is to be found in deep-lying crystalline rocks, such as granites. The anticlinal theory as applied to cinnabar was developed by Dr. J. A. Udden, State Geologist, and is discussed in Bulletin No. 1822, April, 1918, published by the University of Texas.

The difference between the anticlinal distribution of cinnabar ores and the anticlinal accumulation of bitumen is that mercurial fumes in solution were limited to previous conduits furnished by the rocks traversed, following joints, fissures, fault planes and contacts, and invading any pervious structure coming in their way. In impervious rocks the ore is confined to joint cracks, and occurs as fissure veins, measuring from a small fraction of an inch to several feet in thickness. In general the greatest amount of ore occurs in fissured and faulted parts of anticlines, domes and arrested monoclines.

In the Terlingua district of Texas, cinnabar is found in diverse kinds of rocks, ranging from limestone to sandstone, and in intrusive igneous rocks in these sediments. Two mines are in operation near the Shafter silver mine, in the Chisos Mountains. This district covers about 1200 square miles and is said to hold the most extensive reserves in the world. The effect of the Tariff Act of 1922 on quicksilver was immediately reacted on domestic production, and active prospecting has not only extended the limits of the Terlingua area, but what is far more important, has discovered coal of fine quality near the mines. The region is bare of trees and vegetation of all kinds, and the point of production is about 100 miles from the railroad. This unexpected solution of the fuel problem therefore is a direct result of the stimulation afforded the industry.

One company which has been producing rich cinnabar ore continuously for more than twenty-five years, has recently uncovered new bodies of ore in the lowest level of its mine, in the Terlingua district. The completion of the K. C. M. & O. R. R. from Alpine to Presidio, will bring railroad transportation within thirty miles of the operation.

The extent of the Terlingua quicksilver area has never been clearly defined; cinnabar ore appears in many outcroppings for several miles around, and has also been discovered on the Mexican side of the Rio Grande.

The principal sales market for quicksilver is San Francisco, although New York is the actual distributing point. It is shipped in wrought iron flasks, uncrated, 425 flasks constituting a carload. The Texas product goes principally to New York. Were it not for the tariff differential, the industry would be unable to compete with Italian and Spanish imports.

Uses

Quicksilver has a wide variety of uses, principally in explosives, drugs and chemicals. During the war lead azide was developed as a substitute for fulminates. A crystal of the dry azide is so sensitive that it will explode when brushed with a feather.

Mercuric sulphide is used as a vermillian pigment, the nitrate in the manufacture of felt hats, and metallic mercury in thermostats, thermometers, barometers, for amalgamating gold and silver ores, for anti-fouling paint in marine work, in boiler scale compounds, and dental work, and in mercury vapor lamps and electrical apparatus.

The invention of a new mercury vapor boiler promising great fuel economy and increased power station capacity will, if continued tests prove conclusive, create an increased demand for quicksilver. The present requirements of the boiler are stated to be 5¼ pounds of quicksilver per h.p., but it is hoped to decrease this amount to 3½ pounds per h.p. The coal consumption at this plant is reduced from 1.4 to 0.8 pounds of coal per k.w.h.

Chapter XXI

BUILDING STONES, MARBLE, GRANITE

The increasing cost of lumber, and the rapid depletion of the forests, have precipitated a demand for stone buildings. This demand is the more pronounced as people become cognizant of fire hazard. Excluding New England, the great marble and granite resources of the nation lie in the Appalachian mountains from the Potomac to the Tennessee rivers. Probably no country in the world offers its citizens so wide a choice of variety and source of building material for its public edifices, and its dwellings, as does the United States. From plain cold marble to massive granite, and from orbicular gabbro-diorite to serpentine and opaline granite, limestones and sandstones, the builder has but to choose, and a source will be found economically available.

Marble offers a wide diversity of color and texture. When free from metallic impurities it is also an excellent material for switchboards and electrical purposes. Imported marble does not stand exposure as does domestic stone, hence practically all the exterior and monumental marbles and at least 60 per cent of those used for interior finish are of domestic origin.

The principal wholesale market for marble is New York City. The product is rarely finished at or near the quarries, manufacturing and marble-dressing operations being widely scattered. Local markets would frequently be developed if finishing plants were operated near the source of supply. There is no restriction to such a practice anywhere in the United States except in New York

City, where for more than 20 years the local labor organizations have refused to handle finished marble.

The cut and sawn stone is sold by the square foot up to slabs 2 inches in thickness. In blocks it is sold by the cubic foot, which averages 175 to 200 pounds rough cut. The usual block is 4 feet by 5 feet by 7 feet. Deposits which will not quarry 2 feet by 3 feet by 5 feet do not pay to operate.

It is stated that the cost of sawing and finishing exceeds the block price, which in turn equals the average cost of freight and setting. So that with the builder's profit added the final purchaser pays 3½ to 4 times the quarry block price. This could be reduced if, as suggested above, freight charges and handling were lessened by the operation of finishing plants at or near the quarry.

Both the marble and granite industries have suffered intermittently from labor troubles, but in 1922 the "American Plan" was widely adopted. This permits the training of apprentices to replenish the ranks of skilled workmen, and its adoption has resulted in from 24 per cent to 177 per cent increased production in the various building stones.

Serpentine, sandstone and **limestone** building block have also reflected improved labor conditions and shown marked increase in consumption.

Important and valuable by-products of these quarries are paving block, rip-rap, and crushed stone. A radical change in block pavement construction has been effected by heating the sand for asphalt mastic, which is then mixed and poured hot into the joints. By this method an impervious joint is made, and a cemented union of the blocks results. This has brought Belgian block pavement into renewed favor for heavy traffic.

Virginia

Granites or granite gneisses are found throughout the Piedmont section of Virginia. The chief quarrying centers are around Richmond, Petersburg and Fredericksburg, although the occurrences are widely distributed. A very hard dark granite is found from Petersburg to Burkeville, in Dinwiddie and Nottaway counties, and at Buena and Winston, in Culpeper county. A light gray granite is quarried at points in Henrico and Spotsylvania counties.

Black marble at Harrisonburg, Rockingham county; white and green striped marble at Alta Vista, Campbell county; green marble at Goose Creek, Loudon county, and pink marble at Gate City, Scott county, add to Virginia's building stone resources. The Cambrian sandstones along the western slope of the Blue Ridge are capable of unlimited development.

Pulaski county sandstone is shipped for building purposes all over the state. The quarries near Fredericksburg, Stafford county, supply a light gray sandstone which was used in the construction of many public buildings in Washington. Other sandstone deposits exist in Augusta county. A beautiful green marble also occurs at Virgilina, Halifax county; and brown sandstone at Manassas, Prince William county, and Kermit, Scott county.

West Virginia

The building stones of West Virginia are many and varied. They have been described in Vol. IV of the West Virginia Geological Survey.

North Carolina

North Carolina is rich in quarries which produce a wide choice of building and monumental stone. Of special importance are the epidosites or epidote granite of Madison county, the leopardite of Mecklenburg county and the orbicular gabbro-diorite of Yadkin county. These rare and beautiful stones take a high polish and are without competition in their class.

The principal granites of North Carolina have been listed as follows: Medium grained green, and coarse grained pink granite, in Wilson county.

Light gray, and granite gneiss, in Buncombe and Henderson counties.

Dark gray granite in Vance county.

White, pink and cream granites from Rowan county.

Greatest of all granite areas in the state is Mount Airy, Surry county, where a white granite is produced, specked with biotite. This stone is of uniform texture and capable of adaptation to any form.

Wake, Carteret, Rockingham, Granville, Franklin, Johnston, Nash, Madison, Stanly, Davidson, Alexander, Mecklenburg, Gaston, Cleveland, Davis, Polk, Warren, Anson and McDowell counties all have large and available deposits of granite.

The Bailey, Nash county granite is gray, and the Neverson, Wilson county granite is pink. Both are good for large columns and interior decorations. Much of the Nash county area is undeveloped. At Harris, Rutherford county, along the Clinchfield Railroad is a mammoth monolith of granite covering over 20 acres, free from overburden. This stone is an excellent quality and suited to monumental purposes.

Marble is quarried at Murphy, Cherokee county, and occurs in McDowell, Mitchell and Swain counties. At Intermont and Linville Falls, along the Burke-McDowell county border, marble of extraordinary whiteness occurs. It is highly crystalline and takes a high polish.

Sandstones are quarried with varying demand in Lee, Anson, Chatham, Orange, Rockingham, and Stokes counties; and serpentine in Ashe, Buncombe, Caldwell, Clay, Forsyth, Wake, Orange, Stokes, Surry, Wilkes and Yancey counties. Other building stones of quartzite, pegmatite and sandstone are found along the Clinchfield R. R. in McDowell, Mitchell and Yancey counties.

In the neighborhood of Bennett, Chatham county, are three deposits of rhyolite convenient to the railroad. This material is suitable for all kinds of building and crushed stone and concrete.

With such an imposing array of building materials, it is logical to inquire why greater development and wider markets have not been attained. An illustration is had in the case of the Rolesville granite on the border of Franklin and Nash counties, which was opened in 1893 and given railroad service in 1922. This was equally true of the Mount Airy and the Rowan county deposits, famous for generations, but unavailable commercially until transportation facilities were afforded. Freight rates from the mountain districts of Cherokee, Swain and McDowell counties have retarded development of the marbles found in those counties.

South Carolina

South Carolina also produces excellent granite at Rion, Rockton and Winnsboro, Fairfield county. Chesterfield, Laurens, Edgefield and Lexington counties have substantial deposits of which the Laurens county granite is harder than any others in the state. Spartanburg citiens have recently opened up the Pacolet quarry which was formerly operated for crushed stone, with a view to cutting dimension stone at greater depths if the dry seams are found to disappear. This dry seam condition also affects the gneissic rock in Greenville and Pickens counties, where the output is devoted to ballast and concrete. The Southern Railway reports gray granite at Rock Hill, York county, and Kershaw, Kershaw county, and light gray marble at Westminster, Oconee county.

Georgia

The building and monumental stones of Georgia have long occupied an important place in the trade. Georgia marble production approximates two million dollars yearly, but practically none of it is finished in the state. The quarries in DeKalb county, nine miles east of Stone Mountain, are especially adapted to cutting dimensional stone of irregular form.

At Rockmart, Polk county, is a light cream colored limestone sold as Caen stone. The Elberton, Elbert county, granite is a beautifully marked gray stone, easily worked.

Brown and white marble are produced at Varnell's Station, Whitfield county. The *Directory of Commercial Minerals*, published by the Central of Georgia Railway, lists Clarke, Clayton, Coweta, Crawford, Fulton, Haralson, Harris, Henry, Jasper, Lamar, Meriweather, Monroe, Morgan, Muscogee, Newton, Oconee, Pike, Putnam, Spalding, Taylor and Upson counties as having available granites; and Chattooga and Floyd counties for marble; from which it may be seen that no shortage of raw material exists in the state.

Roughly it may be said that the granite area, excluding the ten northwestern counties, includes that part of Georgia north of the "Fall Line," which extends from Augusta through Macon to Columbus.

The marble belt of Georgia is about 60 miles long and one to three miles wide, along the L. & N. R. R., in Fannin, Gilmer, Pickens and Cherokee counties. These beds are over 200 feet in thickness, and vary from very coarse to very fine grained.

Two miles from Holly Springs, Cherokee county, is a deposit of serpentine which is found in contact with talc. It occurs in the form of a lens, about 600 feet in length and 150 feet in width, and is evidently an igneous intrusion.

Near Cuthbert, Randolph county, Georgia, is a fossiliferous crystallized limestone formed by the action of spring water and resulting in distinctive types of travertine differing from the imported material of the same name, frequently of volcanic origin. In trade it is frequently known as "Mexican onyx."

Kentucky

Sandstone, both cut and sawn, is produced in Kentucky in Rockcastle and Rowan counties. It is very fine grained and is used for mantles, and burial vaults. Harlan, Knox and Whitley counties have similar deposits which have duly been worked for rough construction.

The limestone quarries of Warren county produce limestone for both building and monumental purposes. Although much broken stone comes from Kentucky, the instances mentioned appear to comprise the dimensioned stone resources.

Tennessee

There are granite deposits in Carter county, Tennessee, along the narrow gauge railroad between Johnson City and Cranberry, which have the appearance of Milford granite and offer promise sufficient to induce development.

The Cumberland Mountain sandstone along the N. C. & St. L. R. R. is a creamy pink and is very popular. It is cut in thin blocks like brick, and dressed on the ground to fit.

More marble is shipped from East Tennessee than any other state. It goes into wainscoting, tiling, counters, table tops, etc. It is found in all shades from light gray to dark red, and is easily worked, and accessible to the railroads. It takes a high polish, has great strength, and competes successfully with any other field. The Holston variety, quarried in Knox county, is best known, but there is an excellent undeveloped deposit in Davidson county. There is opportunity for the introduction of modern quarry methods.

The Lincoln county marble has never been adequately opened up. It is operated near Flintville, and the product takes a fine polish. It is cut into special sized ornamental building brick and sold as "polished brick." A similar deposit is found in a cave near Lynchburg, Moore county, where the roof and floor are of solid marble. There is a good opportunity with this type of marble to specialize in this form of building material which finds a ready market in Chicago and other distant cities.

At Crab Orchard, Cumberland county, gray marble

occurs. Buff and brown sandstone of extreme hardness and fine grain are found in Putnam, Cumberland, Overton and Fentress counties along the Tenn. Cen. R. R. There is also one quarry for sandstone building block in Franklin county, operated for construction at the University of the South.

Alabama

The Alabama marble deposits in Talledega county have been extensively worked. The public buildings of Birmingham are largely constructed of it. It competes favorably with the East Tennessee product. These deposits extend into Shelby county to the west, and reappear in Lee county to the southeast.

Several grades and colors are operated at Centerville, Bibb county along the Mobile and Ohio R. R. The buff stone takes a high polish and can be cut into 4 to 5 ton dimension stone. There is a large quantity available and undeveloped.

Near Dudleyville, Tallapoosa county, a serpentine outcrop gives indications of a considerable quantity of "Verde antique."

One of the largest quarries in the South is the limestone quarry at Rockwood, Franklin county. Sandstone building block is used locally, and shipped to other states, from Hartsells, Morgan county.

Reference is made to Bulletin No. 28 of the Alabama Geological Survey for detailed description of the Alabama limestones and building stones.

Mississippi

On the Laurel branch of the G. & S. I. R. R. in Mississippi, is a hill three-quarters of a mile wide and three-quarters of a mile long on the railroad side of Leaf River, which is easily accessible to transportation. This hill is a pseudo-granite which takes a high polish, and forms a valuable asset to the state.

In northern Mississippi a white sandstone outcrops along the Illinois Central R. R. in enormous quantities. The bluffs are 40 feet high, and bedded 2 to 6 feet in thickness. This stone has been tested, and found to have a crushing strength of 12,000 pounds per square inch.

Hinds, Rankin, Franklin, Jefferson and Claiborne counties have available gray sandstone which shows a crushing strength of 4000 to 5000 pounds per square inch.

The Vicksburg limestone, which extends across Mississippi from Vicksburg to Waynesboro, is found in buff and in blue-gray, which takes a high polish and makes a beautiful, ornamental stone.

Arkansas

Batesville granite has made Arkansas building stone famous. Similar deposits of greenish gray, almost pure feldspar, taking high polish, are largely undeveloped, in Pulaski and Saline counties, Arkansas.

Magazine, Logan county; Hartford, Sebastian county, and Cutterfield, Hot Spring county, all have building stone deposits but slightly developed, along the lines of the Rock Island and the Missouri Pacific Railroads. Small stone is cut at Searcy, White county, from local sandstones.

Independence county marble is strong and quarries well, but does not take a high polish.

Louisiana

Building stone in Louisiana is at a premium. At Pine

Prairie, Evangeline parish, along the Rock Island and the Oakdale & Gulf Railways, is a good marble which is in statewide demand.

The Winnfield marble in Winn parish is of high grade and value as limestone, but of slight value for building stone on account of its seaminess. By comparatively little stripping, however, it could be exposed for over a half mile, and further prospecting might very possibly develop sound beds. On either side of the Winnfield quarry, are bluffs of calcareous sandstone with pyrite concretions which would mar it for ornamental stone, but would be of no detriment for general construction purposes.

Texas

A specially high-grade of marble, which has been shipped to great distances for public buildings, is found at San Saba, San Saba county, Texas, on the G. C. & S. Fe R. R. Jones, Lampasas and Leander counties all supply limestone in dimensioned block. The Leander county stone is sold as "American Cream White Lens."

A very beautiful stone with numerous oval inclusions of blue quartz, which is very hard and takes a superb polish, is worked in Llano county, and sold as "Opaline granite." Gray granite is also found in Llano and Mason counties, and the red granite of which the state capitol is built, comes from Mason, Llano, Burnet and Gillespie counties.

The Limestone of Williamson county, similar to the San Saba marble, is of uniform texture and fine grain. Throughout central and west Texas are many limestones which quarry in large blocks. Red sandstone occurs in

Ward county and is extensively used in trimmings for brick and stone buildings.

Uses

In addition to building construction, these marbles, granites, sandstones and limestones find outlet in monuments, fountains, mantels, chimneys, park ornaments, railings, steps and pavements, sea walls and abutments, dams, and reservoirs; and the by-product trim goes into concrete, paving blocks, curbing, macadam, and similar uses.

CHAPTER XXII

SAND, GLASS SAND, MOLDING SAND, MOLDING CLAY, GRAVEL, CHERT

Incoherent detrital rock material, coarser than dust, and usually less than one-quarter inch in diameter is classed as sand. Quartz is a major constituent. Its application to such industries as building, glass, molding or polishing serves to classify it, according to its inherent qualities, for particular requirements.

Sand is exceeded in value of annual production among the non-metallics, only by oil, natural gas, coal and stone. Each year there are used in the United States five million tons of molding sand, two million tons of glass sand, a half-million tons of furnace sand, and a quarter-million tons of locomotive sand.

Uses

Glass sand must be of medium grain, 98 to 100 per cent silica, and less than 1 per cent iron oxide. When occurring in certain forms it shades into tripoli (vide Chapter II), and is used for wood fillers, scouring soap and chemical processes. It must also pass 20 mesh; 80 per cent must pass 40 mesh; and 20 per cent must pass 60 mesh.

It has been frequently stated that the three glass sand districts of the United States were in Illinois, Pennsylvania and West Virginia. There are, however, many deposits in the South, of large extent and superior quality. Lack of standardization and inadequate equipment have caused frequent changes of ownership and loss of markets to many operators. The flint glass chemist is careful to eliminate any iron sand, while certain bottle manufacturers can use it without disadvantage. Glass sand carries many trade names, such as silica sand, quartz sand, flint or silex, the difference being mainly in the fineness of the grinding. Flint glass sand is usually 20 mesh. Silica brick and scouring pastes take 40 to 60 mesh. Handsoaps and scouring powders use 90 to 250 mesh, while extremely fine-grained silica, passing 250-500 mesh brings a high price as paint pigment. The 120-140 mesh is the principal demand. Prices range from $2 per ton for the coarser grades to $30 per ton for washed and dried 500-mesh product. Crushing the crude rock is expensive. It is frequently calcined and quenched with water to assist in the breaking up. Only the purest grades will stand the high freights to distant points, which are necessary because of losses in transportation in carload lots.

Lump silica from pure quartzite is used in the electric furnace in the manufacture of ferrosilicon. Such material must be free from lime, phosphorus and arsenic. Ganister rock is a term frequently applied to high refractory siliceous rock, usually 97 per cent or better of silica, and 1 to 1½ per cent alumina, which is suitable for furnace linings. Flint pebbles are used for grinding in pebble mills.

The resulting green tint from iron, when in small quantities, is neutralized in glass by the addition of manganese, selenium, nickel or cobalt. Magnesia causes a higher melting point and is therefore undesirable.

Virginia

The glass sand resources of Virginia have been reviewed by the late Dr. Thomas L. Watson in Vol. II, No.

10, of the Journal of the American Ceramic Society. The Southern Railway exhibits glass sand and quartzite from Mendota, Washington county, Orange, Orange county, and Amelia Court House, Amelia county; the Clinchfield Railway reports development in Clinch Mountain, at Kermit, Scott county; the Norfolk & Western Railway, nine miles west of Salem, Roanoke county, and the Chesapeake & Ohio R. R. at Goshen, Rockbridge county, also report available deposits.

Other deposits are found near Bristol, Washington county; Balcony Falls, Rockbridge county; Greenville, Augusta county, and Stapleton Mills, Amherst county.

The Norfolk Southern R. R. calls attention to the glass sands at Cape Henry, in Princess Anne county. They lie above water level and are available to both rail and water transportation, with cheap oil by steamer. This location offers unlimited raw material for the glass industry.

West Virginia

West Virginia is the center of supply for its own 65 glass plants as well as those in Eastern Ohio and Western Pennsylvania. The Baltimore and Ohio R. R. on both the main line and many of its branches traverses large areas of high-grade deposits. West of Corinth, Preston county, is a medium-grade glass sand with pebbles suitable for sand blast. East of Charleston on the Chesapeake & Ohio is another glass sand deposit of plate glass grade. Vol. IV of the West Virginia Geological Survey deals extensively with these and lesser deposits. The counties of importance in the industry are Monongalia, Morgan, Summers, Preston, Randolph, Taylor and Upshur.

North Carolina

North Carolina practice in mining feldspar and mica has been to leave the quartzite on the dump. Much of this quartzite has recently been found to be easily crushable, and 99.9 per cent silica. The large quantities of this by-product material in Gaston, Cherokee, Avery, Mitchell and Yancey counties, offer inducement for glass manufacture in connection with nearby fuels, or for shipment to existing plants at advantageous freight rates. A saccharoidal quartz sand is also shown by the Southern Railway, from Asheville, Buncombe county.

South Carolina

Most of the silica sand of South Carolina is too fine grained for plate glass purposes, as most of it will pass more than 60 per cent through 60 mesh. Near Dixiana, in Lexington county, on the south side of the Congaree River, is a deposit of fair grade. Good sand for concrete purposes is found in Lexington and Beaufort counties. The United States Geological Survey also reports available glass sand at Blackville and Ulmers, Barnwell county, and Pee Dee, Clarendon county.

Kentucky

Carter, Hardin and Hart counties, Kentucky, along the Chesapeake and Ohio R. R. have abundant supplies of sandstone suitable for crushing. Window glass sand is shipped from Olive Hill, Lawton and Tygart, Carter county. Other deposits, not developed, are along Beechy Creek, Calloway county, and Ludlow, Kenton county. South of West Point, Hardin county, and also near Tip Top, in the same county, along the Illinois Central R. R. is a sand rock which is crushed for glass making.

Tennessee

The Tennessee deposits in operation are at Black Fox, Bradley county; Tazewell, Claiborne county, and Cleveland, Bradley county. Much of this is shipped to Chattanooga, for manufacture with by-product gas.

Reserves are found in the saccharoidal sandstones of Benton county, and the friable sandstones of Anderson, Blount, Knox, Montgomery and Sullivan counties. The Tennessee Central R. R. also reports good glass sand along its line in Overton, Putnam and Cumberland counties.

The question has been raised, and opens a vista worthy of research why it would not be practicable not only at Chattanooga, but at other points in the South where by-product gas is available, to manufacture glass pig, and ship it to various points for ultimate fabrication.

Georgia

The oil refineries and storage at Savannah, Chatham county, Georgia, as a source of gas fuel, make the sand deposits along the Savannah and Ogeechee rivers of more than passing interest. The rail and water facilities of the port are additional advantages for glass manufacture.

North and east of Blakely, Early county, is a six-foot bed of yellow sand, underlain with an extensive bed of white silica sand of glass grade.

Four miles south of Kite, Johnson county, is a four-acre deposit of window glass and bottle grade sand six feet in thickness.

Sugar Valley, Gordon county, and Lumber City, Telfair county, have glass sand in the Southern Railway exhibit.

At Rocky Face, Whitfield county, is sand rock suitable for bottle glass.

There is no company south of Tennessee which manufactures glass bottles, although one Southern soft-drink manufacturer brings 800 carloads of bottles annually from North of the Ohio River.

Whenever glass or pottery sand finer than 120 mesh is required, all present methods of separation are too slow. To meet this difficulty a whirlpool separator, operated by centrifugal force, has been placed on the market by Dr. R. T. Stull, formerly with the Central of Georgia Railway.

Dr. A. V. Henry, head of the ceramics department of Georgia Tech, recently stated that the lime-silicate sand in virtually all of south Georgia is ideally fitted for glass making. It has recently been discovered that the sand in Okeefeenokee Swamp is of first grade for plate glass. This deposit extends from the southern part of Ware county into Baker, Columbia and Milton counties, Florida. Deposits are also noted at Zenith, Crawford county, Butler and Howard, Taylor county, east of Columbus, in Muscogee county, near Dublin, Lawrence county, and along the Savannah River near Augusta, in Richmond county.

Tift Hill, just east of Albany, Dougherty county, has an area of 400 acres and is estimated to contain fourteen million cubic yards of sand, from 10 to 40 feet deep. Analyses made at Georgia Tech show 98.01 per cent silica, 0.27 per cent iron oxide, and compare it favorably with glass sand from Illinois, West Virginia and Pennsylvania.

Florida

Glass making has never received serious consideration

in Florida, until about 1922, although its proximity to Mexican and Texas oil fields by water, and its vast deposits of peat for producer-gas offer many inducements. A large plant is now in operation in Jacksonville, with both rail and water connection.

Glass sand occurs as noted above, in three northern counties, in the Okeefeenokee Swamp, and also in Marion county, along Lake Weir. The dunes in Escambia county, near Pensacola, are clean white sand almost devoid of iron and over 99 per cent silica. Glass sand and high-grade concrete sand are screened and double washed at Lake Wales, Polk county.

Alabama

Glass making in Alabama is merely a matter of bringing by-product gas and raw materials together. A good silica sand occurs at Piedmont, Calhoun county; around Russellville, Franklin county, and at Gadsden, Etowah county. Just outside of Birmingham is a fine deposit of sandstone which is crushed and used at Gate City, Jefferson county.

In St. Clair county, near Odenville, along the S. A. L. Railway is a sand deposit said to be the lowest in iron of any in the South.

Mississippi

In Smith county, Mississippi, where the Laurel branch of the G. & S. I. R. R. crosses Leaf River, is a deposit of glass sand.

On Horn and Cat Islands, in Mississippi Sound, are excellent glass sands of almost unlimited quantity. These islands are about 12 miles from the mainland, which point in turn is about 75 miles from the nearest Louisiana gas fields and the Mississippi lignites.

In the Southern part of Washington county, below Greenville, is another low-iron sand, along the Y. & M. V. R. R., and not far from the Mississippi River. At numerous points along Pearl River, in Hinds county, and one mile south of the Tennessee River in Tishomingo county, are other deposits.

Higginbotham Hollow, near the Noxubee-Winston county line, is a canyon whose erosion shows about 60 feet of remarkably pure glass sand with about 20 foot overburden. This offers a steam shovel or drag-scraper loading proposition.

Louisiana

There is much activity in Louisiana over prospective glass plants. The question of making glass pig is receiving attention. Two old sea terraces carry pure silica sand, one of which is sharp grained and the other rounded, the one being Cretaceous, the other Quarternary.

For a considerable period, glass sand was shipped from Eagle, Washington parish, north of Bogalusa, to the glass works at Shreveport, but the difficulty of getting box cars to keep it clean caused the operation to close down. Increased developments in the Monroe gas field make it possible to reopen this deposit. Also, the second largest glass plant in the world is now in operation at Shreveport, so located because of the natural gas supply. Another new plant was recently installed at Monroe, Ouachita parish. The future for the industry is, therefore, bright.

Arkansas

Glass plants are in operation at Fort Smith and Texarkana, Arkansas. Vast deposits of exceptionally pure sand are found along the Missouri Pacific R. R. in the White River valley, and notably at Guion, Izard county. The Saline county deposits have been intermittently operrated. Pine Bluff, Jefferson county, Crowley's Ridge, Green county, and various areas in Carroll and Madison counties are also recommended. The great sandstone formations of Arkansas are rich in silica sand of low iron content.

Texas

The only glass plant in Southeast Texas is at Three Rivers, Live Oak county. There are numerous occurrences of glass sand along the Gulf in Refugio county.

Beginning at Tordia Hill, in southwest Wilson county, is a strip of pure sandstone running northeast and southwest for 25 miles into Gonzales county. It is several hundred feet wide and forms the hill tops. About 100 feet below this is a similar bed. Natural gas is found 25 miles west.

Along the G. C. & S. Fe Ry. at Santa Ana, Coleman county, is an almost inexhaustible supply testing more than 99 per cent silica, alongside of a plentiful supply of natural gas. It is locally known as "pack sand."

On the C. R. I. & P. R. R., near Amarillo, Potter county, a glass sand deposit was opened up, but later compelled to shut down, due to adverse freight rates. The deposit is of excellent window-glass quality. At Denison, Grayson county, is another undeveloped deposit.

Uses

In addition to its use for direct glass manufacture, silica sand is also found for waterproofs and paper, emery cloth, pottery glaze, scouring and filter mediums, paint and wood filler, valve grinding, putty, metal polishes, mechanical erasers and rubbers, enamels, statuary, stucco, fine cement work, foundry facings and partings, asphalt and composition flooring and roofing, nail polishes, dentrifices and chemical processes. A helpful article on glass sand requirements will be found in Vol. LXXIII of the proceedings of the A. I. M. & M. E.

* * * * * *

Next in importance from point of consumption, and of far greater importance from the standpoint of scarcity of supply, are **molding sand** and **molding clay**. The molding sand resources of the great glacial lake beds of the North and East are approaching depletion. About seven million tons per year are required. Foundries making heavy steel castings desire a sand high in silica and fusing point, with coarse grain. Those making smaller castings use a finer grain. Some molding sands have a natural bond, thus reducing the addition of fire clay, molasses, water and other items of expense in handling and preparation. A good molding sand needs mud and aluminous material such as is found along the upper terraces of many rivers on the west side of the Alleghany Mountains. It must also be sufficiently porous to permit the escape of gases. Sands for foundry work are obtained either from siliceous sandstone or unconsolidated deposits of sand, gravel and sandy loam. They are known as molding sand, core sand, steel sand, fire sand and parting sand.

West Virginia

In West Virginia these sands are found along the Ohio and Monongahela valleys. South of Moundsville, Marshall county, and near Gallipolis, Mason county, are active operations. In Marion and Monongalia counties the upper river terraces are worked from Point Marion to Fairmont and Grafton. In many cases, however, as at Van Voorhis, Washington county, Pennsylvania, on the lower Monongahela River, the property is more valuable for building lots than for molding sand.

Virginia

To meet a demand for additional sources of molding sand, the Virginia Geological Survey has recently issued a report covering that state. The principal supplies are in the Coastal Plain, where the sands are equal to the best. Limited areas, also, of the upper river terraces are good. Transportation facilities are excellent.

Several deposits are worked along the R. F. & P. R. R. between Alexandria and Richmond. Most of this, like the sand at Woodford, Caroline county, and Petersburg, Dinwiddie county, is shipped to local foundries.

North Carolina

North Carolina has recently undertaken a survey for the purpose of assisting foundry interests in locating new deposits. Already a good sand has been found along the upper terraces of the Neuse River, near Selma, Johnston county. Others are being tried out from Hamlet, Richmond county, and Winston-Salem, Forsyth county.

South Carolina

The only South Carolina deposit which has come to the writer's attention is located near Columbia, Richland county.

Kentucky

There are excellent foundry sands in Crittendon county, Kentucky, but only one line of railroad in the county, remote from the deposits. Along the Chesapeake & Ohio R. R., however, from Maysville, Mason county, to Mentor, Campbell county, is molding sand and clay of such high grade it is shipped all over the United States.

These deposits extend east to Ashland, Boyd county, along the Chesapeake & Ohio R. R., but have not been developed to the east of Maysville.

Tennessee

Large areas of suitable molding sand are found in Western Tennessee. Extensive shipments are made from Bruceton, Carroll county and Saulsbury, Hardeman county, and sixty different localities are now being tested by the Bureau of Standards.

Florida

The State Geologist of Florida says in his annual report for 1922: "The possibility of locating deposits of molding sands should not be overlooked."

It is probable that the Lake region of the state will show available deposits. Other likely areas are along the Escambia and Apalachicola rivers.

Georgia

Only a small quantity of furnace-grade sand has been produced in Georgia. South of Albany, Dougherty county, along Flint River there are deposits of fine-grained, loamy sand which is used in local foundries, replacing that formerly shipped in from the North.

Shipments are also made to local foundries from Yellow River, near Almon, Newton county.

Undeveloped deposits also occur in beds from ten to

fifteen feet thick from Portersdale northward to the Central of Georgia Railway in the same county.

At Hephzibah, Richmond county, lying below a paper and pottery clay, and topped by a good firebrick clay, is a ten-foot bed of molding sand.

Alabama

In Alabama, at the junction of the W. of A. and the L. and N. R. Rs., near Selma, Dallas county, is an undeveloped bed of promising quality.

Mississippi

Five miles south of Hattiesburg, Forrest county, Mississippi, between that city and Richburg, is an iron and brass molding sand on the N. O. & N. E. R. R., which has proven of exceptional value. A similar undeveloped deposit is reported in the same county at Petal, just north of Hattiesburg. The state geologist reported in 1923: "In several parts of the state molding sands occur in large quantity." In Smith county is also a deposit of high-grade which has been used to a limited extent in local foundries.

Arkansas—Texas

Limited quantities are produced from Arkansas and Texas for local consumption, but no large deposits have as yet been located.

Vol. LXXIII of the Proceedings of the A. I. M. & M. E. contains an article of value on requirements of molding sand.

Standard methods for testing molding sands have been evolved, so that flaws may be prevented in castings, and proper venting qualities obtained.

Uses

Sand, in general, for cement, concrete, sand blasting, fertilizer filler, engine sand, roofing, bedding stock cars, coal washing processes, filling for golf courses and tennis courts and road building is found in all the Southern states.

The era of good road building has brought many of these deposits to the front, not only for use in the construction of these roads, but to be hauled over them. The Cat and Horn Island sands in Mississippi Sound are used for sand blasting, in removing scale from steel plate, in shipyard work, in preparing bridges for painting, and in scouring marble and similar edifices.

Alabama

At Chehaw, Macon county, Alabama, is a coarse, sharp sand which after washing is excellent for concrete construction. Good gravel is also screened from the same deposit.

At Arrowhead, sixteen miles from Montgomery, Montgomery county, is a similar deposit.

Mississippi—Louisiana

Many sand lime brick plants have sprung up in the movement for better buildings, as at New Orleans. Along the New Orleans and Great Northern R. R. in Mississippi, Monclure, Hines county; Hopewell, Copiah county; Monticello, Lawrence county; and Condron, Marion county, are deposits of sand and gravel, which are shipped in trainload lots to New Orleans for concrete and building construction and road ballast.

North Carolina

The sand banks of Lenoir county, North Carolina,

about one mile south of Kinston, are 20 feet deep, with a gravel bed which is being sold for road construction purposes, and shipped over the A. C. L. R. R.

Florida

Sand and **gravel** are widely scattered over the greater part of Florida, and are being scientifically utilized in all forms of construction. So also is the coquina rock of the St. Johns county area in that state.

Mississippi

The extensive erosion of Coastal Plain formations and their subsequent deposition as sands, along stream channels, has provided nearly every county in Mississippi with available sand for concrete, for road building, sand lime brick and mortar.

* * * * * *

Gravel, like construction and building sand, is abundantly found in most of the Southern states. In Virginia, exclusive of railroad ballast, about 1½ million tons are produced annually, from over twenty counties; North Carolina produces about ¾ of a million tons, from twenty-five counties; South Carolina and Georgia approximately half a million tons each from all parts of both states.

An interesting deposit of sand and gravel lies in Chesterfield county, Virginia. It covers some 60 acres to a depth of twelve feet, with a stream of water running down the center of the field.

One mile north of Cheraw on Huckleberry Creek in South Carolina, between the Atlantic Coast Line R. R. and Pee Dee River is a 700-acre deposit of gravel and sand about 30 feet in thickness of which about 150 acres are reported as good ballast gravel.

Arkansas and Alabama produce around 900,000 tons per annum, while Kentucky, Tennessee, Louisiana, Mississippi and Texas range from 1½ to three million tons yearly.

In Tishomingo county, Mississippi, the Tennessee River gravels lie from 30 to 75 feet thick, for a distance of several miles along the Southern Railway. Great gravel beds have been opened up by the G. & S. I. R. R. in Simpson county, Mississippi, and also along the G. M. & N. R. R. The Central of Georgia Railway reports gravel beds along its lines in 10 counties of Georgia and two in Alabama. The S. A. L. and the A. C. L. R. Rs. have similar supplies in the Carolinas.

Thus, we see that, excepting only Southeast Texas, there is no shortage of road building or concrete gravel anywhere in the South.

* * * * * *

Chert, or flint, is very hard, compact, siliceous material usually occurring with limestone. It is known by various local names as "cement gravel," "cement clay," etc. When found with dolomite it is in the form of nodules, which as the dolomite weathers, become a residual product. It possesses excellent binding quality, but becomes excessively dusty under drought and heavy travel.

Granites, marbles, gneisses and traprock all serve as road building material in sections where they abound.

Virginia

Any hard broken stone which will bind well is known as "road metal." Along the R. F. & P. R. R. in Spotsylvania county, Virginia, gravel is supplied for road building and washed for ballast, concrete and locomotive sand. About 930 acres are held in reserve, wholly undeveloped. The state has ample reserves for all requirements.

North Carolina—South Carolina

These materials occur west of the "Fall Line" in North and South Carolina, in massive, gravel and nodular formations. At Lillington, Harnett county, on the Norfolk Southern R. R. two grades of sand gravel are produced, one for ballast and washed sand for concrete; the other a clay gravel exactly right in mixture of sand, clay and gravel for road building. It is used all over the state. Other deposits are found along the A. C. L. R. R. in southeast Harnett county.

Pure chert does not occur in South Carolina. There is much residual quartz from decomposed granite, but the crushed stone from the granite quarries is superior. The Lafayette gravels occur along the Seneca River in Anderson county.

In Barnwell county, near Dunbarton, on the A. C. L. R. R. and along the Savannah River on the C. & W. C. R. R. are cement gravel pits which ship their product north and east. This is an area of quartz glacial gravel and cement clay.

In the northeastern part of the state, Dillon, Dillon county, and between Bennettsville and Marlboro, in Marlboro county, are extensive deposits of hard sharp gravel along the A. C. L. R. R. The iron oxide content makes these admirable for bonding metal. There is ample water for washing, and topographical conditions are good for excavating, with gravity haul to the railroad. There are about 5000 acres in the Bennettsville deposit, with an average depth of 20 feet, of which 50 per cent is the highest type sharp gravel and the balance the best grade of building sand.

Georgia

All Georgia, north of the "Fall Line," extending from Augusta to Columbus, has widely distributed chert and traprock. The latter, also known as diabase, is produced near Talbotton, Talbot county, and Newnan, Coweta county, on the Central of Georgia and the A. & W. P. R. Rs. The Lee county cherts are for the most part inaccessible to transportation. In northwest Georgia, along the Central of Georgia Railway in Catoosa, Chattooga, Floyd and Polk counties chert is found in abundance.

Florida

The hard marls of Florida shade into broken coquina rock and chert. They are used for road surfacing in Volusia and southern Putnam counties. The Miami and Palm Beach limestones are used extensively for ballast on the F. E. C. Ry. Flint rock residual from dolomite deposits is crushed and used as concrete aggregate and railroad ballast. This is found principally west of Ocala, near Williston, Levy county, and is used by the A. C. L. R. R. from St. Petersburg, north.

Alabama

One of the prominent Alabama sources of road material is at Rice's Spur, Macon county, on the W. of A. Ry. This is a cement gravel and ships ten to fifteen cars a day for highway purposes to Alabama, Georgia and Florida.

A similar and undeveloped deposit of chert, clay and gravel is found at Milstead, Macon county. Good sand for concrete is also available.

Along the Frisco lines at Sulligent, Lamar county, and Winfield, Marion county, ballast and road metal are shipped East and West.

The A. C. L. R. R. secures ballast from the gravel beds of the Alabama River near Mount Lowery.

Washed sand is prepared at Cook's, Montgomery county; the largest single operation on cement gravel is at Cantalou, Montgomery county, which loads forty to fifty cars per day.

Near Bessemer is a 40-acre chert tract which supplies Jefferson county with road material at a royalty of 5 cents per cubic yard.

Kentucky—Tennessee

Middle and Eastern Kentucky and Tennessee have an abundance of road materials from the limestone, dolomite and sandstone deposits described in Chapter XXII and Chapter XXV. At Camden, Benton county, Tennessee, is a pseudo-novaculite which is sold as "Camden chert." This deposit is along the N. C. & St. L. R. R. Other deposits have not been opened because they are more remote from transportation. Quantities of ballast gravel are loaded along the same road at Perryville, Perry county.

Mississippi

The state of Mississippi has vast deposits of road material and chert. Special freight rates have been granted for the movement of this material within county limits.

About two miles from the railroad, at Leesdale, Franklin county, on the Mississippi Central R. R. is a bed of cement gravel.

From Braxton, Simpson county, to Mt. Olive, Covington county, along the G. & S. I. R. R. and extending east and west from Silver Creek, Lawrence county, across Pearl River flats, are small hills and domes of very hard, compact chert and gravel. On the west end the deposit outcrops as rotten limestone.

From the north line of Forrest and Lamar counties, extending southward, are large deposits of wash gravel. They become steam shovel propositions, the pits afterward seep full of water which is used for washing the gravel and for separating the sharp silica sand, which should find a market for glass making or concrete. The district is served by the Mississippi Central, the G. & S. I. R. R. and the N. O. & N. E. R. R.

Extensive gravel pits have also been opened at several points along the G. M. & N. R. R. at Richton and elsewhere.

Copiah county has a 25-foot thick gravel bed near Georgetown. De Soto county ships about 25 carloads a day on the Frisco lines from Olive Branch. The streets of Hernando, De Soto county, are paved with local chert, which underlies the western third of the county.

Along the Y. & M. V. R. R., in Adams county, are numerous gravel pits and quarries. The road building materials of Amite county are 70 per cent chert, the balance being a sand clay which makes excellent binder.

Carroll county chert is improved by washing, for the removal of excess loamy sand.

Outcropping above the limestones in Tishomingo county is a 50-foot bed of buff chert of road size. This deposit is unfortunately several miles from the railroad.

Bulletin No. 16 of the Mississippi Geological Survey gives detailed accounts of tests of many of these materials in Wilkinson and other counties.

Louisiana

Gravel and sand in Louisiana are secured principally from Profitt's Island in the Mississippi River, between Port Hudson and Baton Rouge; and from Washington and St. Tammany parishes along the N. O. & G. N. R. R. The former is about 120 miles from New Orleans. In the mouth of the Ouachita River are also some well washed beds. Eagle, Jenkins and Price Spur, on the Bogue Chitto branch in Washington parish, and Sun, St. Tammany parish, ship considerable quantities of cement and loose gravels.

Arkansas

The road materials of Arkansas come as broken stone from the granite, sandstone and limestone belts described in Chapters XXII and XXV, and from the Ouachita and Saline Rivers. Saline county along the Missouri Pacific and the C. R. I. & P. R. Rs. has large gravel beds as yet untouched, and from Ivan to Fordyce, Dallas county, on the C. R. I. & P. and Cotton Belt R. Rs. is another.

Arkansas chert is found throughout the Arkansas River valley, and along the White and Black Rivers, as isolated patches above present water level, where they have been deposited in their travel from northwestern Arkansas and Southwestern Missouri.

Crowley's Ridge, which centers in St. Francis county, is a solid gravel ridge available to the Missouri Pacific and the C. R. I. & P. R. Rs., and its material supplies many counties in Eastern Arkansas. Extensions of this deposit also ship over the Cotton Belt lines.

From Little Rock, Pulaski county, westward to Dallas, Polk county, and southwestward to Howard county, the broken novaculites and cherts are available, excellent and abundant.

Texas

In Brewster county, Texas, are found alternating beds of gray limestone, black chert, black shales and chert conglomerate. These are served by the Southern Pacific R. R. at Marathon.

"Caliche" is the result of evaporation, leaving calcium carbonate and silica and forms the cap rock of many hills in Western Texas. It is used as road metal in dry country. The G. C. & S. Fe Ry. distributes road material from pits at Romayor, Liberty county; Roganville, Jasper county; Blum, Hill county, and Dyer, Fort Bend county.

The only portion of the state which suffers for high-grade road material is the Panhandle.

In addition to the use of chert as road building material, when the matrix is pure sand it is utilized for concrete; it is broken up for use as pebbles in grinding mills, and has been successfully used for tube mill lining.

Chapter XXIII

PHOSPHATE ROCK, PHOSPHORIC ACID, MINERAL FERTILIZERS

Phosphate rock is basically calcium phosphate, frequently combined with calcium carbonate and other minerals. It is commonly known as hard rock and pebble rock. The Tennessee deposits are of oolitic type, and are locally known as brown and blue rock. To be valuable for fertilizers under present methods of reduction, it should contain at least 50 per cent of tri-calcium phosphate, or "bone phosphate of lime." When this percentage passes 70 the price rises rapidly.

Approximately 85 per cent of the production in the United States comes from Florida, and 97 per cent of this is pebble rock. While acid phosphate is the pre-eminent fertilizing agent produced by 100 manufacturing fertilizer plants in the South, 57 also produce sulphuric acid. With improved methods it has become possible to mine at much greater depths than formerly. The maximum limit of 15 feet overburden has now been extended to 60 feet under favorable conditions. As the recoverable rock exceeds 2000 tons per acre, the allowable overburden may reach from 7 to 10 cubic yards per ton of rock.

The reserves of the United States have been estimated at six billion tons. Late in 1922 over 80,000 acres of Florida phosphate lands were withdrawn by the Government, in various portions of 31 counties in that state. The industry, in so far as it is affected by the fertilizer trade, is a seasonal one. For twenty-five years the world got its phosphate rock from the beds of salt water rivers around

Beaufort, S. C. This rock runs 55 per cent to 60 per cent phosphate. The entire district is underlaid with it. As the higher-grade rock of Florida came into the market it gradually superseded Carolina rock, which remains a reserve to be utilized upon demand.

The whole fertilizer problem is interwoven with the production of nitrates, and the various processes of catalysis; with acid and non-acid phosphate; with fertilization by raw phosphate; with powdered and with liquid fertilizers; with super and double-super phosphates; and with volatilization methods for the utilization of low-grade raw material. All these in turn are affected by the demand for sulphuric acid and other co-products. Sulphuric acid is the king of chemicals. It is used in the manufacture of nitric, hydrochloric and other acids, and has, until recently, been the sole agent in the manufacture of phosphoric acid.

In the volatilization process, phosphoric acid results from the ignition of phosphate rock, silica sand and coke. The white fumes of phosphorus pentoxide combine with the moisture of the air and are precipitated as phosphoric acid. When potash silicate, such as feldspar, is ignited with lime, the potash is liberated. The electric furnace has assumed importance in the development of the volatilization process because it makes possible the absolute control of temperature, and produces a 90 per cent phosphoric acid, which is shipped in concentrated form as a liquid, and in the form of sodium, ammonium and calcium salts, which go into the chemical industry. Other processes combine acid phosphate with air-derived synthetic ammonia and potash.

The non-acid process permits the use of phosphate rock

high in iron and aluminum content, which makes available enormous beds of rock hitherto of no commercial importance. By this method the rock is treated with a solution of potash in water, and dried. The potash solution acts as a flux and the dried product, when ground, is commercial fertilizer representing a 100 per cent extraction of potash and phosphate. Both of these methods eliminate the use of sulphuric acid. In addition, since heat is essential, oil, coke or coal may be substituted for the electric furnace in many locations where cheap fuel and local rock deposits are available and where electric power is remote. The average grade of phosphate rock contains 32 per cent of phosphoric acid. By the sulphuric acid method only 16 per cent of soluble acid is obtained. The production of double acid phosphate, therefore, means a saving of one-half in freight, greater efficiency in the use of our raw material and substantial labor saving in distribution.

The distribution of raw phosphate rock for fertilizer has been largely confined to Tennessee. Experiments have shown that if sulphur be composted with ground raw phosphate rock, bacteria in the soil will rapidly oxidize the sulphur to sulphuric acid, which acts on the raw phosphate within a short time, yielding as high a percentage of phosphoric acid as is found in commercial acid phosphate.

In addition to the fertilizer industry, phosphates enter into the calcium and sodium compounds. Until 1907 phosphates of calcium and of sodium were made from bone, while at the present time 95 per cent is from mineral origin.

The use of peat, marl and limestone as fertilizers is

discussed in Chapters VI and XXV under their respective headings.

Florida

The deposits of phosphate rock in Florida may be divided into two general classes: Those held by chemical companies and those under reserve by the Government. The latter, amounting to 84,842 acres, are listed by the United States Geological Survey under serial number 17,320, a copy of which may be obtained on application.

South Carolina

The phosphate zone of South Carolina extends from a point about 20 miles north of Charleston to Beaufort, along the southeast coast of the state, and inland about 30 miles. The land rock occurs from 8 to 30 inches in thickness. The river rock was much of it derived from the land and occurs in loose boulders in the river bottoms. It has been estimated that there are at least 5,000,000 tons of 60 per cent phosphate still in the ground. Improved machinery, the electric furnace method of extraction and depletion of higher-grade deposits will cause a resumption in the Carolina beds.

Tennessee

The blue rock of Tennessee was discovered in 1893 and the brown rock in 1896. The former is found in ledges like coal and is usually mined by underground methods. The latter occurs in pockets and sometimes in nodules in a lime-clay matrix, and must be dug, washed and dried. The blue phosphate runs from 2 to 4 feet thick in Lewis and Maury counties, and is overlaid with the Chattanooga black shale. Around Gordonsburg, Lewis county, this shale is surmounted with kidneys of black phosphate. It is necessary to prospect with the core drill for blue rock.

The center of the brown rock district is Mt. Pleasant, Maury county. These deposits extend southward from Columbia and Mt. Pleasant to Pulaski, in Giles county. The high-grade rock originally mined ran as high as 80 per cent phosphate. The average of present shipments is around 70 per cent. There are enormous areas in middle Tennessee running from 40 per cent to 60 per cent. They are in an agricultural section, with good transportation facilities, and offer a field for beneficiation like the Carolina rock.

In the electric furnace process of making phosphoric acid, quartz is necessary as a flux. This central Tennessee rock is imbedded in a sandy lime matrix carrying approximately 20 per cent silica. To the west of the blue phosphate district are scattered deposits of white phosphate in Decatur and Perry counties. This has apparently formed in underground caves and channels by solution and deposition and requires prospecting. The beds already opened run 80 per cent to 90 per cent clear phosphate. All over middle Tennessee is a layer of black shale from a few inches to a foot in thickness, and carrying practically pure kidneys of phosphate varying in size from a walnut to an egg. These kidneys are so pure that they are very friable and must be handled with care to avoid loss by disintegration.

In Johnson county, in Eastern Tennessee are many low-grade deposits from phosphatic limestone. Near Mountain City are several hundred acres of gray-white rock, easily worked and fluctuating from 30 to 70 per cent in phosphate. In southeast Hamilton county near Apison is a nodular deposit with blue matrix in one part of the bed and black shale in the balance. This rock is being utilized for the electric furnace process. Along the line of the Tennessee Central railroad the phosphate rock deposits are overlaid with fifty feet of sandstone, offering regular underground mining conditions.

The rock does not slack in the open air and is exceptionally good for export.

Kentucky

Only brown rock is found in Kentucky. It varies from 1 to 6 feet in thickness with from 2 to 10 feet of overburden. A deposit is reported along the N. C. & St. L. Railway in Hickman county, running 78 per cent phosphate. The only operation in the state is in Woodford county. Similar deposits occur in Fayette, Franklin, Scott, Clark and Jessamine counties.

Mississippi

In Smith county, Mississippi, on a north and south ridge, just east of Leaf River, is a fossiliferous phosphate rock outcrop. Below this are boulders up to 7 or 8 feet in diameter, showing 22 per cent phosphate. Extending northwest and southwest in Smith county is an area 7 miles long and 1 mile wide which is covered by broken ledge rock and boulders, some of them 20 feet in length, of similar character. This is a favorable field for prospecting.

Texas

Traces of phosphate rock have been found in Texas, but, so far, not in promising quantity or quality.

Arkansas

But little attention has been paid to phosphate mining in Arkansas. The rock is commonly found asociated with the manganese deposits. In northwest Independence county, along Lafferty Creek, the blue rock is stripped on the hillside until the increased overburden makes underground methods preferable. Fuel being plentiful, the rock is dried to lessen freight charges by roasting it on piles of wood. This rock runs as high as 72 per cent phosphate. There is need for systematic prospecting all over the state. The counties known to carry workable phosphate rock are Independence, Stone, Izard, Baxter, Marion, Searcy and Newton. Deposits have been reported in Little River, Hempstead, Pike, Clark, Garland and Montgomery counties.

Uses

In addition to its use for fertilizer, phosphoric acid finds its greatest market in the clarification of sugar juices. Various densities are required, and it must be free from arsenic and other impurities. Its advantages lie in whiter sugar, quicker crystallization and greater yield. The raw sugar liquid is first treated with lime, neutralized by phosphoric acid, filtered, evaporated and crystallized. It serves a similar purpose in the jelly and preserving industries. On account of the shortage of tartaric and citric acid, it is extensively used for bottled soft drinks and soda fountain beverages. As a syrup, the acid is used in medicine. A 50 per cent solution of the acid is used in the manufacture of rustproof metallic compounds as a pickle. Calcium phosphate is the active base of baking powder, mixed with bicarbonate of soda and cornstarch. It also enters into all the self-raising flours. The salts of phosphoric acid are used to soften water, and for boiler scale compounds. It also finds a place in dental preparations.

Chapter XXIV

LIMESTONE, MARLS, CHERT AND THE CEMENT AND CALCIUM ARSENATE INDUSTRIES

In discussing limestone it is necessary to confine our attention in this chapter to those forms of limestones which enter into agriculture, as in marls and fertilizers; to its use in the cement industry; to its chemical and metallurgical applications; to its part in the manufacture of calcium arsenate; its use as building stone being covered in Chapter XXII, and in the form of chalk in Chapter V.

Limestone is usually of bluish-grey color in a wide variety of appearances. Its presence may be readily detected by acid. It is frequently found in combination with carbonic acid, magnesia, alumina, silica and iron. One of its purest forms is as calcite or calcium carbonate. Dolomite is calcium-magnesium carbonate. Chalk is a soft pure limestone, composed of microscopic marine shells.

As defined by the Bureau of Standards, stone lime is simply broken lime rock. Quicklime is the calcium product as it comes from the kiln, which may be crushed and sold as ground lime. Lime putty is a plastic mixture of quicklime and water. Hydrated lime is quicklime slaked with just enough water to produce a dry powder, instead of a putty. This latter should not be confused with air-slaked lime; hydrated lime is a hydroxide and will absorb carbonic acid when exposed to air and will "set" while air slaked lime, being already a carbonate cannot absorb carbonic acid and will not set.

When the lime in dolomite is so combined as to render it non-slaking and at the same time retaining its refractory qualities, dolomite bricks show high fusion temperature, high specific gravity, great strength and low porosity. Such bricks have been made of 90 per cent dolomite by the Bureau of Mines.

The open-hearth process requires one-man sized lime rock; blast furnaces and steel mills take it crushed, while cement mills usually require run-of-quarry size.

Limestone is an essential to the soil, not as a fertilizer, but to correct acidity, so that legumes, such as clover, peas and alfalfa, will grow successfully. These, in turn, restore nitrogen to the soil. Exhausting the limestone in the soil is like overdrawing a bank account, while liming the soil liberally is like building up a savings account. For agricultural purposes the lime is usually ground to one-quarter inch or finer.

Uses

The uses of lime are so varied and so numerous that only the major ones may be enumerated here. The reader is referred to Chemical and Metallurgical Engineering, February 15, 1922, Vol. 26, No. 7, pages 294-300, for a detailed list. In addition to agriculture, building, steel making and cement manufacture, lime is used in the preparation of wood pulp, for water purification, in refining sugar, as chicken grit, for paint and asphalt filler, in tanning, in glass manufacture, in the oil, fat and soap industries, the making of cyanamid, for purifying illuminating gas, for railroad ballast and road building, for sand-lime brick, in alkali works, for sheep dipping, in the composition of disinfectants, in the manufacture of glue, as a food preservative, in the vulcanization of rubber, for cold-water paints, in the saponification of oils, in medicines, in the manufacture of paper from cotton linters and bagasse, as a precipitating and coagulating agent, for neutralizing acid water, in the production of ammonia, as an absorbing medium, in connection with aluminum for making cleaning mixtures, as an ingredient of insecticides, for the lubrication of dies in the wire industry, for bleaching rags in the manufacture of high-grade rag paper, as a mordant in the dyeing industry, and as a catalyzing agent.

West Virginia

The West Virginia limestones have been more completely surveyed than those of any other Southern state. Detailed county reports have been published by the West Virginia Geological Survey. The limestone around Martinsburg, Berkeley county, will run 96 per cent calcium carbonate in carload lots, with silica under 2 per cent. If care is used in the preparation the silica content can be reduced to 1½ per cent. There is much of this undeveloped territory which needs a railroad, to the south of Martinsburg and east of the Cumberland Valley. Pittsburgh is the present natural market. Near Keyser, Mineral county, is a good open-hearth or chemical lime. There are several deposits in this county more available than those in Jefferson county. These were formerly operated on a small scale and are available for agriculture, ballast and building lime. The Berkeley county limestones, being low in silica and magnesia, go to the open-hearth steel plants; the Hampshire county deposits near Romney go to and are available for the blast furnaces of Pittsburgh, Johnstown and Baltimore. This section is somewhat handicapped by freight rates.

About 6 miles north of Harpers Ferry, Jefferson county, is a splendid dolomite deposit running the theoretical percentage (54 per cent calcium carbonate and 45 per cent magnesium carbonate). The same deposit is being operated at Millville, Jefferson county, southwest of Harper's Ferry. The product goes to Pittsburgh for basic linings and flux. It runs less than 1½ per cent silica, which is the limit for high-grade basic material. Transportation by a railroad extension from Berkeley on the Cumberland Valley to Harpers Ferry would open up a large area of this valuable material. Parsons, Tucker county, is the center of another limestone area. A limestone belt extends across the state from northeast to southwest; from Manheim, in Preston county, through Port Spring, in Greenbrier county, to Princeton, in Mercer county. Lime plants are in operation at Charleston, Kanawha county, Fort Spring, Greenbrier county, and a smaller one in Berkeley county.

Virginia

The whole Valley of Virginia is a limestone formation, unlimited in quantity and quality. The various grades are quarried and used for agriculture, building, burnt lime and chemical lime, both quick and hydrated. For economic reasons, quicklime is preferable in agriculture because freight charges are on lime alone, while for building purposes hydrated lime is better because it is more uniform. In Shenandoah and Rockingham counties, west of Mount Jackson, and from Strasburg and New Market to Harrisonburg is a deposit erroneously called barytes, but which is clear calcite, running 95 per cent to 98 per cent calcium carbonate. Limestone is found at Cedar Valley and Middleton, in Frederick county, and continues to Lexington in Rockbridge county. Other deposits in Virginia will be found in connection with the treatment of Marls and Cement, later in this chapter.

North Carolina

The best North Carolina limestones are those of Henderson county, which average 94 per cent calcium carbonate. On the Murphy branch of the Southern Railway in Cherokee and Swain counties, are a number of deposits, all running 90 per cent or better, and some of the Swain county deposits run as high as $93\frac{1}{2}$ per cent. Freight rates and heavy railroad grades, however, make expensive hauling to competitive markets. These should receive consideration in the development of the state's limestone industry. At Hot Springs and Paintrock in Madison county are other exposures worthy of investigation. A north and south belt extends through Catawba, Lincoln and Gaston counties; and in Wilson county a soft limestone shading into marl has been worked. Along the southeast coast, near Rocky Point, Pender county, a large limestone property has been opened up by the state for road building purposes, and extensive reserves lie at the back. This is 2 miles from a railroad.

South Carolina

The situation in South Carolina is of extreme importance and more than ordinary interest. This state having less mineral resources than many others, and lying midway in the great north-and-south route of tourist travel, needs cement plants and road building material. Near Gaffney, Cherokee county, is a limestone formation reposing at an angle of 45°, which runs from 57 per cent to 97 per cent calcium carbonate. The product was used in 7 iron furnaces between Blacksburg and Gaffney. The chief difficulty lies in the fact that only the middle of the deposit is of high grade, the sides containing too much magnesium. Across the state to the southwest, in Greenwood county, is an apparently high-grade calcite, but its commercial extent has not been determined. Reference will be made to South Carolina marls later in this chapter.

Georgia

Limestones suitable for all purposes are found in abundance in Georgia. The most extensive deposit is the Knox dolomite found in Catoosa, Walker, Chattooga, Floyd and Polk counties in the northwest corner of the state. These counties support an active lime industry, and enjoy excellent transportation and labor facilities. At Clinchfield, Houston county, a cement plant was recently opened. To the southwest, between Bainbridge and Donalsonville, on both sides of Spring Creek in Decatur and Seminole counties, as well as along the Georgia-Florida line, north of River Junction on the A. C. L. R. R. are scattered deposits of commercial limestone. Twenty-eight limestone bearing counties are listed by the Central of Georgia Railway along its lines in Georgia. These are described in detail in their *Mineral Directory*.

Kentucky

The Bowling Green limestone of Kentucky is a very superior stone, originally a petroleum-bearing rock, which has since bleached by evaporation. In Rockcastle, Madison, Bath and Rowan counties occurs a blue free-stone extensively quarried. At Olive Hill, Carter county, and Limeville, Greenup county, are extensive deposits running high in calcium carbonate. Although large areas of the state are underlain with limestone formation, the deposits are frequently interbedded with shale and sandstone, and are relatively thin.

Tennessee

The only good limestones in the western part of Tennessee are found in Montgomery, Robertson, Houston, Hickman and Dickson counties. The product from Erin, Houston county, goes to the sugar refineries of Mississippi and Louisiana. The Bon Aqua limestone, on the line between Hickman and Dickson counties, runs 99 per cent calcium carbonate. There is a considerable quantity of this at present undeveloped. Middle and East Tennessee contain excellent limestones for all purposes. They are for the most part easily accessible. Cumberland Mountain is all limestone. There is a plant at Knoxville, Knox county, preparing ground lime; an available limestone deposit at Apison, Hamilton county, and calcite deposits along the Southern Railway at Newport, Cocke county and Clouds, Claiborne county.

Alabama

On the headwaters of Little Patsaliga River in Crenshaw, county, Alabama, and accessible to the railroad at Luverne, is a calcite deposit of considerable extent. In the Odenville district of St. Clair county, 22 miles east of Birmingham, and taking Birmingham district freight rate, is a limestone running better than 97 per cent and on the outcrop alone are many millions of tons available. In the entire southern tier of counties an abundance of limestone occurs, and the Selma chalk beds around Montgomery and Demopolis run from 75 per cent to 85 per cent calcium carbonate. Shelby and Etowah counties, likewise, have an abundance, with rail and water facilities for transportation. In Lee county, 20 miles west of the Chattahoochee River, is a deposit of highly crystallized dolomite, so free from magnesia that it is used for whitewash. A high-grade limestone is also found along the Southern Railway at Russellville, Franklin county.

Reference is made to Bulletin No. 28 of the Alabama Geological Survey for detailed description of the Alabama limestones and building stones.

Florida

Florida production has, until recently, been confined to Marion, Citrus, Broward and Palm Beach counties. As the drainage of the Everglades progresses, additional limestones and marls are evident in the counties affected. Near Blountsville, in Calhoun county, is a vast deposit of dolomite, analyzing 45 per cent calcium carbonate and 30 per cent magnesium carbonate, which is being used as a vitalizer for sandy soil. The south Citrus county deposit occurs as boulders imbedded in marl, rather than stratified. There is a demand in the Ocala district for builders' lime and ground limestone. The Marion county deposits around Ocala average 99 per cent, while the Jackson county limestone around Mariana runs 99.6 per cent calcium carbonate. The Miami and Palm Beach rock carries about 85 per cent. These deposits will be discussed at greater length under "Building Stones", in Chapter XXII and under "Cement."

Palm Island, Monroe county, in Florida Bay, midway between Miami and Key West also has excellent marls and limestones.

Mississippi

Mississippi has an abundance of limestone. From

Tishomingo county in the extreme northeast, extending westward through Alcorn county, and southward to Noxubee county are beds of limestone and Selma chalk. From Warren county on the west to Wayne county on the southeast, is a limestone anticline. Northwest of Jackson, along the Y. & M. V. R. R., is an exposure several miles in length. These beds vary from 80 to 95 per cent calcium carbonate. The Selma chalk, being more friable, is better adapted to agricultural purposes, while the carboniferous limestone from Tishomingo county is well suited to structural uses, flux, etc.

A recently disclosed and apparently valuable deposit, showing better than 85 per cent calcium carbonate, lies north of the Laurel branch of Leaf River in Smith county, and extends westward across the intersection of Rankin, Smith and Simpson counties, crossing the main line of the G. & S. I. R. R. between Star and Braxton, on the Rankin-Simpson county line. This is locally quarried in blocks approximately 12 inches by 12 inches by 18 inches for chimney and other construction. It is presumably a lateral extension of the Vicksburg-Waynesboro anticline, extending into Franklin and Jasper counties, and offers excellent opportunities for development to supply the sugar refining and cement industries along the Gulf Coast. The depletion of the timber reserves of the district render it imperative to the railroads operating through Southern Mississippi to create new sources of traffic. A very soft and pure lime deposit occurs along the G. M. & N. R. R. near the Chicasaw-Pontotoc county line. One of the handicaps in the development of agricultural lime has been the prohibitive freight rates. But in Mississippi, Alabama and Georgia certain railroads are now hauling agricultural lime free of charge to intrastate points along their lines in order to develop agriculture.

Louisiana

The great limestone deposits of its neighboring states are, unfortunately, missing in Louisiana. But three sources have been found of commercial quality and quantity. At Coochie Brake is a yellowish-blue sandy limestone which quarries readily but which contains quantities of iron pyrites nodules. At Bayou Chicot, in Evangeline parish is a dark-gray, finely-grained limestone, formerly burned for agricultural lime. The third is near Winnfield, in Winn parish, and served by three railroads. This is a highly crystallized blue and white rock, seamed with calcite and occasional masses of spar, and is probably an extension of the Waynesboro-Vicksburg limestone of Mississippi. Drill holes have shown it to exist for from 900 to 1100 feet in depth over an area of 200 acres. The crushing strength is given as 27,300 pounds, hardness 12.1, specific gravity 2.7, and loose weight (50 per cent voids) 168 pounds per cubic foot. A plant with 24,000 tons per month capacity operates to supply ground lime for agriculture, chemical lime, crushed limestone and screenings for roads, ballast, concrete, etc., riprap for levees and quarry waste for roads and railroads. The nearest competing supply is from the Birmingham district, Little Rock, and New Braunfels, Texas.

There are 134 sugar refineries in the state, all of which use lime, and the wood pulp and water purification plants also consume considerable quantities. Costs are given as 61½ cents per ton under present conditions; this figure could probably be reduced with increased equipment and output. The strategic location of this deposit makes it of special economic importance to the entire state.

A new phase of the lime industry is being introduced in Southern Louisiana, through the development of the oyster and clam shell deposit on Isle de Coquilles. The reef extends for 3 miles and has been proved to a depth of 30 feet over an area of 7000 acres, thus blocking out eighty million cubic yards. It is located 28 miles from New Orleans and can be barged to the L. & N. R. R., only three-quarters of a mile distant from the reef. These shells averaged on 15 analyses, 97 per cent calcium carbonate.

The process is to powder the shells to 300 mesh, after which the product is passed into a dust collector, where it falls by gravity into a flume fired by crude-oil burners, introduced into the side of the flume. The passing heat current pulls the fine powder forward and bathes each particle with flame as it passes down the flumes. The burned lime is finally collected in a pot and allowed to cool, after which it is withdrawn in iron dump cars to storage bins, from which it may be sacked and shipped as required. Builders' lime, thus prepared, is 97 per cent pure, 3 per cent silica and no iron. It will remain for two to three weeks in nascent condition as calcium oxide or "activated lime." For chemical purposes it is hydrated, precipitated, dried and reburned. This produces an element different from calcium oxide, which is almost a catalyzer, and which is analogous to ozone as compared to oxygen. At Morgan City, St. Mary parish, on the Atchafalaya River, a similar oyster shell deposit is available.

Arkansas

The limestone counties of Arkansas are Baxter, Independence, Izard, Stone, Searcy, Marion, Newton, Boone, Madison and Benton. The White River line of the Missouri Pacific R. R., which passes through the center of this northern tier, distributes the product over a wide area. The calcium carbonate content is high, and northern Arkansas lime supplies the sugar, paper and agricultural industries of Southern Louisiana. Over four million dollars have been invested in plants which receive their raw material from the Batesville district and the acid plant at Little Rock. A very fine deposit of chalk is found in Clark, Hamstead, Little River and Sevier counties in southwest Arkansas. At White Cliffs, Little River county, it is estimated that there are 150,000,000 tons in one deposit, available to the Frisco and the Kansas City Southern Railways. It runs 89 per cent to 91 per cent calcium carbonate. At Pinnacle, Pulaski county, on the Rock Island line, just west of Little Rock a limestone deposit is reported.

Two cement plants, with an aggregate capacity of 6,500,000 barrels per day, are now under consideration at White Cliffs and Foreman in Little River county to operate on the chalk deposits.

Burnt lime production in Arkansas is also progressing through the installation of three new kilns in the Batesville district.

Dolomite, high in metallic magnesium, is found in Baxter and Marion counties and with the projected hydro-electric development in this section, offers an inducement in the manufacture of light-weight alloys.

Texas

The Texas limestones are found in two groups, the first extending in a narrow north-and-south belt from

Grayson county, through Dallas and Austin to Bexar county below San Antonio, with an easterly branch across Fannin, Lamar and Red River counties. The second is a massive gray deposit, 5000 feet in thickness, showing a wide variation in magnesia content, forming the backbone of the Franklin mountains along the western edge of El Paso county from the Rio Grande to the New Mexico boundary. Large quantities are quarried and used as smelter flux for foundation, for road making and for cement. The shell deposits of the Gulf coast, like those of Louisiana, are now receiving active consideration. In Comal and Hays counties along the M-K-T and the I.-G. N. railroads the quarries are operated for ballast, concrete and structural purposes, and the fine dust is shipped by carload for direct application to the land.

* * * * * *

Marl is a mixture of clay and calcium carbonate frequently combined with shells, mica, glauconite or silica. When subjected for long periods of time to percolating waters the deposit usually becomes so hard it is necessary to crush it for agricultural purposes. Its value is directly proportional to the calcium carbonate, phosphoric acid and potash content. Certain marls because of their texture and lime content are also valuable as cement material. During recent years the demand for agricultural lime has rapidly increased. As between production costs and freight rates the latter are by far of the greatest import to the industry. Thus it happens that limestones and marls in profitable operation in one state may be delivered only at a prohibitive cost in another. Certain of the shell marls decompose more rapidly than others. The green sand, or glauconite marls, because of their potash and phosphorous content are always in demand.

Virginia

The entire Coastal Plain of Virginia carries a wide distribution of green sand and shell marls. Fresh-water marls abound in the entire valley west of the Blue Ridge. When these marls are used in the manufacture of cement it is necesary to make the selection with special reference to low silica sand content. Near Smithfield in Isle of Wight county is a marl deposit of special purity, available for water shipment. One quarter of the total area of the state is underlain with glauconite marl. There are 117 operators in lime products.

A deposit of fresh-water marl four miles north of Staunton, Augusta county, is operated for direct application to the land. The deposit is powdered and about thirty feet deep, with less than one foot of top soil, and covers 55 to 60 acres. It reaches the B. & O. R. R. at Verona.

Two miles back of Cloverdale, in the extreme southern part of Botetourt county, and at Marl Brook, Buena Vista and Riverside in Rockbridge county, along the N. & W. Ry. are deposits of similar grade, but not pulverized. These must be ground before shipment.

In Alleghany county, along the C. & O. R. R., about ten miles north of Covington, and at Barber are marls analyzing 98 per cent calcium carbonate. These are partly developed and are shipped to considerable distance on account of their purity.

North Carolina

The same general conditions exist in the Coastal Plain of North Carolina. In Wilson county is a marl and clay deposit, avilable to two railroads, which is of considerable extent, and undeveloped. A similar deposit is to be found in Edgecombe county, near Sharpsburg.

Three miles northeast of Dublin, Bladen county, on the south bank of Cape Fear River, is a shell marl deposit running 60 per cent to 75 per cent calcium carbonate. This bed is six feet thick, with five to twenty-five feet sand and clay overburden, and is available for river transportation. It lies three miles from the Virginia & Carolina Southern Railway. Four miles southeast of Eliazbethtown and ten miles from Dublin; also at Clarkton, twelve miles from Elizabethtown and fifteen miles from Dublin, in the same county, are high-grade deposits of marl which may be shipped for direct agricultural application without grinding. In Craven county, near New Bern, the state has operated a marl plant. This deposit runs from 90 to 95 per cent calcium carbonate, but frequent sand pockets make it difficult to operate profitably.

South Carolina

The marl deposits of South Carolina are found along the river banks of the Coastal Plain. Much of the overburden has been removed by erosion. One of the difficulties of operation in South Carolina has been the large amount of ground water; and the fact that the upper portion of the beds is frequently leaner than the lower portion. The best located deposits, and which run from 90 to 95 per cent calcium carbonate, lie in eastern Calhoun county and extend down the south bank of the Santee River across Orangeburg county to the Berkeley county line. In the extreme southeastern corner of Florence county, between the Pee Dee and Lynches rivers, is an undeveloped hard-shell marl bed, along the river bank, which analyses 90 per cent, or better, carbonate of lime. This is of sufficiently high grade to interest any phase of industry requiring calcareous material. It lies 15 to 20 feet above normal water, and is about 2½ miles distant from the Seaboard Air Line Railway. There are also immense quantities of marl 15 to 20 miles below Augusta, Georgia, between Modoc and Parksville, McCormick county, South Carolina, along the C. & W. C. R. R., which run 75 per cent to 85 per cent calcium carbonate, contiguous to several pockets of good brick clay.

Georgia

The Georgia Coastal Plain, especially along the Chattahoochee, Flint and Savannah rivers, is a continuation of those deposits in the states farther north. All grades of marl are to be found in practically all the Southern states.

Between Fort Valley and Bon Air in Houston county, on the Central of Georgia Railway, is a marl deposit so pure as to be available for any chemical requirement. In Chatham county is a shell marl deposit, eight miles from the railroad, but available to transportation on the Savannah River.

Florida

The rapid growth of industry and of the extensions of good roads in Florida has directed attention not only to the available limestones, but to the marls as well. Lying, as it does, wholly within the Coastal Plain, considerable area in the central part of the state is underlain with marl, much of it at or above water level. Near Blountstown, Calhoun county, is a combination marine-marl deposit, high in decomposed animal matter, calcium carbonate, ammonia, phosphoric acid and potash, which is loaded onto the cars and shipped to neighboring towns for direct application to the land.

These marls are usually found contiguous to the limestones. In Volusia and southern Putnam counties they are used for road surfacing.

Alabama

Alabama is a distinctly limestone state, shading from the hard stone on the northeast through the Selma chalk to the Coastal Plain marls and shell beds on the south. Around Mobile is a large deposit of shell marl.

Mississippi

Mississippi, likewise, has extensive supplies of marls, associated with the various limestone deposits already described. In Smith county, north of the Gulf and Ship Island R. R., is a belt from 200 to 600 feet wide and extending for 15 to 20 miles, of greenish marl, full of shells and decayed marine matter. It has been drilled to a depth of 50 feet and gives off a very offensive odor. It is apparently an ancient deposit of oysters and seaweed, and shows under analysis 4 per cent potash and 15 per cent nitrogen.

Louisiana

Louisiana is possessed of but little marl. In the extreme northern part of the state are a few scattering deposits of ordinary grade.

Arkansas

Adjacent to the chalk deposits of Arkansas and forming contact with them in Hempstead, Pike, Clark, Howard and Sevier counties, are conglomerate marls running over 3 per cent in potash. An undeveloped marl bed lies at Forrest City, St. Francis county, along the C. R. I. & P. R. R.

Texas

The harbor line of San Patricio county, Texas, around Aransas Bay, is lined with marl, deficient in silica for cement purposes, but rich in shell lime. As "mud shell" it is sold by trainloads for road making purposes. It makes a good automatic binder, and exists in unlimited quantities. In Nueces county is a rich deposit of shell marl available to both rail and water transportation.

* * * * * *

The **cement** industry is interwoven with and dependent upon a supply of high-grade limestone or marl, with suitable clays or shales, fuel at a reasonable cost, and distribution facilities, over a wide area. The importance of a wide distribution of cement plants throughout the South cannot be overestimated. The rapid depletion of the forests with consequent rise in the price of lumber, the great increase in building construction in Florida and other Southern states, and the natural tendency toward fireproof construction, have caused an unprecedented demand for brick, stone, cement and concrete buildings. The good roads movement, likewise, with railroad extensions, culverts and bridges, has still further drained the present cement resources of Southern plants.

It has been estimated that if every cement plant now built and building in the South were to operate at full capacity, there would still be a shortage of 3,000,000 barrels per year in this territory. Unlike most products, cement is used, but not consumed. Wages, labor, quarrying, transportation and financing represented in concrete construction, become permanent contributions to the country's social and industrial progress. In 1924 Portland cement production in the states of Alabama, Georgia, Kentucky, Tennessee, Texas, Virginia and West Virginia amounted to 17,508,000 barrels. It is probable that within a year additional plants will be in operation in Florida and Louisiana.

Inasmuch as a substantial portion of the output of some of the existing plants goes to states north and west, it is logical that a promising field exists in Mississippi, Arkansas and the Carolinas for the cement industry. There is also room for additional plants in several of the producing states, notably Texas. There are a number of locations, as indicated in the discussion of limestones and marls in the earlier portion of this chapter, where raw materials abound, where coal is cheap and water and rail transportation available.

Virginia

In addition to the limestones listed, shales and marls especially adapted to cement manufacture occur in Augusta, Nelson, Isle of Wight and Giles counties, Virginia; Mercer county, West Virginia; numerous localities in Kentucky and Tennessee, and in all the counties in the limestone formations of Arkansas and Texas.

North Carolina

One of the most promising locations for a cement plant in North Carolina is near Sharpsburg, Edgecombe county. Other locations exist to the south.

Alabama

Across the southern tier of counties in the St. Stephens limestone of Alabama, as well as the Selma chalk beds east and west of Montgomery, and around Odenville, St. Clair county, fuel and cement materials may in many cases be handled by gravity to an advantageous site along railroad or river. A similar condition obtains at Stevenson, Jackson county, on the Southern Railway.

Florida

Citrus county, Florida, offers good rail facilities and Tampa affords both rail and water shipment for incoming fuel and delivery of finished product. River Junction, Gadsden county, also could receive coal from Chattahoochee River plants.

Georgia

Georgia only produces one-half the cement requirements of the state. Both raw materials and fuel are available at many points on the various railroad systems and also on the Flint and Chattahoochee Rivers.

Mississippi

Mississippi offers many advantageous locations for the industry. These have been dealt with in Bulletin No. 1 of the State Geological Survey. In addition to the local lignites, coal is available from nearby Alabama fields as well as the sub-bituminous product recently opened up at Louisville, Winston county.

Louisiana

The oyster shell beds along the Gulf coast of Louisiana, especially at the mouth of the Atchafalaya River, are now under consideration by the cement industry. The marls near the Winnfield limestone deposits are also suitable. The shales, marls and shell deposits at Morgan City, St. Mary parish, are similar to those near Houston, Texas, and will doubtless be developed at an early date.

Texas

Brown, Dallas, Tarrant, Harris and Nueces counties, Texas, have sufficient reserves to support additional cement plants whose output can all be consumed within the state.

No attempt has been made in this chapter to discuss natural cement, the great field and future being for Portland cement. Many of the plants formerly making natural cement have gone into the shale brick industry. A new process has recently been evolved by the Louisville Cement Company, which makes a natural cement for both outside and inside wall finish by mixing a resinous gum compound with cement rock. The product is said to be very durable.

West Virginia

Jefferson and Mineral counties, West Virginia, and numerous localities in the James River basin of Virginia, carry deposits of dolomite and of natural cement rock.

In general, it may be said that no shortage of cement materials, fuel, labor or transportation exists in the South.

There is an entire series of special cements which have been created to meet special requirements. These are:

(a) Titaniferous iron ore and lime rock.

(b) Fusion of the above, separating the metallic iron and grinding the slag.

(c) Cement containing from 25 per cent to 45 per cent lime, less than 20 per cent silica and iron oxide, and from 10 per cent to 60 per cent titanic oxide.

(d) Iron and cement, as in (b), whose slag contains a high proportion of alumina and less than 20 per cent of silica.

(e) Iron and cement by fusing a mixture of aluminous low silica iron ore with lime, and proceeding as above.

Until recently alumina cement utilized pure bauxite. Under the new processes the titaniferous and aluminous iron ores offer a source at much lower cost.

* * * * * *

Calcium arsenate is prepared by oxidizing white arsenic with nitric acid, treating it with sodium hydrate and precipitating with milk of lime. Until recently ore carrying more than 1 per cent of arsenic was penalized at the smelters, but the increased demand for insecticides has brought about the removal of the penalty. In fact, a high arsenic content may, at present prices, bring more than the other metal contents, for which the ore is originally mined.

Uses

Glass manufacturers consume about 3000 tons of white arsenic annually. Sheep and cattle dips and medical purposes require 500 tons, and insecticides call for 10,000 tons per year.

White arsenic is largely a by-product from flue dust and smelter fumes. A recent process has been brought out in Alabama for dissolving arsenical sulphides in an alkaline sulphide and leaching out the arsenic. It is claimed for this process that less than 1 per cent of the arsenic remains in the tailings. In connection with the arseno-pyrites deposits of Clay and Randolph counties, Alabama, along the A. B. & C. R. R., and in Tallapoosa and Chambers counties on the Central of Georgia Railway, the production of calcium arsenate in that state holds encouraging promise.

In North Carolina arseno-pyrite is found with gold at Kings Mountain mine in Cleveland county. It is found in similar combination in Cabarrus, Gaston, Union and Watauga counties.

An American group has recently bought a large arsenical iron mine in Saskatchewan, Canada, for the purpose of extracting the arsenic and shipping it for insecticide manufacture in the Southern states, contiguous to the great limestone deposits and abundant hydro-electric power.

The States of Louisiana and Alabama have taken the lead in calcium arsenate manufacture. Its great application is as an eradicant of the boll weevil. With available raw material and power in the center of a great consuming market, it is logical to anticipate further plants in other cotton-growing states. Any of the high-grade limestone deposits referred to earlier in this chapter are equally available for the manufacture of calcium arsenate.

Chapter XXV

ASBESTOS, GYPSUM, MINERAL WATERS

Asbestos is the only commercial fibre in the mineral realm. The United States holds first place in the manufacture of asbestos products, but produces only 1 per cent of the world's output of the raw material. The principal imports come from Canada and South Africa.

It is usually white, gray or green, and may be either fibrous amphibole or fibrous serpentine, known as chrysotile. It occurs in three types—cross fibre, slip fibre and mass fibre. Amphibole is usually mass fibre; chrysotile may be either cross or slip fibre, but never mass fibre. Because of its non-combustibility, non-conductivity of heat and electricity, and its fibrous nature, more different uses have been found for it than man has devised for almost any other known material. From the time when the Emperor Charlemagne mystified his guests with a table cloth which he threw into the fire to cleanse it to about the year 1870, over a period of a thousand years, asbestos failed of commercial recognition. It was considered a freak; a chunk of rock as heavy and dense as marble, and yet composed of such delicate strands it can be woven, carded and spun, like wool, cotton or silk. Its appearance is highly inflammable, yet flame has no effect. Unaffected by atmospheric conditions, it withstands all the assaults of time.

To get one ton of asbestos fibre of various grades, it is necessary to mine and process at least fifteen tons of rock. It is graded into four grades, from the long-spinning fibre, used in the weaving of textiles, to the broken bits used in cement, shingles, etc. Fifty per cent of the entire manufactured product goes to the automobile trade. The annual consumption in brake lining alone produces 70,000,000 lineal feet, of which 15,000,000 feet is for new cars and the balance for replacements.

No notice is ordinarily taken of the chemical analyses of asbestos, except that iron is detrimental when the product is to be put to electrical use. "Asbestic" is the trade name for sand in which particles of asbestos are imbeded. Due to keen competition among the producers and to increased uses for lower-grade materials which, in turn, utilize by-product material and so lessen the cost of production, the market price of asbestos has persistently dropped. Chrysotile, because of its long, silky fibres, leads the market, while amphibole, in spite of its brittleness, because of certain particular characteristics, is replacing short chrysotile fibres. Chrysotile loses its strength when subjected to a temperature of 1200° F., while amphibole does not disintegrate at 6000° F. Powdered chrysotile shows rounded or flaky particles when examined under the microscope, while powdered amphibole shows the smallest particles to be fibrous or elongated.

Virginia

Amphibole was mined in Franklin and Bedford counties, Virginia, about 20 years ago. The material was in slip fibre, the veins varied much in thickness and shaded into peridotite. Small shipments were made, but the developments were not promising.

North Carolina

Passing into North Carolina, the beds become purer and thicker, and there are more occurrences of chrysotile as well as amphibole. These deposits have not as yet been actively developed. At North Wilkesboro, Wilkes county, is a 100-acre deposit of chrysotile, in slip fibre about one-quarter inch long. In Macon county, out of Toxaway, Transylvania county, and beyond Sapphire Lake, in Jackson county, are a dozen deposits, varying from friable slip fibre to the long, silky variety. Chrysotile is also found at Glenville, Jackson county, on Elk Creek in Ashe county and along the western slopes of the Rich Mountains in Watauga county, near the mouth of Squirrel Creek, and on North Toe River. These are all of fair length and fineness, but little work has been done to determine their extent. Amphibole is found on Yellow Mountain, Mitchell county, and on Skyuk Mountain, near Tryon, Polk county. There are large quantities in these deposits, comparable to the Georgia operations. It also occurs at Micaville, Yancey county, and near Bakersville, Mitchell county, along the Clinchfield Railroad. It is a soft, flexible fibre of considerable tensile strength and, when milled, gives an excellent product. Deposits are also reported at Cane River, Yancey county, and near Brindletown, Burke county.

Georgia

The Georgia asbestos deposits have been described in Bulletin 29 of the Geological Survey of Georgia, the *Commercial Mineral Directory* of the Central of Georgia Railway; *Mineral Resources* by the United States Geological Survey, and articles in the Engineering and Mining Journal-Press. Amphibole has been extensively mined in Habersham, Rabun and White counties. About eight miles northeast of the Sall Mountain mines in White county, on Wolfpit and Mack Mountains, mass slip and cross fibre deposits occur.

Amphibole is found in Carroll, Clayton, Fulton, Meriweather and Morgan counties; and chrysolite in Coweta county, along the Central of Georgia Railway.

Alabama

Asbestine rocks, such as actinolite, occur with serpentine and soapstone in Tallapoosa county, Alabama, both north and west of Dadeville. To the northeast, but remote from the railroad, long fibre asbestos is reported and samples submitted are very promising. For many years, in Chambers and Randolph counties, actinolite slabs were used to line bake ovens.

Tests at the United States Bureau of Standards and other laboratories have indicated that Southern asbestos surpasses Canadian and other imported products in its acid, gas-resisting and non-shrinking qualities.

Uses

To list the detailed uses of abestos would entail many pages. They may be comprehensively classified as follows: Steam packings, fireproof curtains, cloth, twine, rope; pipe coverings for heat, cold and acid; linings for safes, stoves and furnaces; bricks, boards, moldings, aprons, belting, blankets, blocks, boots and shoes, braid, braided tubing, bushings, cements, cord, doors, gas burners, gloves, locomotive lagging, listing lumber, mats, packing paints, rests, ribbon, tables, tapes, thread, mill boards, plasters, paints, wallpaper, cards, fireproof supports, filters, clothing, flooring, upholstery, carpeting, paper, electrical insulation, soundproof filling, protected metal, shingles, roll roofing, felt, gaskets, washers, ventilators, mineral wool, gas-grate backs, kitchen utensils, brake lining and brake blocks.

Glass apparatus is repaired with asbestos paper or twine, which is first soaked in sodium silicate and afterward treated with calcium chloride solution.

Asbestos shingles are made of ground asbestos fibre mixed with Portland cement and water, and united into sheets by 40,000 pounds pressure per square inch. These shingles are then stored for 90 days, and when thoroughly "cured" will neither decay, rust nor curl.

Asbestos protected metal is made by saturating asbestos felt with asphalt, which contains hexachlorinated napthalene, so that when exposed to fire, the non-combustible vapors of the chlorinated napthalene dilute the vapors of the asphalt so that it will not support combustion. The product weighs about one-third more than galvanized iron; is susceptible of mixing in dark colors, such as maroon, green and brown and when erected costs from one and a half to two times as much as painted galvanized iron, but carries a low maintenance cost. It is manufactured in shapes and weights corresponding to other metal roofings.

"Fibre talc," or "asbestine," is a double silicate of lime and magnesia, and is a rival of blanc-fixe for paper filler, dental modeling wax, blotting paper, filter paper and copying paper. It is also used for jewellers' polish, imitation stone and fire-fighting chemicals.

* * * * * *

Gypsum, as selenite, satin spar, alabaster, or gypsite, is about one-third lime, one-fifth water and one-half sulphur trioxide. When occuring as selenite it is not infrequently found in beautiful clear crystals up to 3 or 4 feet in length.

Alabaster is fine grained and compact, gypsite is composed of small soft crystals in a clay and silica matrix, and satin spar has a velvety fibrous appearance.

It always lies close to the surface and frequently does not even carry an overburden. The United States is the principal producer and mines about 3,000,000 tons annually. France, Great Britain and Canada are the principal competitors.

Uses

Seventy-five per cent of the product goes into the building trade, small amounts are used for dental plaster and in the manufacture of plate glass, and the balance is used principally for fertilizer.

When three to five pounds of finely powdered gypsum per animal per day are added and thoroughly mixed with barnyard manure, the soluble nitrogen is preserved, and the lime and sulphur of the gypsum added to the fertilizing value of the compost. It also serves as a stable and barnyard deodorizant and fly preventative. It is estimated that one dollar's worth of gypsum will preserve three dollars' worth of soluble nitrogen. Gypsum is also a valuable addition with ground rock phosphate to supplement the necessary sulphur, which decreases under vegetation and leaching much faster than the phosphate content.

Of the ten necessary chemical elements essential to agriculture (carbon, hydrogen, oxygen, nitrogen, sulphur, phosphorous, calcium, potassium, magnesium and iron), gypsum supplies two and increases the supply of a third. If the new processes by which soluble phosphate is made without the use of sulphuric acid assume substantial proportions and displace acid phosphate, the use of gypsum in agriculture would increase from 100,000 tons annually to many times that amount.

Virginia

The Virginia gypsum deposits occur in Washington and Smyth counties and are described in Bulletin 8 of the Virginia Geological Survey and Bulletin 697 of the United States Geological Survey. There remains much undeveloped property at present remote from transportation. Concentration has taken place in the same valley as the salt deposits, not unlike that of the "dome" deposits in the Gulf states. Originally mined by open cuts, it is now operated from a shaft on a combination of room-and-pillar and stoping methods.

Tennessee

Gypsum is reported south of Walland, Blount county, Tennessee. It has never been developed, but is logically located along a fault line, which has been traced from Washington county, Virginia, southwestward to the Rome (Georgia) fault.

Florida

The deposits of Sumter county, Florida, are undeveloped, but there is a 3 to 12 foot bed about 60 miles north of Tampa, estimated to contain several hundred thousand tons, as well as smaller deposits on neighboring "islands" in a swampy area, about 15 miles from the nearest railroad. In view of the abundant limestone in this region, good roads and truck transportation should solve the problem. The bed could be operated by steam shovel or floating dredge.

Mississippi

Gypsum has been reported from Rankin, Madison and other counties in Mississippi, but the occurrences are lenticular, filled with clay, and too impure and sporadic to offer any substantial industry. Recent developments along the Jasper-Smith county line west of Louin, on the G. M. & N. R. R. indicate a persistent deposit of gypsum in a three-foot vein.

Louisiana

In Calcasieu parish, Louisiana, on Belle Isle, along the Gulf coast, and in Cameron and Winn parishes, gypsum of 100 to 540 feet in thickness has been encountered at depths of from 300 to 1600 feet. If a sufficient coast or export trade could be developed, these could be operated by shaft, as in Virginia.

Arkansas

Surface gypsum is found in Pike and Howard counties, Arkansas, and under Sevier county to the west. It varies from 3 to 14 feet in thickness. In Augusta, Woodruff county, it is found ten feet thick, 100 feet below the surface. None of the deposits in this state have been continuously operated, but they are sufficiently pure to make plaster of Paris, or for agricultural purposes. Three miles south of Murfreesboro and extending to the Little Missouri River is a twelve-foot bed of selenite with from twenty to forty feet overburden of clay gravel and thin-bedded sandstone.

Texas

The gypsum strata of Texas form a belt 50 or more miles wide extending southwest from Hardeman to Sterling county. They dip to the west and underlie the entire Llano Estacado and again outcrop in Culberson, Reeves and Pecos counties. The Hardeman county bed varies from ten to fifty feet in thickness.

Gypsum also occurs in several of the salt domes in the

coastal oil fields. Five miles southeast of Falfurrias, Brooks county, is a mound of pure crystal gypsum, covering three land sections. It has been drilled to a depth of 1100 feet, and could be opened as a hillside quarry. It is pure enough for any purpose, and is probably the best and largest deposit of pure crystal gypsum in the United States. It lies near the S. A. & A. P. R. R. and the Gulf Coast lines.

Uses

The use of gypsum, or "land plaster," for fertilizer purposes has already been noted. It is also a retarding ingredient of Portland cement, and when calcined becomes plaster of Paris, wall plaster, Keene's cement, dental plaster and plate-glass polish. It is mixed with other material for blackboard crayons and match heads, and is a base for certain paints. Insecticides, relief maps and models, statuary, molds for rubber stamps and terra cotta trim, surgical casts, decorative friezes and hat blocks all depend on gypsum, but plaster and wall board, partition blocks and inside trim, furnace and pipe covering, "staff" for temporary buildings and tiling in storage warehouses and laundries where wall-sweating is objectionable, are the large consumers. Technical paper No. 155 of the United States Bureau of Mines discusses gypsum products and their preparation and uses.

* * * * * *

Mineral waters are considered as for table use, medicinal use, and in the manufacture of soft drinks. The industry is an old one and well established. As Board of Health supervision, however, has improved public water supply in many cities, there have been many small producers who catered to local trade who have gone out of business. Increasing population, on the other hand, has increased the pollution of many sources of supply, so that the systematic supplying of offices, hotels, dining cars and steamships with pure bottled drinking water has led to large investment for bottling equipment and delivery service. There is a general tendency toward the development of hotels and resorts at or near the recognized therapeutic springs, especially where their location is such as to offer seasonal inducements.

The *Mineral Resources* of the United States on "Mineral Waters in 1923," published by the United States Geological Survey, contains a list by postoffice and county of all the springs, wells or bathing facilities reported for that year.

Virginia

Virginia leads all the Southern states in mineral waters, both in variety and quantity. Out of 60 companies which have produced in the state, about 30 are now in active operation.

West Virginia—North Carolina—South Carolina

West Virginia lists seven; North Carolina, six, the best known of these being probably the Bailey Radio spring at Ivy, twenty-five miles north of Asheville. South Carolina has six springs. Of the latter, one is distinctly medicinal spring and the others are lithia water.

Georgia—Florida—Alabama—Mississippi—Louisana

Eleven springs in Georgia, eighteen in Florida and four in Alabama offer a variety of waters, while Mississippi lists four and Louisiana two watering places of this type. Besides those mentioned in Mississippi, the chalybeate and sulphur waters in Iuka Springs, the arsenical and lithia waters for the treatment of malaria, Cooper's well, Castillian Springs, and Way, and Arundell Lithia Spring at Hattiesburg, Forrest county, all indicate a merited and growing industry.

Arkansas

The mineral waters of Arkansas are well known, through the exploitation of Hot Springs. Mountain Valley, Eureka Springs and Little Rock also offer similar inducements.

Kentucky—Tennessee

The springs of Kentucky, ten in number, and thirteen in Tennessee, are, many of them, well known, and several of them maintain health resorts which have been in operation for many years.

Texas

The industry in Texas centers around Mineral Wells, Palo Pinto county. Six additional wells are reported in Lamar, Eastland, Falls, Hunt and Nacogdoches counties. There are also hot sulphur wells around San Antonio, Bexar county, and hot alkaline waters at Kennedy, Karnes county.

Thus it will be noted that every one of the Southern states has four or more medicinal springs or wells. Systematic advertising and greater publicity would doubtless assist in developing them all.

CHAPTER XXVI

BIBLIOGRAPHY

The publications and authorities listed below have been freely consulted and utilized in the correlation of data. In certain cases, where comprehensive monographs have been issued and are of recent date, they have been specifically referred to in the text. The author has made frequent reference to the files of the Engineering and Mining Journal-Press, the Manufacturers Record, the Mining Congress Journal, the Mineral Resources of the United States, and the various publications of the State and United States Geological Surveys. To have included specific page and volume references would have made the work unwieldy. Any particular source of information, however, can be obtained from the files of the American Mining Congress.

Adair's New Encyclopedia.
Agriculture Department.
Alabama Geological Survey (particularly Bulletin No. 28).
Alderson, Dr. V. C.: "Oil Shale Industry."
Alexander, M. L.: "Survey of the Natural Resources of Louisiana."
Alpha Aids.
Americana.
American Appraisal News.
American Bankers' Association Journal.
American Ceramic Society Journal.
American Chemical Society Journal.
American Institute Mining and Metallurgical Engineers, Inc.
American Zinc Institute, Inc., Bulletins.
Andalusia (Ala.) Daily Star.
Arizona Mining Journal.
Arkansas Geological Survey.
Armstrong, L. K.: "Washington Non-Metallics."
Army Ordnance.
"Asbestos."
Ashley, Dr. G. H.: "Practical Classification of Coals."
Badu, N. J.
Baker, C. L.: "Review of the Geology of Texas."
Ballou, Joel.
Baltimore & Ohio R. R.

Bayley, W. S.: "High Grade Clays of the Eastern United States"; "Magnetic Iron Ores of East Tennessee and Western North Carolina"; "Magnetite Iron Ore"; "Brown Hematite Ores of Western North Carolina."

Bellah, L. P. (Ind. Agt., N. C. & St. L. Ry.).

Berry, E. W.: "Physiography and Geology of the Coastal Plain of Virginia"; "Limestone and Marl Deposits of North Carolina."

Berry, H. M.: "Mining Industry in North Carolina."

Berwick, Dr. Dudley.

Birmingham (Ala.) News.

"Blast Furnace and Steel Plant."

Blue Book of Southern Progress (Manufacturers Record).

Bose, Emil: See Baker, C. L.

Bowles, H.

Branner, Dr. John C.: "Clays of Arkansas."

Branner, Dr. George C.: "Outlines of Arkansas' Mineral Resources—1927," et al.

Brazleton, T. E. (G. C. & S. Fe Ry.)

Brewer, W. M.: "Mineral Resources of the Upper Gold Belt of Alabama."

Brick and Clay Record.

Bromm, L. W. (Ch. Clerk to Agr. & Ind. Agt., C. &. O R. R.)

Brown, Fred W.: "Sources of Our Nitrogenous Fertilizer."

Brown, Paul J.

Bryson, R. H. (Ind. Agt.—Miss. Cen. R. R.).

Bulletins and Reports: Alabama — "Geological Survey of Alabama"; Arkansas—"Arkansas Geological Survey"; Florida —"Florida Geological Survey"; Georgia—"Geological Survey of Georgia"; Kentucky—"Kentucky Geological Survey"; Louisiana—"Louisiana Department of Conservation"; Mississippi —"Mississippi State Geological Survey"; North Carolina— "North Carolina Geological and Economic Survey"; Tennessee—"State Geological Survey of Tennessee"; Texas—"Bureau of Economic Geology and Technology of Texas"; Virginia—"Virginia Geological Survey"; West Virginia—"West Virginia Geological Survey."

Burchard, Dr. Ernest F.: "Portland Cement Materials and Industry in the United States."

Bureau of Mines.

Bureau of Standards.

"Business."

Calhoun, Dr. F. H. H.: "Limestone and Marl Deposits of South Carolina."

Campbell, Dr. M. R.: "Deep River Coal Field"; "Valley Coal Fields of Virginia."
Canadian Chemistry and Metallurgy.
Cardwell, G. A. (Agr. & Ind. Agt., A. C. L. R. R.).
Carolina, Clinchfield and Ohio Ry.
Center, E. S., Sr. (Ga. Ry. and A. & W. P. R. R.).
Central of Georgia Ry.
Century Dictionary.
Ceramist.
Chemical Age.
Chemical and Metallurgical Engineering.
Chevalier, C. G.
Christian Science Monitor.
Clark, W. B. See Berry, E. W.
Clarke, George H.: "Mica Deposits of Alabama."
Coal Catalogue.
Coal Mining Institute of American Proceedings.
Colorado School of Mines, Bulletins.
Commerce Department.
Commerce Monthly.
Commerce Reports.
"Concrete."
Conference of Governors, Washington, D. C., 1908.
Country Gentleman.
Crider, A. F.: "Cement and Portland Cement Materials of Mississippi."
Crouse, Dr. C. S. (U. of Ky.).
Cummings, F. P.
Current News.
Cushman, J. A. See Berry, E. W.
Dabney, Dr. Chas. W.
Darton, N. H.: "Economic Geology of Richmond, Virginia and Vicinity."
Davis, Watson: "Story of Copper."
Daw, H. L. (Div. Freight Agt. N. & W. R. R.)
De Bardeleben, Henry T.
Denison, Walter.
Directory of Commercial Minerals in Georgia and Alabama
—Central of Georgia Railway.
Drane, Brent S.: "Mining Industry in North Carolina."
Earp-Thomas, G. H.: "Peat As a Carrier for Bacteria."
Eckel, E. C. See Burchard, E. F.
Economic Geology in North Carolina.
Electric Controller and Manufacturing Company.
Electric Journal.

Encyclopedia Britannica.
Engineering and Mining Journal.
Engineering and Mining Journal-Press.
Ferguson, H. J.: "Tin Deposits Near Irish Creek, Virginia."
Ferguson, Jim G.: "Arkansas Handbook"; "Industrial Arkansas"; "Minerals in Arkansas"; "Oil and Gas Fields of Arkansas."
Fernstrom, H. (Ch. Engr.—Virginian Ry.).
Florida Geological Survey.
Forbes, B. C.
"Foundry."
Fuller, John T.
Gale, H. S.: "Miscellaneous Non-Metallic Products."
Ganier, A. F.
Geological Society of America, Bulletins.
Georgia Geological Survey.
Glunk, Robert: "Louisiana Lignite."
Green, G. W. (Ind. Dept.—Frisco Lines).
Griffith, C. J.
Grimsley, Dr. G. P. (Geological Engineer, B. & O. R. R.).
Gunter, Herman.
Guthrie, K. R. (Ind. Dept.—A. T. & N. R. R.).
"Gypsum Industries."
Hackett, Allen S.
Hand, J. H.
Harris, G. D.: "Rock Salt, Its Origin, Occurrence and Importance in Louisiana."
Hastings, E. M. (Ch. Engr.—R. F. &. P. R. R.).
Hayes, C. W.: "Metals and Non-Metals in the United States."
Hays, W. S.
Hess, Dr. F. L.: "Zirconiferous Sandstone."
Hertzog, E. L.
Hopkins, O. B.: "Asbestos, Talc and Soapstone Deposits of Georgia."
Illinois Central R. R.
Industrial Dept. C. R. I. & P. R. R.
Industrial and Engineering Chemistry.
Interior Department.
Iron Age.
Iron Trade.
Iron Trade Review.
Jackosky, J. J.: "Electrical Manufacture of Carbon Black."
Jefferson (N. C.) Herald.
Jillson, Dr. W. R.

Joffe, Jacob S.
Jones, H. S.—(G. M. & N. R. R.).
Journal of American Institute of Architects.
Journal of Industrial and Engineering Chemistry.
Journal of Western Society of Engineers.
Kentucky Geological Survey.
Kimball, K. W.   See Campbell, M. R.
Knight, F. P.
Knoxville (Tenn.) Sentinel.
Kopman—Dept. of Conservation, Louisiana.
Ladoo, Raymond B. (Bureau of Mines): "Talc and Soapstone."
Land of Resources (Ind. Dept.—Tenn. Cen. R. R.).
Laughlin, G. F.   See Berry, E. W.
"Lignites of Louisiana."
Lindsey, W. H.
Lloyd, Dr. Stewart J. (University of Alabama).
Logan, W. N.: "Pottery Clays of Mississippi"; "Clays of Mississippi."
Louisiana, Department of Conservation.
Louisiana Survey.
Lowe, Dr. E. N.; "Iron Ores of Mississippi"; "Marls and Limestones of Mississippi"; "Road Making Materials of Mississippi."
Lucey, Matt (Ind. Dept.—Mo. Pac. R. R.).
Lindgren, Dr. W.   See Hayes, C. W.
Luckel, L. O.
McCallie, Dr. S. W.: "Handbook of Mineral Resources of Georgia."
McDonald, F. H.
McGurty, H. A.
McKeand, C. A.
Madison, H. M. (Ind. Agt.—S. A. & A. P. R. R.).
Mallory, J. M. (Ind. Agt.—Central of Georgia Ry.).
Manson, M. E.
Manufacturers Record.
Meade, R. K.
Melcher, J. C.
Memphis (Tenn.) Commercial Appeal.
Metal Industry.
Miller, Dr. Benj. L. See Berry, E. W.
Miller Survey.
Mineral Resources.
Mineral Resources of the United States.
Mining and Metallurgy.

Mining Congress Bulletin.
Mining Congress Journal.
Mining Magazine.
Mining Topics.
Mining Truth.
Mississippi Developer.
Mississippi Facts.
Mississippi State Chamber of Commerce: "Mississippi Builder."
Mississippi State Geological Survey.
Mitchell, Col. R. A.
Mitchell, S. B.
Morse, P. F.: "Petroleum Prospecting in Mississippi"; "Bauxite Deposits of Mississippi."
Munn, M. J.: "Fayette Gas Field of Alabama."
Murray's English Dictionary.
Myers, W. M. (Bureau of Mines).
Nashville (Tenn.) Banner.
National Petroleum News.
Natural Resources.
Nelson, Dr. Wilbur A.
Nelson's Encyclopedia.
Newan, O. D.
New Jersey State Agricultural Experiment Association Bulletin.
New York Herald-Tribune.
New York Sun.
New York Times.
Nicholson, F. L. (Ch. Engr.—N. S. R. R.).
"Nickel."
Niel, R. E. L.
"Nitrate."
North Carolina Geological and Economic Survey.
North Carolina Natural Resources.
Norwood, Dr. C. J. (University of Kentucky).
Oddie, Senator T. L.
Oil, Paint and Drug Reporter.
O'Kelly, E. B. (Ind. Agt.—A. C. L. R. R.).
"Paper."
Paper Trade Journal.
Pearson, C. H.
Peavy, Arthur.
Peele, Robert: "Mining Engineers' Handbook."
Peeler, T. L. (Ind. Agt.—M-K-T R. R.).
Pennybacker, J. E.

Perry, J. M.
Peterson's Development Company.
Philadelphia Evening Bulletin.
Philadelphia Inquirer.
Popular Mechanics.
Portland Cement Association.
Power Plant Engineering.
Pratt, Dr. Jos. Hyde: "Corundum, Its Occurrences and Distribution"; "Tin Deposits of the Carolinas"; "Western North Carolina, Inc."; "Zircon, Monazite and Other Minerals." See Berry, H. M.
Prouty, W. F.: "Graphite Industry in Clay County, Alabama."
Railway Mechanical Engineer.
"Raw Material."
"Reactions."
Reports—Interstate Commerce Commission.
Reports—Federal Trade Commission.
Research Group News.
Resources of Tennessee.
Ries, Dr. H.: "Clays, Occurrences, Properties and Uses." See Bayley, W. S.
Rt. Hon. Viscount Long of Wraxel: "Mineral Resources and Their Relation to Prosperity."
Robinson, E. L. (Ind. Dept.—M. & O. R. R.).
Ross, Wm. H.: "Fertilizer From Industrial Waste."
Rural New Yorker.
Rust and Rot Prevention—Stone and Tar Products Company.
Safety Engineering.
Salt Lake Survey.
Santana, Chas. (Ind. Dept.—N. O. & G. N. R. R.).
Saturday Evening Post.
Saupe, L. A. (Ind. Dept.—Cotton Belt Route).
Scientific American.
Schneider, W. G.
Scholz, Carl.
Schoup, M. Alfred.
Schwrecht, H. G.
Seaboard Air Line Ry.
Seaman, H. W.
Seaman, R. J.
"Secondary Metals."
Sellards, Dr. E. H.: "Soils of Florida"; "Origin of Hard Rock Phosphate Deposits"; "Pebble Phosphates of Florida."

Shaw, J. B.
Sheet Metal Worker.
Shiras, Tom.
Stuckey, J. L. See Drane, Brent S.
Simpson, A. D.
"Slate."
Slate, Its Uses.
Smith, A. R.
Smith, Edgar L.: "Phosphate Germ."
Smith, Dr. Eugene A.
Smith, H. W.
Smith, Rutledge (Tenn. Cen. R. R.).
Sydnor, W. O. (Asst. Gen. Frt. Agt.—C. & O. R. R.).
Some Facts About Sulphur.
Southern Field.
Southgate, Geo. T.
South's Development (Manufacturers Record).
Spence, Hugh S. (Dept. of Mines, Canada).
Spokane (Wn.) Spokesman-Review.
Spurr, Josiah Edward: "The Marketing of Metals and Minerals."
Sterrett, D. B.: "Mica Deposits of the United States." See Pratt, Dr. Jos. Hyde. See Gale, H. S.
Stose, G. W.: "Geology of the Salt and Gypsum Deposits of Southwestern Virginia."
Stull, Dr. R. T. (Cen. of Georgia Ry.).
Summary-Engineering, London.
Taber, Stephen: "Geology of the Titanium and Apatite Deposits of Virginia."
"Talc and Soapstone."
Taylor, J. J. (Ind. Dept.—G. & S. I. R. R.).
Tech Engineering News.
Tenn. Cen. R. R.
Tenn. River and Tributaries (H. R. Document No. 319).
Tennessee State Geological Survey.
Texas Bureau of Economic Technology and Geology.
Texas Gulf Sulphur Company.
Thompson, C. H.
Thorpe Dictionary of Applied Chemistry.
Thurlow, O. G.
Transactions of American Institute of Civil Engineers.
Udden, Dr. J. A. See Baker, C. L.
United States Geological Survey.
Utility News (Dallas, Texas).
Virginia State Chamber of Commerce.

Virginia Geological Survey.
Waggaman & Wagner: "Ground Raw Rock Phosphate as a Fertilizer."
Wall Street Journal.
War Department: "Fixation and Utilization of Nitrogen."
Ward, Gruver & Co.: "Crude Petroleum and Gasoline."
Warren, Robert.
Washington (D. C.) Post.
Washington (D. C.) Star.
Watkins, Dr. Joel.
Watson, Dr. Thos. L. See Taber, Stephen. "Glass Sand Resources of Virginia." See Hess, F. L. See Berry, E. W.
Webster's New International Dictionary.
Weed, W. H.: "Copper Deposits of the Appalachian States."
Week (Atlanta, Ga.).
Wells, A. E.: "Potash Industry of the United States."
West Virginia Geological Survey.
White, Dr. I. C.
Whitney, Milton: "Fertilizer Situation."
Willett, N. L. (Ind. Dept.—C. & W. C. R. R.).
Wilhoit, H. H. (Southern Ry.).
Williams, Jas. C.
Williams, Jas. P.
Wilmington (N. C.) Morning Star.
Wilson, Philip D.: "Methods of Recording Underground Geological Data, Mine Sampling and Estimation of Ore Reserves."
Wormser, Felix Edgar. See Spurr, Josiah Edward.
Yellville (Arkansas) Mining Reporter.
Young, J. H.

INDEX

A

ALABAMA   Page
- Antimony, possible in 126
- Arseno-pyrites 335
- Asbestos 340
- Asphalt 86
- Barytes 33
- Bauxite 23
- Bentonite 47
- Chalk 43
- Chasers 17
- Chert 302
- Chromite 119
- Clays 219
- Coal 54
- Copper 169
- Diamonds 151
- Feldspar 268
- Fullers' earth 15
- Gems 149, 150
- Gold 162
- Graphite 154
- Gravel 300
- Iron 105
- Lignite 58
- Limestone, agricultural and chemical 320
- Limestone, building 281
- Lithographic stone 257
- Manganese 123
- Marble 281
- Marl 330
- Mica 237
- Millstones 17
- Mineral pigments 40
- Mineral waters 346
- Molding sand and clay 297
- Ochre 39
- Oil shale 83
- Petroleum 73
- Pyrites 176
- Sand 291
- Sandstone 281
- Serpentine 281
- Shales 247
- Sienna 40
- Silver 165
- Slate 250
- Talc 242
- Tin 196
- Tripoli 10

ANTIMONY 125, 126
- Appearance 125
- Characteristics 125
- Deposit in:
  - Arkansas 126
- Identification 125
- Probable deposits in:
  - Alabama 126
  - Mississippi 126
- Uses 126

ARKANSAS
- Antimony 126
- Asphalt 87
- Barytes 35
- Bauxite 24
- Bentonite 49
- Chalk 43
- Chert 305
- Clays 223

                                    Page
- Coal 56
- Copper 170
- Diamonds 151
- Diatomaceous earth, reported in 7
- Feldspar 268
- Fullers earth 17
- Gold 163
- Granite 282
- Graphite 155
- Gravel 300
- Gypsum 344
- Ilemite 134
- Iron 109
- Lead 190
- Limestone, agricultural and chemical 324
- Limestone, building 282
- Lithographic stone 258
- Manganese 124
- Marble 282
- Marl 330
- Mica 237
- Mineral waters 347
- Molding sand and clay 297
- Natural gas 90
- Novaculite 18
- Ochre 41
- Oil shale 83
- Petroleum 76
- Phosphate rock 312
- Pyrites 177
- Rutile 134
- Sand 292
- Sandstone 282
- Slate 250
- Strontium 137
- Talc 242
- Tripoli 10
- Tungsten 140
- Zinc 190

ASBESTOS 337-341
- "Asbestic" 338
- "Asbestine" 341
- Deposits in:
  - Alabama 340
  - Georgia 339
  - North Carolina 338
  - Virginia 338
- Early history 337
- "Fibre talc" 341
- Method of mining and preparation 337, 341
- Occurrences:
  - Cross fibre 337
  - Mass fibre 337
  - Slip fibre 337
- Uses 340

ASPHALT 84-88
- Bitumen from pine stump distillation 87
- Deposits in:
  - Alabama 86
  - Arkansas 87
  - Kentucky 85
  - Louisiana 87
  - Mississippi 87
  - Texas 88
- Earliest recorded use for paving 84
- Uses 87

357

INDEX

B

	Page
BARYTES	30-36
Blanc fixe	30
Deposits in:	
Alabama	33
Arkansas	35
Georgia	33
Kentucky	34
North Carolina	32
South Carolina	33
Tennessee	35
Texas	36
Virginia	31
West Virginia	32
Effect of tariff	36
Forms	30
Lithopone	30
Uses	30
BAUKITE	27-29
Chemical characteristics	28
Deposits in:	
Mississippi	28
Tennessee	27
Discovery of	27
Uses	28
BAUXITE	19-27
Aluminum	19
Affinity for oxygen	26
Alum	20
Aluminum cement	20
Artificial abrasives	20
Essentials of production	20
Forms	19
Improved methods of extraction	20
Objectionable impurities	19
Preparation	21
Deposits in:	
Alabama	23
Arkansas	24
Georgia	22
Kentucky	22
Mississippi	23
North Carolina	22
Tennessee	22
Texas	24
Virginia	21
Origin	19
Uses	24
BENTONITE	45-49
Characteristics	45
Counterpart of montmorillonite	45
Deposits in:	
Alabama	47
Arkansas	49
Kentucky	47
Mississippi	48
Tennessee	47
Texas	48
Uses	45
BERYLLIUM	150
Source	150
Uses	150
BUILDING AND MISCELLANEOUS SAND	285
General areas of deposition	285
Increasing demands for	285
Uses	285
BUILDING STONE BY-PRODUCTS	274-275
Improved paving	274
Uses	274
CALCIUM ARSENATE	335-336
Arseno-pyrites	335

	Page
Deposits in:	
Alabama	335
North Carolina	336
Preparation	335
Sources of arsenic	335
Uses	335
CARBON BLACK	91-92
Decrease of industry in West Virginia	91
Electric process of production	91
Growth of industry in Louisiana	91
Uses	92
CARNOTITE	
Occurrences	131
Uses	131
CEMENT	331-335
Consumption	331
Increased demand	332
New processes for natural cement	334
Opportunities for	332
Oyster-shell beds	333
Production	332
Special cements	334
Uses	331

C

	Page
CERIUM	129, 130, 136
Characteristics	129
Deposits in:	
North Carolina	136
South Carolina	136
Virginia	136
Uses	130
CHALK	43-45
"Cliffstone"	43
Competition with imported	44
Deposits in:	
Alabama	43
Arkansas	43
Mississippi	43
Texas	44
Reported in:	
Georgia	44
North Carolina	44
Tennessee	44
CHASERS	17
Deposits in:	
Alabama	17
Virginia	17
CHERT	300-306
"Caliche"	306
Deposits in:	
Alabama	302
Arkansas	305
Florida	302
Georgia	302
Kentucky	303
Louisiana	305
Mississippi	303
North Carolina	301
South Carolina	301
Tennessee	303
Texas	306
Virginia	300
Local names	300
"Road metal"	300
Uses	306
Usual formation	300
CHLORITE	239
Deposit in:	
Georgia	239
Occurrence	239
Uses	239

INDEX

	Page
CHROMITE	116-119
Characteristics	117
Deposit in:	
Alabama	119
North Carolina	118
Virginia	118
Disadvantages	117
Handicaps of transportation	116
Uses	116
CINNABAR	269-272
Anticlinal occurrences	270
Deposit in:	
Texas	269
Markets	271
Mercury vapor boiler	272
Smelting	269
Uses	271
CLAYS	198-229
Deposits in:	
Alabama	219
Arkansas	223
Florida	214
Georgia	210
Kentucky	216
Louisiana	222
Mississippi	221
North Carolina	205
South Carolina	208
Tennessee	217
Texas	224
Virginia	203
West Virginia	204
Foreign clays	202
General classification	198
High grade	198
Low grade	198
Kaolin	202
Method of shipment	202
Mineral fillers	200
"Off color" clays	201
Porcelain clays	201
Problems of mining	200
Uses	226
Whiteware clays	200
COAL	51-58
Briquettes	54, 55, 56
By-products	54, 56, 58
Deposits in:	
Alabama	54
Arkansas	56
Georgia	54
Kentucky	55
Mississippi	55
North Carolina	53
Tennessee	56
Texas	57
Virginia	52
West Virginia	53
Economic factors	51
Low temperature carbonization	56
Uses	58
COLUMBITE	129, 135, 136
Associations	129
Deposits in:	
North Carolina	136
Virginia	136
COLUMBIUM	129
Associations	129
COPPER	165-171
Alloys	172
Classes of products	166
Deposits in:	
Alabama	169
Arkansas	170

	Page
Georgia	169
North Carolina	168
South Carolina	169
Tennessee	169
Texas	171
Virginia	167
Factor of safety value	173
Growth of industry	166
New fields for research	173
Occurrences	165
Opportunities for new smelters	166
Refining centers	171
Uses	171
COPPERAS	177-178
Deposits in:	
Mississippi	177
North Carolina	177
Tennessee	177
Uses	177
CORUNDUM	147-148
Associated gems	147
Carborundum	147
Competition with imported ore	147
Deposits in:	
Georgia	148
North Carolina	148
Virginia	148
Tests for	148
CYANITE	229, 231
Characteristics	229
Deposits in:	
North Carolina	230
Virginia	230
Uses	230

D

	Page
DIAMONDS	151-152
Deposits in:	
Arkansas	151
Sporadic occurrences:	
Alabama	151
Georgia	151
North Carolina	151
Texas	151
Virginia	151
DIATOMACEOUS EARTH	4-8
Absorbtivity	5
Analysis	5
Color	5
Deposits in:	
Arkansas, reported in	7
Florida	7
Mississippi	7
South Carolina	6
Texas	7
Virginia	6
Derivation	4
Marketed forms	5
Occurrence	5
Problems	5, 6
Qualities	5
Specific gravity	5
Tests	5
Uses	7
Weight	5

E

	Page
ELECTRIC SMELTING	111-115
Application to non-ferrous metallurgy	113
Beneficiation processes	93, 113
"Direct steel" processes	114, 115
Double vs. single voltage	114
Exhaustion of high-grade ores	112

INDEX

	Page
Modified types	114
Power consumption	114
Sponge iron processes	112
Uses	113
EMERY. *Vide* Corundum	

F

	Page
FELDSPAR	265-269
Associated with mica	265
Classifications	266
Commercial grades	265
Dental quality	266
Deposits in:	
Alabama	268
Arkansas	268
Georgia	268
North Carolina	267
Tennessee	268
Texas	268
Virginia	267
Effect of freight rates	266
Forms	265
Methods of separation	265, 266
Objectionable impurities	265
Porcelain manufacture	266
Preparation	265
Problem of standardization	266
Uses	266-269
FLORIDA	
Chert	302
Clays	214
Diatomaceous earth	7
Fuller's earth	16
Gypsum	343
Ilmenite	134
Limestone, agricultural and chemical	321
Marl	329
Mineral waters	346
Molding sand and clay	296
Peat	67
Petroleum, reported in	72
Phosphate rock	310
Rutile	134
Sand	290
Tripoli	10
Zirconium	135
FLUORSPAR	252-255
Deposits in:	
Georgia	254
Kentucky	254
Tennessee	255
Texas	255
Virginia	254
Distribution of product	252
Effect of tariff	253
Method of occurrences	252
Problems of mining	252
Sizes and grades	253
Uses	255
FULLER'S EARTH	12-17
Characteristics	12
Claystone, form of	16
Deposits in:	
Alabama	15
Arkansas	17
Florida	16
Georgia	14
Mississippi	16
North Carolina	14
South Carolina	14
Texas	17
Virginia	14

	Page
Tests	12
Uses	13

G

	Page
GADOLINITE	130-131
Occurrences	130
GEMS	148-151
Classification	148
Deposits in:	
Alabama	149, 150
Georgia	149
North Carolina	148, 149, 150
South Carolina	149
Texas	150
Virginia	149
Uses	158-163
GEORGIA	
Asbestos	339
Barytes	33
Bauxite	22
Chalk, reported in	44
Chert	302
Chlorite	239
Clays	210
Coal	54
Copper	169
Corundum	148
Diamonds	151
Feldspar	268
Fluorspar	254
Fullers' earth	14
Gems	149
Gold	160
Granite	278
Graphite	154
Gravel	299
Ilmenite	134
Iron	104
Lignite	58
Limestone, agricultural and chemical	319
Limestone, building	278
Manganese	123
Marble	278
Marl	329
Mica	237
Mineral waters	346
Molding sand and clay	296
Nickel	142
Ochre	38
Petroleum	71
Pyrites	175
Rutile	134
Sand	289
Sap brown	39
Serpentine	279
Shales	247
Slate	250
Talc	242
Tellurium	137
Tripoli	9
Whiting	44
GERMANIUM	192
Sources	192
Uses	192
GOLD	158-163
Deposits in:	
Alabama	162
Arkansas	163
Georgia	160
North Carolina	159
South Carolina	160
Tennessee	161
Texas	163

INDEX

	Page
Tennessee	280
Texas	283
Virginia	275
Domestic harder than imported.	273
Restrictions on finished marble.	273
Uses	284
Wholesale market	273
MARLS	326-331
Deposits in:	
Alabama	330
Arkansas	330
Florida	329
Georgia	329
Louisiana	330
Mississippi	330
North Carolina	327
South Carolina	328
Texas	331
Virginia	327
West Virginia	316
Method of occurrences	326
Varieties	326
Uses	326
MICA	232-239
Color	232
Deposits in:	
Alabama	237
Arkansas	237
Georgia	237
North Carolina	235
South Carolina	154, 236
Texas	238
Virginia	234
Di-electric properties	232, 233
Difficulties in development	233
Electrical specifications	233
Growth in consumption	232
Method of operation	233, 234
Non-absorbtivity	232
Phlogopite	234
Preparation for market	233
Specific gravity	232
Uses	238
Usual occurrences	232
Various forms	232
MINERAL PIGMENTS	36-42
Adjective pigments	37
Deposits in:	
Alabama	40
Virginia	38
Requirements	37
Substantive pigments	37
MINERAL WATERS	345-347
Occurrences in:	
Alabama	346
Arkansas	347
Florida	346
Georgia	346
Kentucky	347
Louisiana	346
Mississippi	346
North Carolina	346
South Carolina	346
Tennessee	347
Texas	347
Virginia	346
West Virginia	346
MISSISSIPPI	
Antimony, possible in	126
Asphalt	73
Baukite	28
Bauxite	23
Bentonite	48

	Page
Chalk	43
Chert	303
Clays	221
Coal	55
Copperas	177
Diatomaceous earth	7
Fullers' earth	16
Granite	281
Gravel	300
Gypsum	343
Iron	107
Lignite	59
Limestone, agricultural and chemical	321
Limestone, building	281
Marble	281
Marl	330
Mineral waters	346
Molding sand and clay	297
Natural gas	90
Novaculite	18
Ochre	40
Oil shale	83
Paint pigments	18, 40, 41
Petroleum structures	73
Phosphate rock	312
Sand	291
Sandstone	282
Tripoli	10
MOLDING SAND AND CLAY.	294-297
Annual requirements	294
Deposits in:	
Alabama	297
Arkansas	297
Florida	296
Georgia	296
Kentucky	217, 295
Mississippi	297
North Carolina	295
South Carolina	295
Tennessee	296
Texas	297
Virginia	295
West Virginia	294
Specifications	294
Tests for	285
MOLYBDENUM	138-139
Advantages in use	138
By-products	138
Deposit in:	
Texas	139
Pyrex glass welding	138
Treatment	138
Uses	138
MONAZITE	130, 136
Deposit in:	
North Carolina	129, 136
North Carolina	136, 154
Virginia	136
Occurrences	136
MONTAN WAX	64
MONZONITE	128
Deposit in:	
North Carolina	135
Characteristics	128

N

NATURAL GAS	89-91
Conservation of	89
Earliest use in the United States:	89
For fuel	89
For lights	89
Gasoline from	90
Production of gasoline	90

INDEX

	Page
Helium from	90
Industries dependent on	89
New fields	90
Price factor	91
Production, 1923	89
Sources:	
Arkansas	90
Kentucky	90
Louisiana	90
Mississippi	90
Tennessee	90
Texas	90
West Virginia	89
NICKEL	141-143
Alloys	142
Catalytic property	143
Deposits in:	
Georgia	142
North Carolina	141
South Carolina	142
Tennessee	142
Virginia	141
Uses	142
NORTH CAROLINA	
Arseno-pyrites	336
Asbestos	338
Barytes	32
Bauxite	22
Cerium	136
Chalk, reported in	44
Chert	301
Chromite	118
Clays	205
Coal	53
Columbite	136
Copper	168
Copperas	177
Corundum	148
Cyanite	230
Diamonds	151
Feldspar	267
Fullers' earth	14
Gems	148, 149, 150
Gold	159
Granite	276
Graphite	153
Gravel	299
Iron	97
Lead	187
Limestone, agricultural and chemical	318
Limestone	277
Manganese	122
Marble	277
Marl	327
Mica	235
Mineral waters	346
Molding sand and clay	295
Monazite	129, 136
Monzonite	135
Nickel	141
Novaculite	18
Ochre	38
Oil shale	81
Peat	66
Petroleum, test wells	70
Pyrites	175
Rutile	134
Samarskite	133
Sand	288
Sandstone	277
Serpentine	277
Shales	245
Silver	164

	Page
Talc	241
Tellurium	137
Thoria	136
Thorium	136
Tin	194
Tungsten	140
Whiting	44
Zinc	187
Zirconium	129
NOVACULITE	17-18
Deposits in:	
Arkansas	18
Mississippi	18
North Carolina	18
Tennessee	18
Chasers	17
Grindstones	18
Millstones	17
Rottenstone	18
Uses	17

O

OCHRE	36-42
Colors	36
Deposits in:	
Alabama	39
Arkansas	41
Georgia	38
Kentucky	39
Mississippi	40
North Carolina	38
Tennessee	39
Texas	41
Virginia	37
West Virginia	38
Derivation	36
Foreign competition	41
Occurrence	36
Treatment	36
Uses	41
OIL SHALE	78-84
By-products	79
Carbon black recovery	78
Characteristics	78
Comparison of shale oil with well oil	80
Cost of plant installation	79
Deposits in:	
Alabama	83
Arkansas	83
Kentucky	81
Mississippi	83
North Carolina	81
Tennessee	82
Texas	83
West Virginia	80
Difference from oil sand	78
Economic discussion	79
Gasoline recovery	78
Ichthyol	84
Occurrence in Texas	84
Large scale operations necessary	78
Oil yield per ton	79
"OXYGEN-SULPHUR FAMILY"	131

P

PEAT	65-68
Classes of	65
Deposits in:	
Florida	67
North Carolina	66
Virginia	66
Fertilizer filler	65, 67, 68
Micro-organic fertilizer	67

INDEX

Powdered fuel 66
Uses 65
PETROLEUM 69-78
  Consumption, industrial heating 70
  Consumption per capita....... 70
  Deposits in:
    Alabama 73
    Arkansas 76
    Florida, reported in 72
    Georgia 71
    Kentucky 72
    Louisiana 75
    Mississippi, structures 73
    North Carolina, test wells ... 70
    Tennessee 73
    Texas 77
    West Virginia 70
  Fuel conservation 70
  Increase in gasoline and lubricating oil 69
  Losses in refining 70
  Oils from wood distillates...... 70
  Peg models: 74
    Method of construction...... 74
    Value of 74
  Production in the South....... 69
  Reserves in the South.......... 69
PHOSPHATE ROCK 307-313
  Allowable overburden 307
  Blue 307, 310, 311
  Brown 307, 310, 311, 312
  Deposits in:
    Arkansas 312
    Florida 310
    Kentucky 312
    Mississippi 312
    South Carolina 310
    Tennessee 310
    Texas 312
  Government Reserves 310
  Land rock 307
  Pebble rock 307
  Phosphates:
    Uses 313
  Phosphoric acid: 311, 313
    Acid processes 308
    Catalysis 308
    Distillation processes 308
    Non-acid processes 308
    Sulphuric acid process 309
  Raw rock as fertilizer: 308, 309
  Sulphur in connection with .. 309
  White 311
POTASH 259-265
  Annual consumption 260
  Agricultural impoverishment of soil 259
  Deposit in:
    Texas 263
  Effect of tariff 259, 261
  Need for domestic supply...... 259
  Nitrogenous resources.......... 260
  Recovery from:
    Blast furnaces 261
    Cement plants 261
    Feldspar 260, 262
    Glauconite 260, 262
    Sericite 262
  Sources:
    Beet sugar waste 263
    By-product and waste recovery 261
    Feldspar 262
    Glauconite sands 262

    Industrial wastes 263
    Kelp 263
    Lake bed deposits 260
    Molasses distillery waste 263
    Polyhalite 261
    Potash springs 260
    Sericite 262
    Wool washing 263
  Uses 265
PYRITES 174-177
  Arseno-pyrites:............. 176
  Calcium arsenate industry 174, 176
    (*Vide* Chap. XXV)
  Deposits in:
    Alabama 176
    Arkansas 177
    Georgia 175
    North Carolina 175
    South Carolina 175
    Texas 177
    Virginia 175
  Effect of sulphur on importations of 174
  Uses 174

R

REDDLE 41
  Deposit in:
    Arkansas 41
RUTILE 127-135
  Deposits in:
    Arkansas 134
    Florida 134
    Georgia 134
    North Carolina............. 133
    South Carolina 134
    Texas 134
    Virginia 133
  Uses 127

S

SALT 181-185
  Deposits in:
    Louisiana 183
    Tennessee 183
    Texas 184
    Virginia 183
    West Virginia 182
  Difficulties encountered 182
  Methods of mining 182
  Salt cake: 184
    New method of making 184
  Soda ash 182
  Uses 182
SAMARSKITE 129
  Deposit in:
    North Carolina............. 133
  Uses 129
SAND 285-294
  Annual consumption........... 285
  Colorization due to iron........ 286
  Deposits in:
    Alabama 291
    Arkansas 292
    Florida 290
    Georgia 289
    Kentucky 288
    Louisiana 292
    Mississippi 291
    North Carolina............. 288
    South Carolina 288
    Tennessee 289
    Texas 293
    Virginia 286

INDEX

	Page
West Virginia	287
Effect of magnesia	286
Glass pig	292
Glass sand	285
Lump silica	286
Neutralizing mediums	286
Range of price	286
Size	286
Sources	286
Specifications	286
Trade names	286
Uses	285, 293
SANDSTONE	273, 274
Deposits in:	
Alabama	281
Arkansas	282
Kentucky	279
Mississippi	282
North Carolina	277
Tennessee	280
Texas	283
Virginia	275
West Virginia	275
Uses	284
SAP BROWN	39
Deposit in:	
Georgia	39
SELENIUM	132
Sources	132
Uses	132
SERICITE	239
Occurrence	239
Uses	238
SERPENTINE	274, 275
Deposits in:	
Alabama	281
Georgia	279
North Carolina	277
Uses	274
SHALES	245-247
Deposits in:	
Alabama	247
Georgia	247
North Carolina	245
South Carolina	246
Tennessee	246
Virginia	245
West Virginia	245
Grades	245
Uses	245
SIENNA	36, 37, 40
Deposit in:	
Alabama	40
SILLIMANITE	198
SILVER	163-165
By-product production	164, 165
Deposits in:	
Alabama	165
North Carolina	164
South Carolina	164
Tennessee	164
Texas	165
Virginia	164
New industrial demands	164
Uses	165
SLATE	247-251
Chemical characteristics	247
Centers of consumption	248
Deposits in:	
Alabama	250
Arkansas	250
Georgia	250
Tennessee	249
Virginia	249
West Virginia	249

	Page
Transportation problem	248
Uses	251
SOUTH CAROLINA	
Barytes	33
Cerium	136
Chert	301
Clays	208
Copper	169
Diatomaceous earth	6
Fullers' earth	14
Gems	149
Gold	160
Granite	277
Graphite	154
Gravel	299
Ilmenite	134
Iron	99
Lead	188
Limestone, agricultural and chemical	318
Manganese	122
Marble	278
Marl	328
Mica	154, 236
Mineral waters	346
Molding sand and clay	295
Monazite	136, 154
Nickel	142
Phosphate rock	310
Pyrites	175
Rutile	134
Sand	288
Shales	246
Silver	164
Talc	242
Thoria	136
Thorium	136
Tin	194
STRONTIUM	132
Characteristics	132
Deposits in:	
Arkansas	137
Texas	137
Uses	132
SULPHUR	178-181
Consumption	178
Deposits in:	
Louisiana	178
Texas	178
Di-electric properties	180
Effect on:	
Concrete	180
Dried fruits	180
Paper pulp	180
Fertilizer experiments with	179
Methods of mining	179
Salt dome formations	179
Uses	179

T

TALC	239-244
Deposits in:	
Alabama	242
Arkansas	242
Georgia	242
North Carolina	241
South Carolina	242
Texas	243
Virginia	241
Grades	240
Market requirements	240
Pyrophyllite	240
Soapstone	239, 240
Specific gravity	240
Trade names	240

INDEX

	Page
Uses	243
TELLURIUM	131
Characteristics	131
Deposits in:	
Georgia	137
North Carolina	137
Tennessee	137
Virginia	137
Uses	132
TENNESSEE	
Barytes	35
Baukite	27
Bauxite	22
Bentonite	47
Chalk, reported in	44
Chert	303
Clays	217
Coal	56
Copper	169
Copperas	177
Feldspar	268
Fluorspar	255
Gold	161
Granite	280
Gravel	300
Gypsum	343
Iron	100
Lead	188
Limestone, agricultural and chemical	320
Limestone, building	280
Lithographic stone	257
Manganese	121
Marble	280
Mineral waters	347
Molding sand and clay	296
Natural gas	90
Nickel	142
Novaculite	18
Ochre	39
Oil shale	82
Petroleum	73
Phosphate rock	310
Salt	183
Sand	289
Sandstone	280
Shales	246
Silver	164
Slate	249
Tellurium	137
Tripoli	10
Whiting	44
Zinc	188
TEXAS	
Asphalt	88
Barytes	36
Bauxite	24
Bentonite	48
Chalk	44
Chert	306
Cinnabar	269
Clays	224
Coal	57
Copper	171
Diamonds	151
Diatomaceous earth	7
Feldspar	268
Fluorspar	255
Fullers' earth	17
Gems	150
Gold	163
Granite	283
Graphite	155
Gravel	300
Ichthyol	84

	Page
Ilmenite	134
Iron	109
Lead	190
Lignite	59
Limestone, agricultural and chemical	325
Limestone, building	283
Lithographic stone	258
Manganese	125
Marble	283
Marl	331
Mica	238
Mineral waters	347
Molding sand and clay	297
Molybdenum	139
Natural gas	90
Oil shale	83
Ochre	41
Petroleum	77
Phosphate rock	312
Potash	263
Pyrites	177
Rutile	134
Salt	184
Sand	293
Sandstone	283
Silver	165
Strontium	137
Sulphur	179
Talc	243
Thoria	136
Thorium	136
Tin	196
Tripoli	10
Tungsten	140
Zinc	190
THORIA	130
Deposits in:	
North Carolina	136
South Carolina	136
Texas	136
Virginia	136
Uses	130
THORIUM	130
Deposits in:	
North Carolina	136
South Carolina	136
Texas	136
Virginia	136
Occurrence	136
Tests for	130
Uses	130
TIN	193, 197
Alloys	193, 194
Annual requirements in U. S.	193
Deposits in:	
Alabama	196
North Carolina	194
South Carolina	194
Texas	196
Virginia	194
De-tinning processes	197
Problems of mining	196
Smelters	193
Uses	193
TITANIUM	126
Occurrence	126
Uses	127
TRIPOLI	8-12
Absorbtivity	9
Color	9
Deposits in:	
Alabama	10
Arkansas	10
Florida	10
Georgia	9

INDEX

	Page
Louisiana	11
Mississippi	10
Tennessee	10
Texas	10
Virginia	9
Derivation	8
Occurrence	8
Porosity	9
Problems	11
Pumiceous rhyolite, form of	9
Qualities	9
Specific gravity	8
Tests	9
Uses	11
TUNGSTEN	139-141
Deposits in:	
Arkansas	140
North Carolina	140
Texas	140
Idiosyncracies	139
Occurrences	139
Uses	140

U
UMBER	18, 36, 37
URANIUM	131
Uses	131

V
VANADIUM	131
Characteristics	131
Uses	131
VIRGINIA	
Asbestos	338
Barytes	31
Bauxite	21
Cerium	136
Chasers	17
Chert	300
Chromite	118
Clays	203
Coal	52
Columbite	136
Copper	167
Corundum	148
Cyanite	230
Diamonds	151
Diatomaceous earth	6
Feldspar	267
Fluorspar	254
Fullers' earth	14
Gems	149
Gold	158
Granite	275
Graphite	153
Gravel	299
Gypsum	343
Ilmenite	133
Iron	95
Lead	186
Limestone, agricultural and chemical	317
Limestone, building	275
Lithographic stone	258
Manganese	120
Marble	275
Marl	327
Mica	234
Millstones	17
Mineral pigments	38
Mineral waters	346
Molding sand and clay	295
Monazite	136
Nickel	141
Ochre	37
Peat	66

	Page
Pyrites	175
Rutile	133
Salt	183
Sand	286
Sandstone	275
Shales	245
Silver	164
Slate	249
Talc	241
Tellurium	137
Thoria	136
Thorium	136
Tin	194
Tripoli	9
Zinc	186
Zirconium	135
VOLCANIC ASH	49
Deposit in:	
Louisiana	49
Uses	49

W
WEST VIRGINIA	
Barytes	32
Clays	204
Coal	53
Granite	275
Grindstones	18
Iron	96
Limestone, agricultural and chemical	316
Limestone, building	275
Manganese	121
Marl	316
Mineral waters	346
Molding sand and clay	294
Natural gas	89
Ochre	38
Oil shale	80
Petroleum	70
Salt	182
Sand	287
Sandstone	275
Shales	245
Slate	249
WHITING	44
Colloidal	44
Crystalline	44
Improvement in domestic	44
Produced in:	
Georgia	44
North Carolina	44
Tennessee	44
Uses	44

Z
ZINC	186-193
Application of electric smelting	186
Deposits in:	
Arkansas	190
Kentucky	188
North Carolina	187
Tennessee	188
Texas	190
Virginia	186
Principal markets	186
Uses	191
Usual occurrences	186
ZIRCONIUM	128
Appearance	128
Deposits in:	
Florida	135
North Carolina	129
Virginia	135
Uses	128